WARSHIP 1996

WARSHIP 1996

Edited by David McLean and Antony Preston

CONWAY

MARITIME PRESS

Frontispiece
A close-up view of the 'X' turret of Queen Mary *with its pair of 13.5in guns from a photograph taken three years before Jutland. Three of the four seamen whose eyewitness accounts are recorded in the article on the 'Loss of the* Queen Mary *at Jutland' managed to escape from this turret, which had already been unseated by heavy German shells. (IWM.A39893) (see page 111)*

© Brassey's (UK) Ltd 1996

First published in Great Britain in November 1996 by
Conway Maritime Press,
An imprint of Brassey's (UK) Ltd
33 John Street
London WC1N 2AT

British Library Cataloguing in Publication Data
Warship 1996
    1. Warships – Periodicals   2. Warships – History
    I. McLean, David and Preston, Antony
    623.8'25

ISBN 0–85177–685–X

Jacket design by Holman Design Partnership
Typesetting in Plantin and page make-up by M Rules
Printed and bound in Great Britain by the
University Printing House, Cambridge.

CONTENTS

EDITORIAL

Technical

In this twentieth year of *Warship* it is, perhaps, opportune to look at the evolving state of warship design in the last years before the millennium, as well as its historical precedents.

Huge strides have been made in the study of hull forms, propulsion and weapons, but paradoxically the overall concept of the warship has changed relatively slowly in the past 50 years. The gas turbine and the diesel engine have virtually displaced the steam turbine as prime mover. Although a number of steam-driven warships remain in service in minor navies, the only steam turbines serving in major navies are in very large aircraft carriers, either on their own or as part of nuclear plants, and in nuclear submarines.

Despite many experiments the traditional monohull remains far more effective for large warships than the 'exotic' solutions such as hydrofoils, hovercraft and surface-effect craft. Special forms, particularly the small waterplane-area twin-hull (SWATH), offer significant benefits in specialised roles, but are at a disadvantage in other roles. Having said that, leading navies are looking at the trimaran hull form as an alternative to the monohull, and several studies are in hand (the Royal Navy is seeking bids for the construction of a demonstrator). The trimaran offers a very stable platform for helicopters, low hull drag (resulting in higher speed for the same power), a measure of protection against torpedo attack and a way to reduce the heat signature of the hull.

Much has been made of 'stealth', but there will never be a way of making ships invisible. At the very least, a ship's wake cannot be hidden, and various other signatures can only be 'managed', not eliminated. In one sense, 'stealth' is a form of electronic camouflage, a means of delaying identification and thus confusing the enemy. The risk is that the publicity given to 'stealth' aircraft is spilling over to the naval world, where it is has a totally different relevance. The shaping of hull and superstructure surfaces and the use of special coatings cannot avoid adding to the cost of procurement. For many important missions 'stealth' is inappropriate.

At a strategic and tactical level, navies have come through a traumatic 50 years since the end of the Second World War. The emotional impact of nuclear weapons, not only on the public but on politicians and the military, led to a near-fatal denial of the need for navies. Those of us with long memories can look back to the era of the 'Four-Minute Warning', and an assumption that navies could only have, at best, a role in the 'broken-backed' phase after the inevitable nuclear holocaust. Recent revelations reveal an almost comical approach to the use of tactical nuclear weapons, including nuclear sea mines laid by midget submarines (with an escape-speed of 5-6 knots) and a bomb so dangerous that a graze during loading might set off a 'low-yield' detonation sufficient to sink the aircraft carrier before it could launch a strike. To be fair, the young sailors and airmen who were willing to use such weapons believed that the alternative was the destruction of civilisation.

Later, sanity prevailed and the risk of 'brushfire' wars was recognised. This brought the aircraft carrier back into favour as the ideal way to defuze crises and to fight local campaigns, despite strident claims from the submarine lobby to give them all the money. In the mid-1960s the air power lobby also tried to convince politicians that carriers could be targeted by intercontinental ballistic missiles (ICBMs). This spurious argument led to the cancellation of the Royal Navy's aircraft carriers *Queen Elizabeth* (CVA-01) and *Duke of Edinburgh* (CVA-02) in 1966, despite continuing evidence that ships at sea are very difficult to target. A year later the sinking of an Israeli destroyer by two small Egyptian missile-boats led to another 'panic', followed by two decades of obsession with fast attack craft (FACs). In 1982 the loss of one Royal Navy warship to an air-launched Exocet missile led many commentators to predict the death of the surface warship, but instead anti-missile defences have proliferated.

The cycle seems to confirm the theory of what might be termed the 'Lissa Syndrome'. In that battle in 1866, the apparent supremacy of Austrian ramming tactics led all major navies to adopt the ram as a weapon of offence. In fact ramming had less to do with Tegetthoff's victory than his superior leadership and a corresponding lack of cohesion in the Italian Fleet. In more recent times Stephen Roskill defined a related problem, the 'Fallacy of the Dominant Weapon', the temptation to ignore the possibility that enemies might also adopt the new technology. A list of such 'dominant' war-winning weapons would be a long one, but some prime examples include the Paixhans shell gun, the monster gun, high-level bombing and radar.

For those of us who study the evolution and use of warships all this becomes self-evident as we get deeper into the subject. In fact no weapon, 'dominant' or not, can triumph in battle unless its operators are well-trained and motivated. The Royal Navy, after its overwhelming victory over Napoleonic France in 1815, gave full tribute to this 'X' factor in its adage, 'It's the Man Behind the Gun who matters'. Translated into modern terms, that simple truth is what makes naval history so complex and rewarding. Without it, we would be nothing more than the despised 'rivet-counters' of popular myth. The details matter, but only if they help to explain how and why certain things happened the way they did.

Antony Preston

Speculative

As we approach the beginning of the twenty-first century, we are living in a time of rapid technological change. Those who sail in warships have good cause to be concerned. Research scientists employed on military projects have already developed some subtle gadgets for use against warships.

The following threats to warships may or may not be coming:

- Self-activating mines which can be buried in the soft seabed and activated by underwater signal.
- 'Smart' torpedoes and mines programmed to attack pre-selected targets.
- Low-cost pilotless aircraft operating from ships to provide reconnaissance and targeting.
- Faster anti-ship missiles with improved resistance to countermeasures.
- Missile ships disguised visually or electronically as something totally different.

Researchers are applying the latest technology to underwater detection and attack. Every warship's 'signature' can be recorded by submarines or strategically placed sensors.

Threats such as these might suggest that warships should evolve into semi-submersible missile platforms with ever-lower profiles, but in practice there is little likelihood that warship design will go that way. The dangers need to be seen in perspective. Warships are tiny specks in relation to the world's oceans, and clouds, bad weather, mountains and islands can make them difficult to find, even in the electronic age. They also have a large number of roles where 'high profile' is more useful than the reverse. The warship is the largest moving military object devised by man – and it is also the most versatile. Amongst military hardware it can undertake far more roles than other war machines such as aircraft or tanks.

Alone or in a battle group it can be a powerful and awesome threat, influencing political events for hundreds of miles around it as it shows itself on the edges of a troublespot or loiters just over the horizon, manipulated with surgical precision by its own government.

On the other hand it can transform itself into a splendid harbinger of peace or *entente cordiale* as it sails by invitation into a foreign port, dressed overall, with all its paintwork cleaned and all its sailors ready to entertain and be entertained by the citizens of the host country. Most readers of *Warship* will know how grand the friendly arrival of a warship into port can be – even if it belongs to a foreign power. A government can often use a warship to signal presence and friendliness in another country's area, which it certainly couldn't do with lumbering tanks or screaming warplanes, which always look and sound aggressive.

Warships on non-military missions, lending support, escorting merchantships, helping in rescue work, carrying out anti-pirate or anti-smuggling duties – in fact any sort of anti-international crime work – need to be 'high profile' and look like warships from a distance. Indeed there is still an obvious need for the conventional naval gun turret. Not only is it important for the profile, but it also has important contributions to make in peace and war. In peace and at pageants it can fire salutes and in times of conflict it can fire shells over many miles. Heavy naval shells have more penetrating power than naval missiles and, as illegally invading troops sometimes find out, the irregular thud of naval bombardment continuing day and night round their positions is enough to knock the stuffing out of them long before the relieving ground troops arrive. Of course there is also the proverbial shot across the bows . . . many targets are not worth a missile but can be called to order by the lob of a shell or the swivel of a gun turret. The basic types of larger warships we know and admire are ideally suited to general policing roles and will hopefully be around for a long time yet. World security and readers of *Warship* need them!

This Issue

When John Roberts asked to be relieved of the helm of *Warship* he had already collected most of the articles for the present issue and supplied these with enough notes to enable the new watch to keep *Warship* up to speed and on course. His hand-over and subsequent helpful signals is acknowledged and appreciated.

This year's contributors, both seasoned and new, have upheld, your editors hope, the strong traditions of scholarship and enthusiasm which is special to *Warship*. The offerings vary in subject-matter and come from authors in no less than six countries. The new team at Conway has enjoyed working with them all. This year the production of *Warship* has gone a few more steps towards electronic publishing with more submissions coming in on disk and the illustrations being recorded digitally and integrated with the text electronically. This trend will continue for the benefit and improvement of *Warship*.

David McLean

THE SWEDISH ARMOURED COASTAL DEFENCE SHIPS

It is appropriate that Sweden, which produced the inventor John Ericsson, also adopted his ideas for turreted monitors enthusiastically. **Daniel G Harris** looks at the policy which evolved between 1861 and 1901

The 1861 parliamentary review of naval forces, aware of the news of the American monitors fitted with the Ericsson Moveable Turret, initiated the construction of four large and ten small monitors in the years 1865–72. The four large monitors were to defend the outer skerries, the smaller the inland waters.

In 1870, the government concluded that Sweden needed warships that could prevent invading forces from landing in areas outside the skerries. Although the four large monitors could operate in fairly heavy weather in open waters, the smaller could not. To remedy the deficiency, parliament allotted funds for the construction of two, later increased to nine, gunboats of the type designed by G. W. Svensson to carry heavy guns. The British gunboat *Staunch*, 180 tons, carrying a 23cm fixed gun, was the model for Svensson's nine *Blenda* class gunboats. The *Blenda* class were twin screw vessels of 500 tons armed with a 27cm gun forward and a 12cm gun aft. The British firm Armstrongs supplied the 27cm guns, which could be trained within an unarmoured turret by being swung to port or starboard. The maximum speed provided by Woolf's two-cylinder compound engine was 12 knots. Since the *Blenda* class had no armour, naval officers pointed out that a single shot from an enemy could penetrate the thin iron plating and probably disable the vessel. Moreover, in heavy seas, these vessels proved unmanageable.

In 1875, Commander F. W. V. Otter, Minister for the Navy, aided by King Oscar II, drew up a plan for presentation to parliament as follows:

1. The Navy was to have the same importance to National Defence as the Army.
2. Without strong Naval defences, an enemy can, without interruption, land strong forces where it will and can maintain communications with its base.
3. National defence is only provided for to a minimum by a fleet intended only for operations in the skerries.
4. A fleet that can operate outside the skerries forces an enemy to take greater risks and employ more forces.

5. The present-day development of naval forces enables an enemy to choose more quickly and confidently his objective and carry out an invasion.
6. The Swedish Navy must consider the foregoing. If given the means, it can offer greater resistance to any assault.

The Minister called for armoured ships with heavy guns to be essential components of the fleet. Such vessels would increase the area of operations to the open waters close to the coast. Moreover, light craft such as torpedo boats required the tactical support of well-armed larger vessels.

The Minister held the Navy's responsibilities to be as follows:

1. To prevent an enemy from occupying our most important ports.
2. To hinder the landing of large numbers of enemy troops on our coasts wheresoever such landing occurs.
3. Where an enemy has succeeded in landing, to cut off its communications with its base and, by operating in our inland waterways, assist our forces to oppose any hostile advances.

Parliament's defence committee refused any action on the Navy Minister's propositions until it had received the views of the ground forces. After receiving the Army's report, the committee's members began to criticize any proposals for armoured ships – Otter had attached some particulars of British, French, and German armoured vessels as prototypes for similar Swedish vessels. That information and the question of fitting rams occupied the defence committee's deliberations. Consequently, the Minister's call for new armoured ships considered by the committee to entail major changes was talked out. Nonetheless, a year later, the committee accepted the Minister's terms of reference for the Navy.

In October 1879, the cabinet, at a meeting presided over by King Oscar II, set up a special committee of experts to determine which types of vessels would best meet the nation's needs. Sweden was concerned about possible Russian aggression. From 1855 she had relied upon the Franco-British treaty of neutrality. Britain and France agreed to protect Sweden, with force if necessary, provided that Sweden neither ceded territory, nor granted fishing rights, to Russia. France's fall in 1870 caused Sweden to look towards Imperial Germany for protection, although she believed a powerful British fleet might enter the Baltic should Russia attack.

The committee accepted the Navy Minister's list of responsibilities, but made it clear its recommendations for new ships would give careful consideration to costs owing to the nation's limited resources. It agreed that a new type of armoured vessel was necessary. The new warship not only should meet the Minister's terms of reference, but be able to protect the islands of Gotland and Öland. In June 1880 the committee proposed six vessels of so-called type 'A', armoured ship for coastal and off-shore operations be built. The type 'A' was to have a displacement of 2,622 tons, two propellers, a speed of 13 knots and be able to steam in heavy weather. The armament was to be two 25.4cm, three 15.2 guns and a single torpedo tube. The vessel was to have heavy armour. For the next two years Parliament took no action, being more interested in discussing the introduction of conscription for the Army than in authorizing naval construction. Finally in 1883, by a majority of six it authorized the release of funds to construct the first of a series of three heavily-armed and well protected coastal defence vessels; the first to be named *Svea*, the first in a series of 12 to be built over the next 22 years.

The Svea class

Director General G. W. Svensson prepared the final plans for *Svea* to be submitted to King Oscar II for his approval. It had been the custom for the monarch to sign his approval of the final drawings since the reign of the ill-fated Karl XII. The practice ended with Oscar II's death.

Svensson increased the vessel's speed by one knot. To carry the two 25.4cm guns in a moveable turret and armour, he had to increase *Svea*'s displacement to 2,931 tons. In 1884, the Crown made a contract with Lindholm's yard, Göteborg, to build *Svea*. Lindholm laid the keel in March and launched *Svea* in December of the following year. Nine months later, the sea trials took place and the Navy took delivery.

Svea's dimensions were length 75.7m, beam 14.48m, draft 5.18m and displacement at full load was 3,278 tons. The hull was built of Motala's bessemer steel plate 1.5cm thick. *Svea*, although having a swan bow, to naval officers' regret, had no ram. Two horizontal compound engines – the Woolf system, drove the twin propellers, six coal-fired boilers provided the steam. The constructors chose horizontal engines because these could be below the water line, and thus had additional protection. The pistons' great weight caused heavy wear and tear. *Svea* made 14½ knots at 3,155ihp on trials and later achieved 15. She could carry up to 260 tons of coal. A curiosity was *Svea*'s two square funnels. These were replaced by round smoke stacks at a later major refit.

The armament comprised two Armstrong breech-loading 25.4cm guns in a single turret; four 15.2cm

GW Svenssons 1883 proposed armoured ship – later Svea *class. Armament: two 27cm guns – changed to 25cm. (Krigsarkivet)*

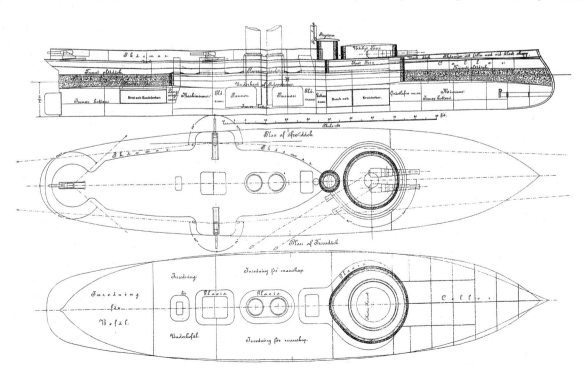

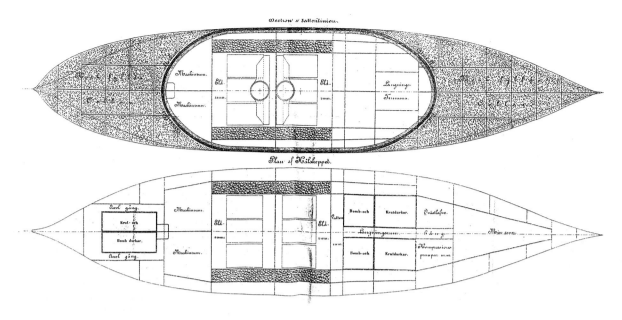

Svea *plan. (Krigsarkivet)*

breech-loading Armstrong guns on Vasseur mountings, each protected by a shield of 25mm armour and 12.7mm-thick roof; two 38mm anti-torpedo boat guns; four 4-barrelled 25mm guns, and in the open fighting top one 10-barrelled machine gun. A single 38cm torpedo tube was in the stem. The torpedoes supplied by Whitehead of Fiume were 6m long and carried 26 kilos of gun cotton. Compressed air drove the torpedo for 400m at a speed of 19 knots. Two searchlights on 'bandstand' mountings were on each side of the hull.

The French Schneider Creusot supplied the armour – Chief Constructor Svensson submitted draughts with explanations in French to the manufacturer to show the proposed methods of bolting of armour to the hull. The water-line armour's thickness was forward 29.7cm, reduced to 14.7cm midships and increased to 19.7 towards the stern. The armour's thickness on the quarters was 22.2cm. The side armour had a 26cm wooden backing extended to 59cm above and 89cm below the water-line. The side armour was attached to 26cm thick wooden backing. Incidentally, the hull was not pierced for scuttles.

The twin turret's barbette armour thickness was front 29.7cm, side 14.7cm and back 19.8cm. The turret armour thickness was 29.7cm front, 27.3cm sides and 24.6cm back. The 15cm gun shields deck armour was 4.9cm thick, covered by cork and ordinary ships' plate. The citadel's armour was 29.7cm. In addition, the hull was subdivided into 194 horizontal and longships compartments. Seventy-two were in the double bottom. The coal bunkers, when full, provided some protection to the hull.

In 1899, *Svea* had a major refit. The turret for the two 25.4cm guns was replaced by a turret for a single 21cm gun. The number of 15.2cm guns in single turrets was increased to seven, three on each side and one aft. Calculations proved that *Svea*'s hull could not carry aft a second turret for a 21cm gun. Bofors made all the new guns. The 21cm gun turret's armour was 19cm and 14cm, the citadels 19cm. The 15cm gun turret's armour was now 11.5cm. The hull was pierced for scuttles as part of the reconstruction. After the refit, *Svea*'s complement of 252 was reduced to 232.

Svea remained in service until 1915. In 1921, after alterations, *Svea* became a submarine depot ship. In 1941, to the relief of submarine crews and the Navy, *Svea* went to the breakers.

In 1884 and 1886, Parliament rejected the Crown's request for funds for the second ship. Nonetheless, a year later, Parliament released sufficient funds to enable the crown to get construction started at Lindholm's yard, Göteborg. The final draughts were only approved in the autumn of 1888. The name of the second vessel was *Göta*. The new ship was to be the fleet flagship and had to accommodate the Admiral and his staff. The yard laid down the keel in 1888 and launched the hull in September 1889.

Göta's dimensions were: length 79m, beam 14.8m, draft 5.1m. Motala Verkstad built the six coal-fired cylindrical boilers (6.25 at) and the two horizontal compound engines that provided 4,600ihp. driving twin screws. Coal bunkers could carry 260 tons. *Göta* also had square funnels. The vessel's total displacement at full load was 3,393 tons. The main armament was two Armstrong 25.4cm guns and four 15.2cm Bofors guns. Five 57mm Maxim Nordenfelt anti-torpedo boats guns were mounted aft, four between the 15.2cm guns and the fifth on the stern. A single 38cm torpedo tube was built into the bow and two, one on each side, were placed on the second deck amidships. Whiteheads of Fiume, Austria, supplied the torpedos. Schuckert of Germany supplied the four searchlights placed on 'bandstand' mountings – two on each side.

The French firm Schneider Creusot supplied *Göta*'s armour, the water-line armour thickness was 29.3cm forward, 24.3 midships and 21.8cm aft. The deck armour thickness was 4.9cm. The 25.4cm turret front armour was 29.3cm thick and the rest 26.8cm. The citadel's armour was 26.8cm thick. *Göta* had a double bottom and 198 subdivisions. It carried two steam picket boats armed with one machine gun and two large spar torpedoes. The complement was 237 men.

The Navy found defects in *Göta* during the initial trials in 1890. After changes and a four-hour full-speed trial at an average speed of 14.9 knots in April 1891, the Navy accepted the vessel. It became a component of the active fleet in July.

Göta was the coastal fleet's flagship from 1891 to 1896. In 1897, she represented Sweden at Queen Victoria's diamond jubilee review of the British fleet at Spithead.

In 1900, the two single torpedo tubes were removed and similar armament to *Svea*'s replaced the original. The replaced guns were set up in coastal fortresses.

Before World War I began, *Göta* was obsolete, but was retained for local defence until 1917. Rebuilt in 1923 as an accommodation vessel, she lay for some years at the Air Force's seaplane base in the Stockholm Skerries. In 1942, *Göta* was scrapped.

Although in 1888 parliament had authorized the construction of the third armoured ship, it only allotted the funds in 1891. Oscar II gave royal assent to the drawings for *Thule* in late January the same year. In May 1891, the Crown accepted Bergsund yard's offer to build *Thule*'s hull. The contract with Bergsund was for the hull and machinery. The Crown was responsible for the fighting equipment's installation at the Stockholm dockyard. *Thule*'s hull differed from *Svea*'s and *Göta*'s by being fitted with a steel ram. The successful use of the ram at the battle of Lissa had impressed many navies including the Swedish. Articles published in the 1880 editions of *Tidskrift-i-Sjöväsendet* held the ram to be the ultimate weapon in sea battle. Consequently, *Thule* had no bow torpedo tube. Bergsund laid the keel in 1891. The Treasury's delays in releasing funds postponed *Thule*'s launch until March 1893 and completion until December.

Thule's dimensions were: length (including ram) 83.66m (excluding ram 78.52m), beam 14.62m, draft 5.1m. The displacement at full load including the ram was 3,305 tons. Bergsund built the engines and boilers – all similar to *Göta*'s. On speed trials in November 1893 at 5,000hp, *Thule* reached 16.9 knots. *Thule*'s funnels were round. Her armament was similar to *Göta*'s, but the two Armstrong 25.4cm guns were on a 30cm higher mounting. As a result, the 25.4 guns were easier to serve, and, consequently, their rate of fire was higher. Bofors manufactured the 15.2cm guns. The two single torpedo tubes, made by the Karlskrona Naval Yard were for 45.7 torpedoes and placed amidships, one on each side.

Thule's refit in 1902 brought about the same changes as described for *Göta*. By 1914, she was of little fighting value and became an accommodation vessel. After the war she was used as a target, being sold for scrap in 1933. The three vessels' names are those of the three Kingdoms that eventually united to become Sweden.

The *Oden Class*

In the autumn of 1892 after the release of funds for the construction of the third *Svea* class vessel, the Crown established a new committee of naval experts which studied the latest developments in naval construction, made proposals for the modernization of existing fleets' components and new vessels, and concluded that the three Svea class vessels met Swedish needs, but suggested that the heavy armament, the positioning of guns, and armour could all be improved. The rate of fire of the 15.2cm guns was too slow.

The committee's recommendations included a fleet of 15 armoured coastal defence vessels, 30 class-one torpedo boats, 15 class-two torpedo boats, and six flotilla leaders. The proposed armoured ships were to have the main armament in two separate turrets and quick-firing 12cm guns. In 1893, Cabinet requested parliament to vote funds for the construction of one new ship. Parliament only granted half the funds in 1893, but, a year later, it released sufficient funds to begin construction.

The Bergsund yard won the contract to build the new ship, to be named *Oden* Its dimensions were: length 86.3m, beam 14.77m, max. draft 5.6m. The hull was divided into 200 compartments and had no scuttles. *Oden*'s machinery, built by Bergsund, comprised two triple expansion engines; total hp was 5,330, driving two 3.93m diameter propellers. The maximum speed attained on trials was 16.8kts. Six Admiralty pattern coal-fired boilers provided the steam. The vessel had two round funnels. Displacement at full load was 3,715 tons. Bergsund launched the hull in March 1896 and delivered *Oden* in June 1897. *Oden*'s main armament comprised two 25.4cm guns, each in its own turret, one forward, one aft. The French Forges et Chantier le Havre manufactured the 25.4cm system Canet-type guns. Bofors supplied four 12cm quick-firing guns which were placed in casemates midships, two on each side. Four quick-firing Bofors 5.71cm guns were in casemates, and two 8mm Maxim Nordenfelt guns in the fighting top. It also supplied two 2.5cm guns for the two picket boats.

The underwater torpedo tube in the stem fired a 45.7cm torpedo. The Navy was now not only buying torpedoes from Whiteheads of Fiume, Austria, but also from the German Schwarzkopf company. The maximum range of the new torpedoes was about 800m and speed about 26kts. The 180 kilo charge was considered sufficient to damage a target.

The French Schneider company supplied the heavy nickel alloy armour, 24.3cm for the water line, 24.7cm for the barbettes and 20cm for the turrets. The turrets' roof armour was 3cm thick. The armour of the citadel was 24.7cm thick. Bofors rolled the lighter armour for the casemates, deck and steering engine space. Thicknesses were 10cm, 4.9cm and 4.9cm. *Oden*'s original complement was 239, later 254. *Oden*, with two newly-completed flotilla leaders, were part of the Stockholm 1897 Art and Industry Exhibition.

Oden's grounding in 1901 brought about special grants for the salvage and repairs. The Navy Department was not only able to extract funds from the Treasury for the

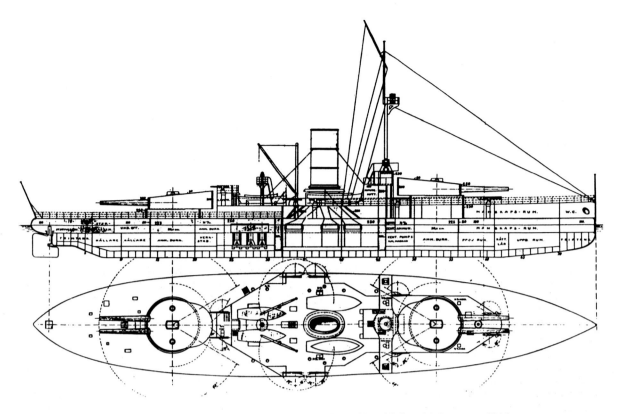

HH Lilliehook and A Schvan: Proposed 4,500 ton 17 knot coast defence ship with four 30.5cm guns, 1906.

Oden *after 1915 reconstruction. Note single funnel and 5.7cm guns on turrets and mainmast removed. (Sjöhistoriska Museet, Stockholm.)*

Oden *class (1896). General arrangement drawing. (Krigsarkivet)*

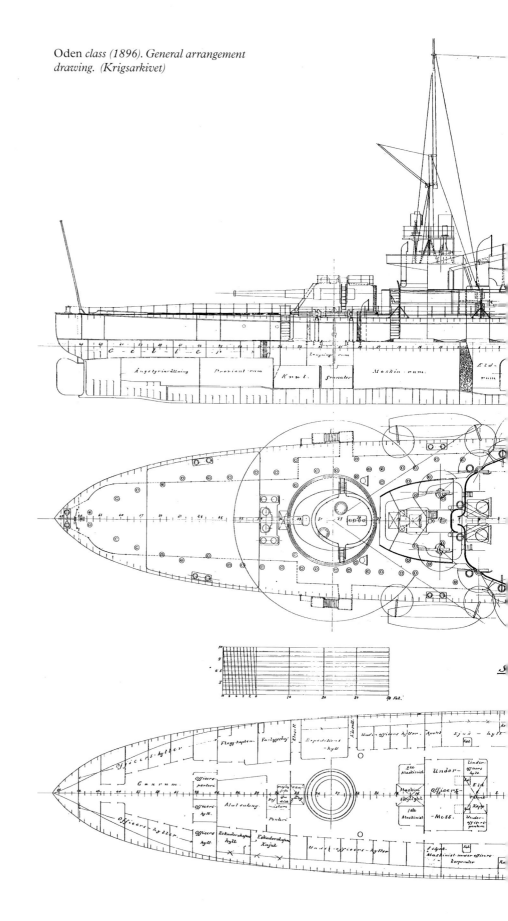

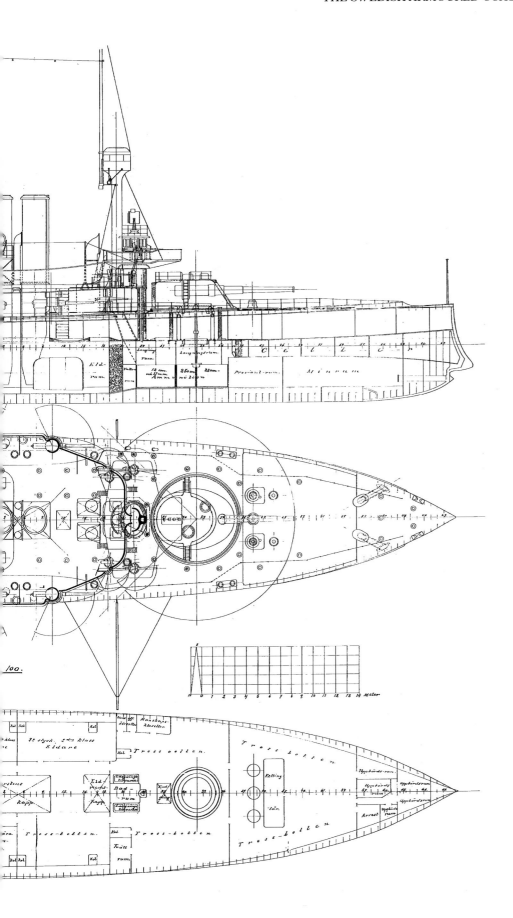

repairs, but also for two additional 12cm guns which replaced two 5.7cm guns in casemates that were now placed on the superstructure. A second reconstruction took place in 1915. It included new boilers and changes to *Oden*'s silhouette. A single funnel replaced the two; both the fore and main masts were exchanged for a lighter and longer foremast with fighting top.

In 1902, *Oden* represented Sweden at King Edward VII's Coronation Review of the British Fleet. In 1913, during exercises in the Sound close to Ven Island, *Oden* rammed and sank the gunboat *Urd*, luckily without loss of life. *Oden* was attempting to fire a practice torpedo at *Urd*. Since the maximum range of the torpedo was only 800m, the attacking vessel had to come close to the target. The confined waters of the Sound made any distance less than a torpedo's maximum range hazardous. After this, *Oden*'s torpedo tube was removed.

Oden was discarded in the 1930s. Attempts to sell the vessel for scrap failed. Finally in 1943, the Karlskrona Royal Dockyard demolished the vessel.

In 1896, Parliament authorised the addition of two more *Oden*-class ships to the fleet because it was concerned about the increased naval construction in Germany and Russia. In 1893, Germany had eight 3700-ton armoured ships, five 11,000-ton battleships under construction, and a large fleet of torpedo boats. Russia had ten 13,000-ton battleships armed with 30.5cm guns, and four more under construction, but had little interest in torpedo craft. The size of the two major powers' fleets hastened the Swedish Parliament's consent to these ships.

In 1896, the Crown placed orders with Bergsund, Stockholm and Lindholm, Göteborg for two 3,720-ton ships to be named *Thor* and *Niord* respectively. The hull dimensions were the same as *Oden*'s. In 1902, an innovation was that the hulls were pierced fore and aft for scuttles.

Bergsund and Motala built the vessels' two 5,350ihp triple expansion engines. Six cylindrical boilers at 10.76kg pressure provided the steam. Both vessels could carry 280 tons of coal. The Contracts required the vessels to attain a speed of 15kts without forced draft. The ships' range at 10 knots was 2,500 miles. The boilers were located in two compartments. A longitudinal bulkhead separated the two triple expansion engines.

Generators provided power for the thirteen electric motors needed for ammunition hoists and fans in torpedo tube and dynamo compartments. The French firm Caret supplied the two 25.4cm guns for *Thor*, but Bofors the two for *Niord*. It was the first time Bofors had made such large guns. Bofors supplied the six 12cm and ten 5.7cm guns. In addition, the two 2.5cm twin-barrel machine guns for the two picket boats and two 8mm machine guns for the fighting top were also of Bofors manufacture. Both vessels had a 45.7cm torpedo tube in the stem. The French Breguet company supplied four 90cm searchlights. The vessel's complement was 254.

The Navy ordered the armour plating from John Brown of Sheffield. That company was rolling a nickel alloy steel called Harvey Steel, superior in strength to that available from French, German and Swedish makers. The new English steel had the advantage of being lighter in weight, saving 200 tons overall. The armour's thicknesses for 50

metres of waterline armour varied from 10cm to 20cm and had a height of 1.48m. The barbettes had 20cm armour, the revolving turret was 19cm thick on the sides and 3cm thick on the roof. The casemate's protection was 10cm thick. Deck armour was two layers of 2.5cm plate.

Bergsund and Lindholm laid the keels of *Thor* and *Niord* in March 1896 and, launched the ships two years later. Both vessels underwent speed trials in 1899. *Thor* averaged 15.5kts. and *Niord* 16kts. In 1902, to provide greater stability, both vessels were fitted with bilge keels. In 1907, *Thor* was adapted for cadet training. She underwent a major refit in 1914 similar to *Oden*'s.

In 1918, *Thor* was part of a force sent to the Åland islands with troops to protect the inhabitants from red Russian forces. Declared obsolete in 1920, the hull lay in Karlskrona dockyard until finally scrapped in 1942.

Niord went through the same refits as *Thor*. Declared obsolete in 1922, the hull was used for accommodation purposes until 1930. In 1931, *Niord* was lent to the Stockholm Social Welfare Committee as lodging for unemployed merchant seamen undergoing some form of training. After use by the Air Force for seaplane crews stationed in Stockholm's Skerries, *Niord* went to the breakers in 1944.

The Swedish *Tidskrift i Sjöväsendet*'s 1898 issue made a comparison between the *Thor* class and the Norwegian *Harald Haarfagre* and the Danish *Herluf Trolle* class vessels; the result of a member of parliament suggesting the Swedish vessel *Thor* was inferior to the Norwegian *Harald Haarfagre*. The Danish and Norwegian fleets were also intended for defence against invasion. The journal published the table set out below:

Table 1:

	Thor (Sweden)	*Harald Haarfagre* (Norway)	*Herluf Troll* (Denmark)
Displacement (tons)	3,300	3,400	3,500
Max. Speed (kts)	16.5	16	15.6
Armament (cm)	Two 25	Two 21	One 24
	Six 12	Six 12	Four 15
	Ten 5.7	Four 7.6	Ten 5.7
Deck Armour (cm)	5	5	5
Turret Armour (cm)	20	20.3	17.5

It is suggested that the *Thor* class vessel was superior to the Danish and Norwegian ships. The Norwegian ship was seized by Germany in 1940 and converted to an antiaircraft vessel. She was returned to the Norwegian Navy in 1945.

Dristigheten (Courageous)

Royal decree of 10 October 1896 required the Navy Board to prepare and submit draughts for a new armoured ship of the *Oden* class by 1 September 1897. The board completed a new set of draughts but these

Dristigheten *after conversion to seaplane depot ship in the 1930s. Note two seaplanes on the stern. In the background old flotilla leader* Jacob Bagge. *(Sjöhistoriska Museet, Stockholm.)*

were not of another *Oden* class ship, but for an entirely new type. The Crown approved the draughts on 5 November 1897.

The source of funds for the new vessel prompted lively debate in the 1897 Parliament. One proposal was to use the surplus arising from the customs duties on food imports. One member reminded the house of an 1888 promise to use such surplus funds for the relief of poverty. He stressed those in need were already suffering from the introduction of conscription and high taxes. Another member proposed raising a loan to cover the ship's construction costs. In 1898, the conservative government requested funds for the construction of the Ofoten railway that connects Luleå with Narvik, and the armoured ship *Dristigheten*. The parliamentarians refused funds for the railway but voted a lesser grant for ship construction.

In the 1899 parliamentary sessions, a new Navy minister, Commander G. Dyrssen, asked for grants to build three more armoured ships. He proposed that the costs of three vessels be spread over a three-year period. Parliament's two houses voted – one for the three new ships, the other against. When both houses voted together as one house, Dyrssen's proposals were approved by a majority of 106. The increased Norwegian naval expenditures may have influenced the members' decision.

In the autumn of 1898, the Crown signed a contract for *Dristigheten*'s hull and engines with Lindholm and Motala. To reduce the turning circle, the stern's dimensions were smaller than the *Oden*'s. The yard fitted bilge keels 4.56cm wide and 35m long on the hull prior to launch. The cost of the hull and engines was 1,910,000 kronor (£127,000 or $633,000 approximately). The hull's dimensions were length 86.9m, beam 14.77m, draft 5.2m. Displacement at full load was 3,600 tons.

Dristigheten's machinery consisted of two 5,400hp triple expansion engines driving two propellers. Eight Yarrow water tube boilers supplied the steam. The Chief

Constructor, H. H. Lilliehöök, had studied ship construction in Britain and America before joining the naval service. He became aware of the British development of the water tube boiler that had the advantages of easier cleaning and could raise steam quicker than in the fire tube boilers fitted to the older vessels. He persuaded the Navy to adopt the Yarrow water tube boiler as standard for new vessels. When *Dristigheten*'s speed trial took place, 5,617ihp and 16.8kts were reached. The bunker's 310 tons of coal gave a 2,900nm radius at 10 knots. The Yarrow water tube boiler became the Navy's standard until 1931 when the French Penhoet-type better met the new oil-fired ships' needs.

Bofors supplied the armament of two 21cm quick-firing guns mounted in single turrets, one forward, one aft; six 15cm quick-firing guns in casemates and ten 5.7cm guns protected by 6.4mm shields. Armstrong Whitworth supplied the two 45.7cm underwater torpedo tubes.

The French Cie Hauts-Fourneaux Acier Chamond supplied the Krupp face-hardened type armour. The turrets' armour thicknesses were: barbette 20cm front, 15cm side and 3cm roof. The waterline armour was 20–14cm thick to a height of 1.48m. The citadel had 20cm so-called Harvey nickel-faced armour. Bofors supplied the casemates' 10cm protection. French 4.9cm armour protected the deck. Schuckert supplied four 90cm searchlights.

Lindholm laid down *Dristigheten*'s keel in October 1898 and she was launched in April 1900. During the trials, the electrical equipment turned the 21cm turrets 304 degrees in 40 seconds; by hand (four men), the time was 130 seconds. Electrically-operated hoists containing a 125kg shell and two 30kg cordite bags took 11 seconds to travel from the magazine to the turret. The hand-worked hoist took 20 seconds. Two hoists served the 5.7cm guns – their speed was six boxes of 12 shots per minute. *Dristigheten* originally had two pole masts. In 1910, a tripod mast with fighting top replaced the foremast. In

1915, two 5.7cm AA guns were placed on top of the 21cm turrets. In 1921, as a cadet training vessel, she visited the Royal Naval College at Dartmouth. Six years later, she was converted, over a three-year period, to a seaplane depot ship. A crane for lifting seaplanes on board, superstructure for workshops, and four 7.5cm AA guns replaced the turrets and the 15.2cm guns. After reconstruction, *Dristigheten* could carry two Heinkel torpedo-carrying aircraft. The plans were to station her in the Stockholm Skerries to service aircraft used for reconnaisance or action. Decommissioned in 1947, the vessel became a gunnery target and went to the scrapyard in 1961.

The Äran *Class*

The three additional coastal defence vessels authorized by the 1899 parliament were *Äran* (Glory), *Wasa* and *Tapperheten* (Bravery). The names were those of the 1780 ships of the line built by the famous naval architect, F. H. af Chapman. The contract to build *Äran* was awarded in October 1899. Lindholm was to build the hull and Motala the engines, the vessel to be completed in twenty-six months. At the same time, Bergsund of Stockholm were contracted to build and deliver *Wasa* in twenty-six months and Kockums of Malmo were to complete *Tapperheten* in twenty-four months.

The dimensions of all three vessels were length 89.7m, beam 15.02m, and draft 5.3m. All were fitted with bilge keels 35m long and 0.7m broad. The machinery to drive the two propellers comprised two 5,500ihp triple-expansion engines. Eight Yarrow water tube and coal-fired boilers supplied the steam. A water-tight bulkhead separated the two engines. The boilers were in three separate compartments. The three ships' contracted speed was 16.5kts which the Navy believed was the average maximum speed of the period's foreign battleships. The ships were to carry 370 tons of coal and have a 3,000-mile radius of action at 12kts. The displacement at full load was 3,735 tons and the complement was 285 men.

The three vessels' armament included two 21cm guns in single turrets, six 15.2cm guns in single turrets, three to port and three to starboard, and ten 5.7cm guns. The British Armstrong Whitworth Company supplied the two underwater torpedo tubes. The ships' two steam picket boats each carried a 3.7cm gun. Bofors manufactured all the guns. The German Schuckert firm delivered four 90cm searchlights.

Krupp of Essen, Germany, supplied the 17.5cm surface-hardened water-line armour. Its length was 50.43m and height 1.78m. It had a teak backing. The 21cm turrets' barbettes' armour was 19cm thick of similar steel. The turrets' front armour was 18cm thick, 14cm elsewhere. The 15.2cm turrets' barbette armour was of 10cm nickel alloy steel; the turrets' fronts had 12.5cm and the rear 6cm. The deck was protected by 4.8cm and the citadel by 17.5cm. Bofors delivered the doors to the 15.2cm turrets and the citadel.

Äran, launched in August 1901, was fitted for the Admiral commanding the fleet and his staff, with special heating arrangements for winter service. On trials in August 1902, maximum speed was 16.07kts. Final delivery took place in September.

King Oscar II christened *Äran* by breaking a bottle of champagne on her bow at the launch. A prelate described the christening of *Äran* with wine as sacrilegious and caused such an uproar that the Crown abandoned the custom. It has never been resumed.

A tripod foremast with fighting top and 2m range finder replaced the fore and main masts in the late 1900s in all three vessels. *Äran* had refits in 1910 and 1914, and was placed in reserve in 1933. In September 1939, the defence department ordered her re-commissioning. Survey of the vessel revealed the deck to be in fairly good condition, but the armament was obsolete. *Äran*'s guns had a maximum range of 9,000 metres in daylight, 2,500 metres at night. It was evident that modern German or Russian vessels with 10–12cm guns having greater range could easily destroy *Äran*. Other equipment such as anchor chain was in poor condition. It broke under test, severely injuring the forecastle crew.

In October 1939, engine room duties became dangerous owing to the severe shaking of piping caused by firing four shots with the two 21cm guns and seven with the 15.2cm. Nonetheless in 1940, four 5.7cm AA guns, two 4cm AA guns, two 2.5 AA guns and two twin barrelled 8mm AA guns replaced the original 5.7cm. The two torpedo tubes were removed. In 1942, *Äran* became a floating barracks; in 1951, the hull was cut down to be a barge.

Wasa, built by Bergsund and delivered in December 1902, seems to have been the 'black sheep' of the *Äran* class. A tripod mast with fighting top and 2m range finder replaced the fore and main masts in 1909. She was placed in material reserve in 1924. Thereafter, the vessel had the minimum of maintenance, the result of funding shortages caused by the government's disarmament policies. In 1939 the Commander-in-Chief of Defence Forces suggested that *Wasa* be used as a floating battery in Malmö. The Navy's commander replied that the costs of refitting *Wasa* for that purpose would be very high and that scarce funds could be better employed elsewhere. The Navy used *Wasa* as a damage control training vessel in Stockholm throughout World War II. Her water-line armour was removed and used by Bofors to make new armour for the new Swedish cruisers *Göta Lejon* and *Tre Kronor* completed in 1947. In 1942, changes were made to the silhouette to make the vessel resemble the 1920 coastal defence ship *Drottning Victoria*.

Tapperheten (Bravery), launched in November 1901, reached a speed of 17.7kts for five hours in the 1903 acceptance trials, during which 6,000ihp was attained. The total construction costs were about 4,500,000 kronor. She ran ashore in January 1914 and was not refloated until July. The salvage costs of 1,340,808 kronor necessitated a special parliamentary grant. *Tapperheten* had the same changes to her silhouette as *Äran* and *Wasa* before World War I began. In 1927, she visited Britain. Thereafter, she was laid up in material reserve at Karlskrona. In September 1939, the Defence Department ordered *Tapperheten*'s commissioning. The survey reported

Tapperheten *after partial reconstruction 1939, camouflaged with white neutrality markings underway in Stockholm skerries 1944. (Sjöhistoriska Museet, Stockholm).*

that the decks were in fair condition but the AA guns, the main armament, were weak and out of date. Fitting out and commissioning took from 9 September to 6 November.

On 7 December 1939, the Swedish Admiralty requested the Cabinet's permission to replace the main armament of *Äran* and *Tapperheten* with *Wasa*'s guns. Bofors was to recondition the two ships' guns. On their return, the *Wasa*'s guns were either to be turned over to the coastal artillery or mounted in requisitioned merchant vessels. The Cabinet agreed to the proposal.

In 1939/40, none of the coal-fired units could reach their designed maximum speed owing to the deterioration of stocks of coal left for several years in open storage. In 1947, *Tapperheten* was struck off and sold for scrap.

Manligheten (Virility) In 1901, Parliament approved expenditures for the *Äran* class's fourth ship. The Cabinet approved the drawings for the new vessel and it received King Oscar II's signature in November. The Crown awarded the contracts for the hull and machinery to Kockums of Malmö and armament to Bofors. The hull's launch took place in December 1905; the acceptance trials in the autumn of 1904. *Manligheten*'s dimensions were length 90m, beam 15m draft 5.3m. Her displacement was 3,450 tons. The machinery, original armament and armour were similar to *Äran*'s. She had improved accommodation and comfort for the crew. Personnel now had cupboards and boxes for their personal effects. These replaced the kitbags and ditty boxes that previously had only been available for crews in older vessels. Other features included a compressor refrigerator and a proper ventilation system with fans and heat exchangers.

Manligheten *after 1940–41 reconstruction and fitting of new bow following damage from German anti-minesweeping device. Ship is underway in Göteborg skerries. Ensign is at half-mast owing to loss of Swedish submarine* Ulven *on German mines. (Sjöhistöriska Museet, Stockholm).*

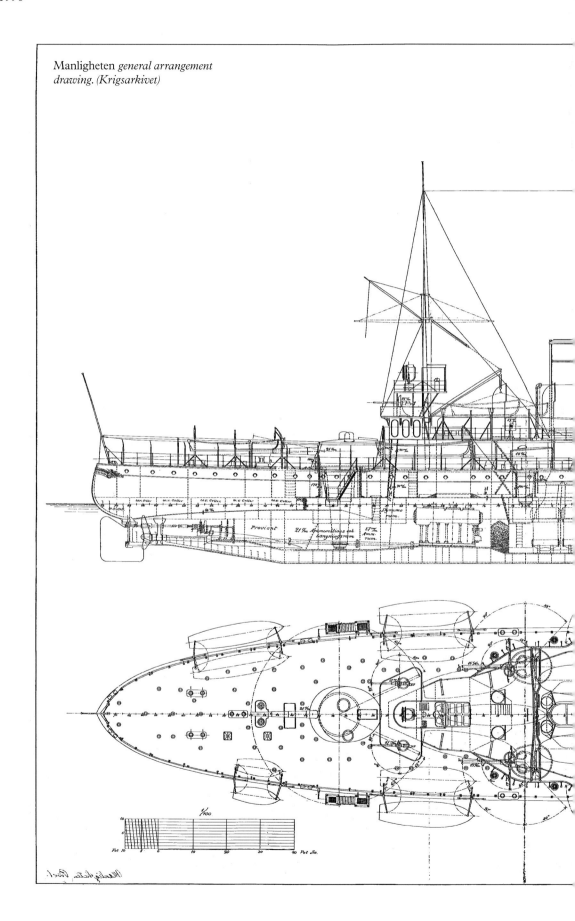

Manligheten *general arrangement drawing. (Krigsarkivet)*

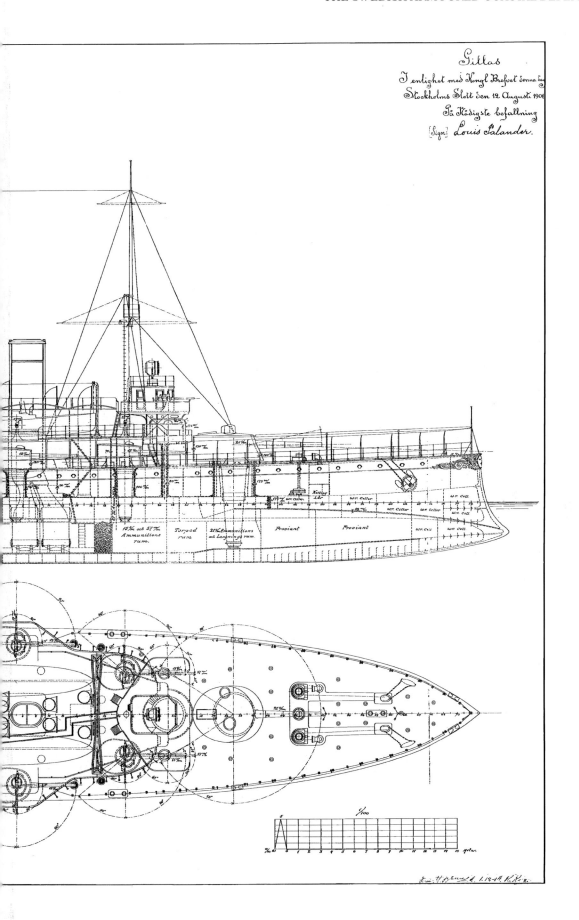

Thor *and* Niord *as built, 1898. General arrangements. (Krigsarkivet)*

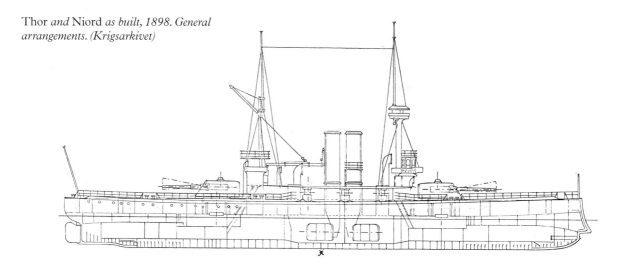

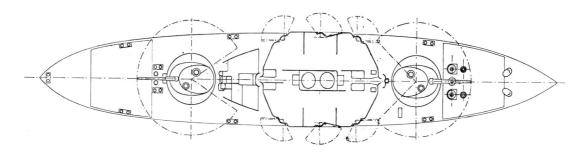

Consequently, the air in the crew space was much improved. Measurements of the carbon dioxide in the air in the severe winter of 1905–06 were found to be comparable to the outside air. Measurements in older vessels revealed the air to be very stale.

Manligheten went through similar refits and changes to silhouette as *Äran*. In 1906, the single tripod mast and fighting top replaced the two pole masts. In the 1930s, two boilers were rebuilt for oil firing. The fuel was produced from oil-bearing shale from Kinnekulle. That low grade oil became of great importance to the Navy in the years 1940–45. In 1936, she was brought into a state of readiness, stationed in Göteborg as part of the west coast squadron. In 1939, the explosion from a German anti-sweeping gear mine caused damage and killed six men. She, two 1917 destroyers and three 1918 submarines were to be in the main force to meet any German invasion force. *Manligheten*'s 21cm guns had a maximum range of 11,000 metres and the 15.2cm guns 9,000 metres. In 1939, German cruisers' 15cm guns had a maximum range of 20,000 metres. The antagonist in 1939/41 was expected to be a German *Admiral Scheer* class pocket battleship. The tactics proposed to meet that threat were for *Manligheten* to lie behind an island with high ground, and, when the Scheer came within range, to come into the open and open fire with all guns. Those tactics would have been difficult since the Swedish vessel had neither fire control system nor combat information centre.

Manligheten went through major reconstruction in 1941. It included the installation of new boilers. Bofors rebored all the guns with new rifling. The refit gave the vessel a new combat centre and fire control system, four new 5.7cm, two 4.0cm and two 2.5cm guns. In addition, *Manligheten* was fitted with a new bow with a pronounced flare that improved seakeeping qualities and kept the foredeck drier. Cowls were added to the funnels. After being in commission throughout the 1939–45 war, the vessel went to the breakers in 1950.

Oscar II The 1901 parliamentary committee's discussions about the last armoured vessel to be built under the 20-year programme concentrated on the amount of protection the new vessel ought to have. The committee cited recent naval actions (probably the Spanish-American and Sino-Japanese wars) as proving that a new vessel would need heavier armour, more medium calibre guns and greater speed. The committee examined three proposals; the first was an improved *Äran*-class vessel with eight 15.2cm guns, the second included the two extra 15.2cm guns and a speed of 18kts. The third proposal increased the number of 21cm guns to four, the 15.2cm to eight and a speed of 18kts. That vessel's displacement would be about 4,800 tons. The estimated cost for the third alternative was 776 million kronor – about 50% more than the cost of an *Äran*-class ship. The committee said two important matters had to be considered – size and costs. The new ships's size must suit its strategic defensive functions, namely to destroy an invader's troop transports at sea, break an enemy's blockade of Swedish ports and maintain control over Swedish coastal waters. Moreover, the ships must be able to navigate the skerries' confined waters and be able to engage an enemy's 'strongest and fastest' ships. The committee held the more units in action, the greater the chances of success. The funds available should determine ships' sizes and numbers. When the committee took a vote, the majority of members recommended the first alternative. The reasons for the rejection of the second and third alternatives were the costs, also beliefs that the larger vessels would have difficulties in the skerries' confined waters. The committee also recommended the construction of two armoured cruisers, more torpedo boats and a submarine.

In 1903, the Navy's administration board requested funds for the 12th armoured ship to be larger, more heavily armoured and armed and faster than the *Äran*-class vessels. The new ship's design was originally closer to the third alternative. However, the Navy Minister, for reasons of political expediency, decided to request parliament for funds for the second alternative. The members agreed to release a third of the estimated total cost of 6,225,000 kronor. The decision that the new ship was to be the fleet's flagship required special arrangements for the fleet's commander and his staff which raised the construction by about 800,000 kronor. In May 1903, Oscar II gave royal assent to the final draughts prepared under the direction of H. H. Lilliehöök. The name of the new vessel was to be *Oscar II*. Motala, Verkstad was to manufacture the engines; Lindholm of Göteborg, the hull.

Oscar II's dimensions were length 95.6m, beam 15.42m, draft forward 5.13m, aft 5.56m. Her displacement at full load was 4,495 tons. The weight distribution was hull 1,025 tons, armour 987 tons, guns and ammunition 594 tons, engines and boilers 640 tons, other equipment 648 tons, crew and stores 86 tons, coal 500 tons, reserve feed-water 15 tons.

The machinery driving two three-blade propellers was two quadruple expansion engines 9,400ihp, built by Motala, that gave *Oscar II* a maximum speed of 18.98kts, attained on acceptance trials. The Yarrow water tube, coal-fired boilers supplied the steam. The vessel's range was 1,100 miles at 17.8kts and 3,550 miles at 11kts.

Bofors supplied the armament that included two 21cm guns in single turrets, eight 15.2cm in four twin turrets, ten 57cm and three 3.7cm guns for the steam picket boats. One underwater tube supplied by Armstrong Whitworth, was placed on each side of the hull. Schuckert supplied four searchlights. Krupps of Essen supplied the turrets' armour. The 21cm barbette armour was 17.5cm thick, the turrets' armour was fronts 19cm and backs 13cm. The 15cm gun turrets' fronts and backs had 12.5 and 6cm respectively. The water-line armour supplied by Schneider of France was 15cm midships reduced to 10cm in the bow and stern. The citadel's armour was 10cm thick covering an area of 23m that included the 15cm guns and 5.7cm gun hoists and the area between the boilers, furnaces and the smoke stacks. The conning tower's armour was 15.7cm. The admiral's tower aft had 10cm armour; the decks 3.7cm. *Oscar II*'s complement as flagship was 335.

Lindholm launched the hull in 1905 but the famous general strike delayed delivery until 1907. During the two-year period between the launch and the completion, an anonymous author published an article in a leading daily in which he maintained that destroyers and submarines were the best vessels to attack invading transports. He suggested that the battle of Tsushima between the Japanese

Oscar II *after 1938–9 reconstruction at sea off Karlskrona (Sjöhistoriska Museet, Stockholm.)*

and Russian fleets proved that *Oscar II* and the cruiser *Fylgia*, then under construction, would have insufficient armament to 'slug it out' with modern battleships and armoured cruisers. In addition, their speed would be too slow to avoid action with more powerful ships. The author proposed that a vessel of 4,500 tons displacement armed with four 30cm, ten 7.6cm guns, and having a speed of 17kts, would meet Sweden's defence requirements. Members of the Navy Administration Board held that a 25cm gun could be just as effective as a 30cm and that 7.6cm guns would prevent short-range contests. The proposal considered at the Swedish Technological Association's January 1906 meeting was discussed but was dismissed as impractical by Navy board members.

Oscar II had problems during firing trials. When the forward 21cm gun was fired at maximum elevation, the hatches of the 15cm guns had to be closed. The firing of the two after twin turrets made stay in the flag officer's tower unpleasant. Those 'teething troubles' caused delays in the acceptance trials that only finished in 1908. Since King Oscar died in December 1907, he may never have seen the ship that bore his name.

The ship went through three refits, the first in 1911 when a tripod mast and fighting top replaced the foremast, the second in 1929 when the main mast was shortened. In 1937, *Oscar II* was in, the Karlskrona dockyard for surveys. In 1938 Germany's seizure of Austria caused a Swedish rearmament programme. The dockyard had to begin a major refit of *Oscar II* to increase its fighting value.

Ten new boilers, including two to burn oil, replaced the old; the main mast was removed. New equipment included a fire control system and a new fighting top with new range finders. In addition, the dockyard installed a gyro compass with repeaters, echo sounding gear, paravanes and three modern searchlights. New 5.7cm AA guns replaced the older model. Two 2.5 AA guns and two twin 8mm guns increased the old ship's fire power. Bofors' late delivery of tooth cog arcs for the 21cm guns delayed the refit's completion until the end of October 1939. The results of rearmament and additional equipment were to increase the vessel's tonnage at full load to 4,850 tons and draft to 5.7 metres.

Oscar II's career included visits to Portsmouth and Cowes in 1907. In 1911, King Gustaf V took passage in her when making an official visit to Emperor Wilhelm, Germany. In April 1918, *Oscar II*, with the new coastal defence ship *Sverige* and elderly *Thor* proceeded to the Åland islands to protect the inhabitants from the maraudings of Soviet forces. A larger German force arrived in May. Difficulties arose between the Germans that had the backing of Finnish provisional government and the Swedish squadron. As a result, the Swedish government withdrew the Swedish warships.

Oscar II formed part of a local defence force at Karlskrona throughout World War II. Struck off strength in 1950, the damage control school used the hull for training for another two years. In 1974, a scrap merchant purchased the wrecked hull.

After completion of *Oscar II*, several committees considered the types of coastal defence vessels to replace those laid down in the late 19th century. The 1909 committee recommended more heavily armed turbine-driven vessels. In 1912, the Götaverken yard, Goteborg, laid the keel of *Sverige*, the first of three new turbine-driven coastal defence ships. Delayed by World War I, the delivery of the third, *Gustaf V*, did not take place until 1922.

Continuous discussions took place between 1922 and 1937 about replacements of the *Sverige* class vessels. In 1937, the Naval Staff proposed an offensive force of cruisers and destroyers. That proposal was unpopular with the politicians. However, the proposal for two large coastal defence ships armed with 15.4cm guns met the politicans' approval. Owing to the outbreak of World War II, none were laid down.

Why were so many obsolete vessels, including the *Äran* class, retained by the Swedish Navy? The *Äran* class vessels' guns, with their flat trajectory and low shooting ranges, were no match for the German and Soviet vessels built in the 1930s. The Navy argued that the older vessels could carry out some neutrality guard tasks. A second reason was that the retention of the old ships enabled the Navy to keep its personnel numbers high. In June 1940, the new defence minister, Mr Edwin Skold, requisitioned turrets built by Bofors for the Dutch Navy. He ordered the Navy to build two cruisers for these turrets with automatic 15.2cm guns. The Navy now got its wish for an offensive force. Nonetheless, Ansaldo of Italy was commissioned to prepare preliminary drawings for a 16,000-ton vessel to be armed with six 28cm guns. The 1942 keel laying of the cruisers *Gota Lejon* and *Tre Kronor*, and large destroyers ended the Swedish Navy's coastal defence ship period.

Sources

Politics
Admiralitets Kollegiets Historia Vol. IV, Stockholm, 1980
Tidskrift – i – Sjöväsendet, Karlskrona, 1873, 1885, 1899
Sandström A, *Pansarfartyg åt Sveriges Flotta*, Stockholm, 1984
Svenska Flottans Historia, Vol. 3, Malmö, 1945
Åhlund B., *Vanmakt till Sjömakt*, Stockholm, 1994

Construction, Machinery and *Armament*
Engström, I. A., *Års berättelse i Skeppsbyggeri*, Stockholm, 1899
Holmquist, A., *Flottans Beredskap 1938/40*, Stockholm, 1972
Sandström, A., *Pansarfartyg åt Sveriges Flotta*, Stockholm, 1986
Svenskt Skeppsbyggeri, Malmö, 1963
Svenska Flottans Historia, Vol. 3, Malmö, 1945
Halldin, G., *Skeppsbyggmastare, Marin Ingenjörer*, Malmö, 1948
Westerlund, K. E., *Etal Svenska Örlögsfartyg*, 1855/1995, *Karlskrona* 1992

Special Acknowledgement
Captain (E) C. Borgenstam, RSwN, has kindly let me have access to his extensive notes and an unpublished paper about the coastal defence battleships.

THE MYSTERY OF THE LAST VOYAGE OF JAPANESE SUBMARINE *I–52*

There have been many stories of sunken submarines carrying gold bullion, but most cannot be substantiated. **David Miller** looks at the latest case, which raises some intriguing questions.

In June 1995 a headline in the British *Guardian* newspaper announced that 'US team finds gold-laden Japanese submarine 51 years after sinking.' According to the report, the US-led team had just beaten a British team in finding the wreck of *I–52*, which is said to contain an estimated US$15million worth of gold bars. To discover the story behind this latest in the series of 'sunken treasures' we must go back to the signing of the Axis pact by Japan, Germany and Italy on 27 September 1940. This agreement set out a number of high-flown war aims, but suffered from one fundamental flaw, since there was a vast geographical distance between the two Europe partners and their ally in the Far East, a problem exacerbated by Allied control of most of the land, sea and air routes between them.

When Japan entered the war in December 1941, Axis naval cooperation mainly involved submarine attacks by Germany and Japan (and, to a lesser extent, Italy) in the Indian Ocean. Initially the German boats returned to France after their operations, but eventually a base was established in Japanese-occupied Malaya, at Penang, followed by two smaller bases in Singapore and Soerabaya. The Axis partners also sent supplies to each other. In general terms, the Germans despatched prototype equipment, including items such as disassembled aircraft and their engines, plans, and samples of ammunition, plus some raw materials such as mercury. They also presented two U-boats to the Japanese as examples of the very latest design and construction practice. For their part, the Japanese were less forthcoming concerning new equipment and weapons, although they did send some plans and samples to Germany, and there is no trace of them ever having offered a submarine to the Germans. Their supplies to Germany were, instead, raw materials such as rubber and molybdenum, as well as drugs, particularly opium and quinine.

At first, the trade was conducted by blockade-running merchant ships, but, like the surface raiders, these were gradually eliminated by the Allies until, in February 1944, Hitler forbade any further voyages. That left submarines and a number of voyages were undertaken between German-occupied ports in France and the Far East.

The Germans were very short of operational U-boats and were thus loath to use their own submarines as transports, so they persuaded the Italians to convert some of their submarines (which had proved unsatisfactory as attack boats) for use as transports. These were converted at Bordeaux and sailed for the Far East in 1943 and some reached Singapore. They were still there on 8 September 1943 when Italy capitulated to the Allies and the boats lying in Singapore were taken over by the Japanese for a short period and then handed over to the Germans. Some set out on the return journey, but none reached Europe.

The Germans continued to send U-boats to the Far East right up to the very end of the war. When making the return voyage to France all U-boats carried a relatively small amount of additional cargo. The Japanese Navy sent five submarines to France (see Table 1) of which three reached France, but of those three, only one ever completed the return voyage to Japan. The last submarine to be sent to France was *I–52*, which sailed from Singapore on 23 April 1944 and is known to have had a rendezvous with a German submarine on 23 June in the mid-Atlantic; it then disappeared until it was found by the treasure hunters in 1995.

The Submarine

During World War Two the Imperial Japanese Navy's (IJN) I–class submarines were the largest in any navy. The designation was derived from their hull numbers, which used the letter 'I', the initial letter of the Japanese word *junsen* (cruiser). They were intended for operations in the

No photograph of I–52 *is known to exist, but* I–16, *shown here, was of almost identical size and appearance, except that* I–52 *had a second 140mm (5.5in) gun abaft the conning tower.* I–52 *had an unrefuelled range on the surface of 27,000 nautical miles, far more than sufficient to sail from Singapore to the French coast without refuelling. Unfortunately for her crew it was necessary to collect three German radio operators for the final leg of the voyage at a mid-ocean rendezvous which proved fatal. (IWM, MH 5953)*

C3/C4 Class

Displacement	2,564 tons surfaced
	3,644 tons submerged
Length:	356.5ft (108.7m)
Beam:	30.5ft (9.3m)
Draught:	16.75ft (5.1m)
Propulsion:	Two diesels; 4,700shp
	Two electric motors; 1,200bhp
	Two shafts

Speed:	17.75 knots surfaced
	6.5 knots submerged
Range:	27,000nm at 12 knots surfaced
	105nm at 3 knots submerged
Operating depth:	330ft (100m)
Crew:	94
Armament:	Six 533mm (21in) torpedo tubes
	19 torpedoes
	Two single 5.5in (140mm) guns
	Two 25mm (1×2) cannon

Five boats of the C1 class were built in 1936–41 as long-range, attack submarines. They were followed by the C3/C4 class which had virtually the same dimensions, but was optimised for long range. This meant that they had much less powerful engines (4,700bhp vs 12,400bhp) six torpedo tubes instead of eight and one 5.5in (140mm) gun instead of two. This enabled much more fuel to be carried, increasing surfaced range from 14,000nm to 27,000nm.

Pacific against United States warships, for which great range and endurance – and hence size – were necessary. Such size also meant, however, that they were much slower to dive and considerably less manoeuvrable under water.

I–52, one of three attack submarines of the C3/C4 class, was laid down at Kure Naval Yard in March 1942 and completed on 18 December, 1943. The new boat's first mission was a supply run to Europe and following work-up it was loaded for its mission and sailed from Kure on 10 March, 1944 under command of Commander Uno, IJN. *I–52* arrived at the Japanese naval base in Singapore in mid-april, refuelled, picked up supplies and then sailed for Europe on 23 April, 1944. Although it was built as an attack submarine and not as a freighter, *I–52*'s size enabled it to carry no less than 516 tonnes of cargo, as well as 16 passengers.

The Allies keep watch

Unknown to either the Japanese or German navies, however, the Allies followed *I–52*'s progress throughout this mission, primarily through monitoring the radio links between Germany and the Far East. The Japanese embassy in Berlin had both diplomatic and naval circuits to Tokyo, as did the Germans, while the latter also had naval circuits to the U-boat bases in Penang and Singapore. All these operated in the medium- and high-frequency (MF/HF) bands and were easily monitored by the Allies, as was to be expected, but what was considered impossible by both the Germans and the Japanese was that the Allies had broken both the codes which were supposed to protect the traffic. The Allied codebreakers followed the submarine's progress closely, noting, for example, the changes in the submarine's codename, which was known on the Japanese links, first as 'Momi' and later as 'Gimmatsu', while on the German naval circuits, it was known as either 'Tanne' or 'Föhre.' These two words are, in fact, synonymous in German, being alternative names for the pine-tree.

Earlier voyages to France had shown Japanese submarine crews to be inexperienced in the ways of Allied anti-submarine warfare (ASW) operations, which were especially intense in the Bay of Biscay. Thus, it became the practice for a German U-boat to rendezvous (RV) with the incoming Japanese visitor in mid-Atlantic and to place a small German party on board, which was equipped with extra communications and radar warning equipment, and was required to give expert advice during the final leg of the voyage and also maintain communications with Captain U-boats (West). By this stage in the war, headquarters of *Befehlshaber der U-boote* (BdU) (commander of the U-boats) had moved back to Berlin, leaving Captain U-boats (West) at Lorient in operational command of U-boats in the Atlantic.

Detailed instructions had been agreed in the previous September concerning procedures at an ocean rendezvous, describing how the two submarines were to effect a meeting, what to do if they could not find each other, and also their reactions to being discovered by Allied ships or aircraft. Concerning the latter, if one of the submarines had 'an excessive diving time' (a polite reference to the Japanese submarine) and it detected the attacking aircraft sufficiently early, either visually or by radio direction-finding (RDF), then it was to submerge, indicating that it was doing so by flying a red flag. If, however, it was unable to dive in time, it would fly a green flag and fight it out on the surface. Once the alarm was over, the two submarines were to move to a new rendezvous 120 miles due west of the position where they had submerged, arriving there precisely 24 hours later.

Armed with these instructions and with the three-man liaison party aboard, the Type IXC/40 U-boat, *U–530* (*Kapitän-Leutnant* Kurt Lange), sailed from France on 22 May, 1944. For some reason, part of the rendezvous instructions were changed on 9 June, well after *U–530* had sailed. Lange was told to arrive at the RV at 2115 GMT on 22 June and, after surfacing, to await *I–52*'s arrival. If contact had not been established by 2400 the German submarine would remain at the RV, listening on its hydrophones, while the Japanese submarine carried out high-speed runs for the first ten minutes of each hour until dawn. If still not in contact, the procedure would be repeated on the following two nights. In addition, the success signal was now to be given when 150 miles from the RV rather than 120, as previously ordered. The new orders also took account of the recent Allied invasion on June 6 and said that 'should the invasion situation require it' the Japanese submarine would be instructed to go to Norway instead of to France. It must be presumed that Lange would have shown this to KL Schäfer before he left for the Japanese submarine.

Meanwhile, *I–52* reported on 11 June that it had reached 10°N 31°W and, despite the distance travelled from Singapore, Commander Uno told his superiors that he still had sufficient fuel for a further 12,000 miles at 11

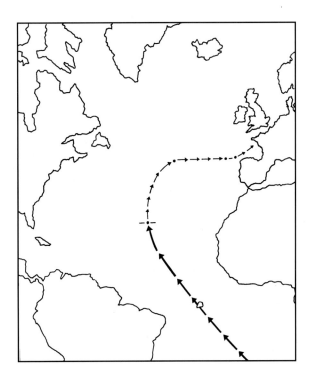

The track of I–52 *up the mid-Atlantic.*

⟶ *confirmed track*

⟶ *assumed track if not sunk near Azores*

—•— *RV with* U–530 *(23 June 1944)*

knots, and provisions for 3 months. On 23 June the two boats rendezvoused exactly as planned, as recorded in *U–530*'s *Kriegestagebuch* (war diary):

1930 hours. Arrived at rendezvous EG 5288.
2315 hours. Direction Finder 280 degrees.
2320 hours. Surfaced. 'Tanne' in sight.
2330–0145 hours. Transferred equipment. Transferred *Kapitänleutnant* Schäfer, *OberFunkMeister* Schulze, *OberFunksMaat* Behrendt.

This event has been confirmed to this author by an eye-witness, the former *Leutnant-zur-See* Carl-Felix Schüler, who was a watchkeeper aboard *U–530* during this voyage. He writes that: '*Kapitänleutnant* Schäfer served as the 'navigating officer' for a Japanese submarine through the Bay of Biscay to Brest. We met that submarine and transferred him.'

But, as a result of Allied monitoring, a US Navy task group (TG.22.2), commanded by Captain Vosseler, USN, was just over the horizon. TG.22.2 comprised the carrier *Bogue* (CVE–9) and destroyer-escorts *Haverfield* (DE–393), *Janssen* (DE–396), *Willis* (DE–395), *Francis M Robinson* (DE–220) and *Willhoite* (DE–397), and had been searching for the two Axis submarines since June 15. As a result, according to the eye-witness Schüler, '. . . After we had stowed the rubber dinghy we were attacked by (one?) aircraft. We submerged. The Japanese

JAPANESE SUBMARINES IN THE TRANSPORT ROLE BETWEEN THE FAR EAST AND EUROPE: 1942–45

Submarine	Class	Departed (place/date)	Arrived (place/date)	Load	Remarks
I–30	B1 Type (I–15)	Penang 22 Apr 42	Lorient 5 Aug 42	Aircraft and torpedo plans.	Operated off African coast before sailing for Europe.
		Lorient 22 Aug 42	Penang 5 Oct 42	One Japanese engineer plus various equipments and plans.	Sunk 13 Oct 42 by mine off Singapore, while en route to Japan.
I–29	B1 Type (I–15)	Penang 5 Apr 43	Penang 13 May 43	Two passengers. Freight, including gold.	a. I–29 met U–180 off Madagascar 23–27 Apr 43. b. This was the only example of a mid-way exchange.
U–180	Type IXD₁	Bordeaux 9 Feb 43	Bordeaux 3 Jul 43	Two passengers. Freight (both directions).	c. Passengers taken from Europe to Far East were Chandra Bose Indian nationalist leader) and his ADC.
U–511 (Ro–500)	Type	Lorient 10 May 43	Penang 16 Jul 43 Kure 7 Aug 43	One Japanese, three Germans.	Transferred to IJN on arrival in Japan as Ro–500, 16 Sep 43. See Note 1.
I–8	J3 Type (I–7 class)	Singapore 1 Jun 43	Brest 21 Aug 43	Took crew for Ro–501. (Ex–U–1224)	See Note 2.
		Brest 5 Oct 43	Singapore 5 Dec 43	Diesel engines, bomb sights, etc.	a. Reached Kure 21 Dec 43. b. Only successful round trip by a Japanese submarine.
I–34	B1 Type (I–15 class)	Penang 13 Nov 43	–	Plans and handbooks for submarines.	Left Singapore 11 Nov 43. Sunk 13 Nov 43 when about to enter Penang harbour.
I–29	B1 Type (I–15 class)	Singapore 16 Dec 43	Lorient 11 Mar 44	16 passengers, all Japanese.	Voyage was without incident.
		Lorient 16 Apr 44	Singapore 14 Jul 44	18 passengers: 14 Japanese, 4 German. Plans for jet and rocket fighers.	Sunk 26 Apr 44 off Manila, while en route from Singapore to Japan.
I–52	C3 Type (I–52 class)	Singapore 23 Apr 44	–	See main story	Sunk in Atlantic.
Ro–501 (ex U–1224)	Type IXC	Kiel 13 Mar 44	–		a. Sunk off Azores 13 May 44. b. See Note 2.

Notes

[1] Hitler presented two German U-boats to the Imperial Japanese Navy. The first, *U–511*, was already in service with the German Navy and sailed from France with its German crew (plus some Japanese passengers). On arrival in Japan it was transferred to the IJN as *Ro–500* and the German officers and sailors were dispersed among other U-boats and bases in the Far East.

[2] The second boat to be transferred, *U–1224*, was brand-new and the IJN sent a complete crew in *I–8* for training and to bring it back to Japan.

submarine opened fire with its anti-aircraft guns. After several bomb detonations the AA fire ceased and we perceived in our immediate vicinity unmistakable sinking noises. It was totally clear to us that the Japanese submarine had sunk.'

What happened aboard the Japanese submarine can only be a matter for speculation. It would seem, however, that Commander Uno decided to fight it out on the surface, possibly because he simply did not have enough time to dive. It must also be a matter of guesswork that, since Schäfer had only just arrived aboard, Commander Uno may not yet have been prepared to accept any advice the German gave him so early in their acquaintanceship. Meanwhile, Lange, who was naturally far more experienced in Atlantic warfare, dived and survived.

Next morning, searching US ships found human remains and flotsham of obviously Japanese origin. There was no other Japanese submarine in the Atlantic at that time which could have been the source of such remains: I–29 had left Lorient on 16 April, 1944 and reached Singapore on 14 July, while Ro–511 had been sunk near the Azores on 13 May. The fate of I–52 would thus seem to have been as conclusively proved as was possible under the circumstances.

A Surprising Post-Script

That should have been the end of the story, but there were two extraordinary sequels. The rendezvous with the Japanese submarine had taken place on the night of 23/24 June, following which Lange was under orders to move at least 150 miles away before making a radio report. In the event, he failed to make radio contact with Captain U-boats (West) on the first attempt and so the German authorities ashore did not know the outcome of the mission until 27 June, when Lange signalled: '. . . Carried out task on 23/6. One unsuccessful attempt already made to transmit information.' Somewhat surprisingly, this signal makes no mention at all of the air attack on I–52, nor of the 'breaking-up noises' so clearly heard by Schüler. So, having no reason to think otherwise, there was considerable optimism ashore and the following day the Japanese Naval Attaché in Berlin sent a signal to his superiors in Tokyo, telling them that '. . . the Germans have received a signal on the 27th to the effect that 'Momi' effected its rendezvous with the German submarine without incident. Liaison officer and others were transferred and crew are all fit.' Unless there was another signal not recorded by Ultra, the naval attache's comment that the crew was 'all fit' seems to have been an assumption based on the fact that Lange's signal did not actually say that they were unwell.

Thus, the Axis partners ashore believed that everything was going according to plan and that the Japanese submarine would arrive at Lorient on schedule. Consequently, Captain U-boats (West) sent out a general signal (29 June) warning that '. . . Japanese submarine "Föhre" is on passage via Square Green MK (Southern half) to Western France. Its present position is approximately Square Green IQ 23, Course North. Appearance.

Length 108 metres, built-in conning-tower, one 14cm gun forward, one 2.5cm twin aft. Be prepared for encounter. Do not hinder.' Ultra noted that the naval grid squares had been encoded and that 'Green MK' was actually Naval grid square BD, while 'Green IQ 23' was Naval grid square DR 20.

It had been arranged that I–52 would report its position some three or four days before reaching the rendezvous off Lorient, but nothing was heard, and the authorities ashore began to feel a little concerned. But then, on 30 July, they suddenly received the signal 'QWF' on the expected frequency, which meant according to the operation order that I–52 was now just 36 hours from the RV. There was some excitement ashore as the Japanese Naval Attaché signalled Tokyo that '. . . Yesterday, the 30th, contact with "Momi" was re-established and it is estimated that it should enter harbour about August 3. The party who are to meet it have left Paris for the port of arrival.' All this puzzled the British experts at Bletchley Park, who frequently knew more about what had happened than either the Germans or the Japanese, and they added a note below the decrypted signal that: '. . . "Momi" ((I–52)) is believed to have been sunk by aircraft to the West of Cape Verde Island on June 24. This is the first definite evidence we have received to the contrary.'

At Lorient the German navy despatched an escort ship to RV with I–52 on 1 August at 0430 and again at 2315, but the expected submarine did not arrive. Also on 1 August, another previously-agreed signal was received continuously throughout the morning and again in the afternoon, so a German ship was sent to the rendezvous on the following day as well, but to no avail.

Obviously frustrated, Captain U-boats (West) sent a radio message to I–52 on 3 August, telling its captain that an escort ship would stand by at the rendezvous yet again, this time on the 4th at 0430, and that if the Japanese failed to rendezvous they were to report the reason. So, the escort ship went out once more, but the hoped-for submarine failed to arrive. The Japanese Naval Attaché, probably by now grasping at straws, thought that this might be due to an error of calculation, so on 5 August he sent a somewhat plaintive message direct to the captain, once again giving him route instructions. '. . . Has there been some error of calculation?' he asked, 'Please inform me again your estimated date of arrival at the above rendezvous point.'

By now, however, another factor was coming into play, since the Allies had invaded France on June 6 and were now sweeping around towards Lorient, making I–52's arrival there potentially very embarrassing. So, the ever-optimistic attaché sent off yet another signal telling the captain that '. . . Although we are not in contact with your ship, we (trust) that it is safe. In consequence of the sudden developments in the war situation in Northern France, it is no longer safe to enter Lorient or any other port on the French coast. You are therefore requested to sail for Norway. Your port of arrival should be Trondheim or Bergen. [Whatever happens] please report subsequent developments by telegram immediately. The German Navy has already been consulted.'

By the following day, however, the attaché was taking a

more realistic view, which was reflected in a very long signal to Tokyo, reporting how he had '. . . begun to entertain doubts as to the safety of the ship.' He suggested that 'QWF' might have been a fake message by the British, although the action taken by the enemy had not tallied with this, as previous experience showed that prior to sending fake messages the British would both precede and follow it by another signal which German Navy's intercept organization, the *B-dienst*, had learnt to recognise, but no such signals had been sent on this occasion. The German navy had given up hope for the Japanese submarine, although the attaché still considered it possible that the captain was trying to make a detour North on his own initiative and without sending a wireless signal.

What was aboard I–52?

Not only did Allied intelligence know about *I–52*'s movements, but it also knew precise details of who and what was aboard. The submarine's crew comprised four officers, seven warrant officers and eighty-four petty officers and sailors. These were accompanied by thirteen passengers: one officer, one warrant officer and four petty officers, together with seven technicians from various Japanese companies, described as being 'men temporarily employed by the Navy'.

In addition, the submarine was carrying 228 tonnes of metals (tin, molybdenum and tungsten), 288 tonnes of opium, 3 tonnes of quinine and 54 tonnes of raw rubber. There were also some cypher books and documents, which had been requested by the Japanese military attaché in Berlin. The most significant part of the cargo, however, was described in detail in a signal from the head of the Foreign Affairs Department of the Ministry of Finance in Tokyo to Financial Commissioner Yumoto at the embassy in Berlin:

1. The gold being sent by 'Momi' on its present voyage is for the replenishing of the gold fund special account, and details are as follows:
(A) Number of Gold bars: 146 (49 boxes).
(B) Total weight of bullion: 2,000,229 grammes 0.
(C) Purity of Bullion: 2,000,003 grammes 5.
(D) Fineness: over 995 fine.
(E) Inherent value 7,700,128 Yen 64 (if one gramme be taken as 4 Yen 80 Sen, 9,600,016 Yen 80.)
2. Please arrange to handle the matter as on previous occasions.

Since this message was sent on 10 June, which was well after *I–52* had left its last port-of-call (Singapore) and in view of its origin in the Ministry of Finance, its authenticity appears unchallengeable. It thus appears that the wreck of *I–52*, located by the American team, should contain 146 bars of gold, which should be worth some US$15 million, at current prices.

This message, however, ends with a reference to 'previous occasions' and there is an earlier signal in the Ultra files dated 2 June 1943, which refers to a 'forthcoming consignment of gold' consisting of 144 ingots and says that it had been agreed with the German authorities that this consignment would be entrusted to a German submarine. One unusual feature of this signal is that, according to the additional comments by Ultra, although received on 2 June, 1943 it was not actually decrypted until 14 July, 1944. It is not, however, clear what caused the British to unearth this signal 13 months after it had been received. So, which U-boat carried this consignment and did it reach its European destination, or does it, too, lie on the ocean bed awaiting another party of treasure hunters?

Three questions thus remain. First, was *I–52* actually sunk by the Avengers? If the answer to that is 'yes', then who sent the message 'QWF' on 30 July, 1944 and for what purpose? The message was on the correct frequency, and was sent in Morse code and repeated regularly, so there seems to be no chance that there was any misunderstanding on the part of the German radio operator. The British may well have known about the coded signal (they seem to have known almost everything else concerning this operation through Ultra) but if they made these transmissions what were they trying to achieve? The only German reaction to 'QWF' was to send a small warship out to the RV, but this was never attacked.

Alternatively, is it possible that *I–52* did not actually sink as a result of the attack by *Bogue*'s Avenger aircraft and that the 'QWF' signal was genuine. But in that case what happened to *I–52*, because it was never actually seen again after 23 June? At this stage, research into the story of *I–52* seems to raise as many questions as it answers and the further investigation of the wreck by the treasure hunters is awaited with interest.

Sources
"Ultra" decrypts in the Public Record Office.
Letters from Carl-Felix Schüler to the author.

ENTENTE CORDIALE, 1865

The large fleets created by Great Britain and France after the Crimean War are seldom given the attention they deserve. **Colin Jones** looks at a rare moment when the armed might of both navies was on parade.

At the end of two weeks almost continuous naval ceremony and pageantry, the editor of *The Times* wrote,

> The spectacle of the two most powerful nations of Europe converting their engines of hostility into instruments of hospitality, and deriving from the symbols of warfare pledges of mutual respect and friendship, cannot fail to be long remembered, and at once to illustrate an honourable alliance and set a happy example to other countries and to other times. In one instance, at all events, two great nations, with distinct if not rival dispositions and prejudices, with differences of character deeply ingrained by ancient histories and traditions, have found even in their former antagonism grounds for mutual respect, and have learnt that their diversities make them the more necessary to each other, and the more potent in advancing the happiness of the world.

The text could be applied to our own times, but it dates from Saturday, 2 September 1865.

It all began with a visit of the French Channel squadron to Plymouth in late July. There the Prince and Princess of Wales had watched from the deck of the Royal Yacht *Osborne*, a naval guard of honour – the British ironclads *Achilles*, *Prince Consort* and *Royal Sovereign*, frigate *Constance* and sloop *Gannet*, and the French ironclads *Magenta* and *Flandre* and sloop (aviso) *Ariel*. An invitation was subsequently given for the British Channel Fleet to visit the French arsenal of Cherbourg for the occasion of the Emperor's Birthday. The events then snowballed into a further visit of the fleet, to Brest, and a reciprocal visit by the French fleet to Portsmouth. The fleets would be accompanied by the highest naval authorities, the French Minister of Marine and the British First Lord of the Admiralty, and a beribboned contingent of officers, including, as the reporters put it, 'half the admirals on the navy list'. It was holiday season in the French and British naval ports, and no expense was spared, either by private individuals or the navies of the two countries, to ensure the success of the whole venture. Those British notables who could not be accommodated in the various Admiralty yachts and despatch vessels were found a place, along with the gentlemen of the press, aboard the troopship *Urgent*.

Simultaneous with the movement of the fleet, there was a yacht race across the Channel from Cowes to Cherbourg. All that was needed, as the Channel fleet steamed out of Portland, was good weather. It was not to be.

The fleet comprised the ironclad frigates *Achilles*, *Black Prince*, *Hector*, *Prince Consort* and *Defence*, the flagship, line of battleship *Edgar*, and the frigates *Liverpool*, *Octavia* and *Constance*. It was under the command of Rear Admiral Sir Sydney Dacres KCB, who had flown his flag in the Channel for the last two years, and who had taken the *Edgar* out of Spithead under sail alone the previous March – the last British ship of the line ever to do so. In the war against Russia he had commanded the battleship *Sans Pareil* in the Black Sea. Out in the Channel they found themselves facing dirty weather, with a heavy south-west wind, force 4 to 6. In these conditions, the *Constance* contrived to collide with the *Liverpool*, carrying away her mizzen chains and quarter boats, and losing her mizzen topmast. In the circumstances, she was considered not up to the requisite standard for a naval display and was sent home. The whole summer had featured bad weather, and the ironclads had frequently fallen into confusion in manoeuvring, leading to fears by Flag Captain Geoffrey Hornby that they would 'crack their shells'. For most of them, though, the visit to the French ports was to show that the training had paid off. Joining the fleet were the turret ironclad *Royal Sovereign*, the ironclad sloop *Research*, the gunboat *Trinculo*, tender to the flagship, and the paddle despatch vessel *Salamis*. The yachts also struck heavy weather, the sailing vessels having a hard time of it, and as for the steamers, the journalists, as they leaned against the bulwarks of the *Urgent*, were able to thank providence that they were not aboard the little paddle vessel *Fire Queen*, whose pitching was perceived as particularly violent.

Nevertheless, the fleet entered Cherbourg harbour at 6.30pm on Monday 14 August, to the resounding thunder of the salutes of the forts. As it was British practice not to salute after 6 pm, the ships came to their moorings silently. The warships were moored in three lines, at the western end of the harbour – the position of honour, and at the end of each line was one of the ironclads of the French Channel Fleet – *Magenta*, *Flandre* and *Héroïne*. There were also two French frigates present, and the British yachts, *Osborne*, *Enchantress*, *Salamis*, *Fire Queen* and *Sprightly*,

The Prince of Wales' yacht Osborne *passes between a guard of honour of the British and French ironclad squadrons in Plymouth Sound in July 1865. From left to right, the warships are: British –* Achilles *(reduced the previous month to a three-masted rig and without a bowsprit),* Prince Consort, *turret ironclad* Royal Sovereign *and frigate* Constance; *French –* Flandre *and* Magenta. *The relatively light rig of the French ironclads is notable.*

found themselves surrounded by yachts and excursion steamers. That night there were fireworks in the Grand Place, and observers were thrilled at the multitude of riding lights of the ships, and how the signal lamps flickered in the darkness. The arrangements had not entirely met with the approval of the captain of the *Edgar*, Geoffrey Hornby, who had wished to make the French port earlier in the day.

> 'My Lords did not leave Portsmouth yesterday morning when they ought because the weather looked threatening.'

Next morning the saluting began in earnest, between the ships and the forts, so that clouds of smoke wreathed the black hulls. As the smoke rolled away, the ships were seen suddenly to be decked in flags. It was the day of the public holiday, and the entertainments and sideshows were well patronised by holiday makers, but the weather became worse as the day progressed, deteriorating into a full south-west gale which hid the ships behind curtains of driving rain. Each of the French battleships was equipped with a steam launch, though of the British ships, only the *Edgar* boasted such an amenity. As a result, communication between ships which had only pulling boats was

somewhat hampered. Nevertheless, things went, damply, as planned, with a *Te Deum* in the Cathedral and a review of the garrison in the Place Napoléon.

At a dinner at the Hôtel de Ville that night, the first of the speeches were made, warmly commending the friendship between the two countries. Speakers noted the cooperation which had been enjoyed between ships of the two nations in recent operations in China and Japan. The Marquis de Chasseloup-Laubat and the Duke of Somerset led in proposing toasts to the respective monarchs while outside there were more fireworks. Perhaps it was the weather, but those who remembered the visit of Queen Victoria to Cherbourg in 1858 ruled them relatively inferior.

Wednesday was fine, with a keen cold wind from the north-west, but the day was to be filled with visits by the British officers to the French ships, and to the great breakwater, the Digue, which was regarded as one of the wonders of the world. It had been built, not as a projection out from the land, but in the middle of the sea. Not only was it 2.3 miles long, but it supported four large gun batteries and protected a roadstead that could contain every warship the French were ever likely to own. The stones of which it was built, it was observed, would make 200 miles

The fleet dressed with flags at Cherbourg on 15 August 1865 for the birthday of Napoleon III. The British flagship Edgar *is in the foreground, with the* Royal Sovereign *off her stern and a French corvette and British yachts off her bow.*

of the Great Wall of China. The extent to which the Cherbourg forts bristled with cannon was also noted. The *Magenta* was subject to minute scrutiny, as representing the strongest type of the French ironclads, though the *Héroïne*, just newly commissioned, was also of interest. Typically of the times, no one had a good word to say about the aesthetic attractions of the ironclads, and inevitable comparison was made with British practice, in particular the wideness of the French gunports and their relative closeness together, which was thought to possibly make the working of the big guns difficult and dangerous. The *Magenta* and *Solferino* were the only two-decked ironclads in the world, but on the whole, the British visitors were not specially impressed. Not only was the armour less than that of many British ironclads, but the absence of shot proof bulkheads at the ends of both batteries was looked on with disfavour. They had two chase guns on the upper deck, twenty-four guns on the main deck and twenty-six on the lower deck. In total, they comprised twelve 50 pounder smooth bores, thirty-six 30 pounder breech loading rifles, and four 80 pounder rifled howitzers. It was noted, however, that the lower deck guns were much closer to the water than was the case in British ironclads, 6 feet compared with 9ft. 3in., and that in practice they were closed and caulked while the French ships were at sea. Thus the ships were reduced to a second rate status in the eyes of many observers. One point in their favour was the armoured conning tower, not to mention the pronounced spur of the ram. The French ships were understood to be fast, and in addition, the method of fixing their armour by screws rather than by through bolts in the British manner was praised. To what extent the armour would resist shot was, of course, an area of lively dispute. Captain Hornby was very envious of the cleanliness of the ships of the French Channel fleet compared with his own, though later when he saw the more familiar dirt of the French Mediterranean fleet he attributed the cleanliness to the ships' being so much in port.

The British were also taken on a tour of the dockyard, in which nine older ships were lying side by side – including ships of the line *Ville de Nantes, Napoléon, Austerlitz* and *Bayard* and frigate *Clorinde*. Building were two more wooden ironclads, believed to be of the *Magenta* type, though only their keels and beaks could be seen,[1] as well as three first class avisos and a corvette. The three-decked cavalry transport *Aveyron* was fitting out for Cochin China.

There were a few curiosities easily passed over. One was the 'submarine gunboat' *Le Plongeur*, described thus:

This novel creation of naval architecture is shaped externally like a tortoise, is between 40ft. and 50ft. in length, and propelled by a kind of locomotive engine of about 12-horse power, driving a pair of screws at her stern. Its bow consists of a sliding port, fixed at an angle of about 45 deg., and which forms the gunport. *Le Plongeur* has been experimentally constructed to attack and destroy an enemy's fleet with perfect immunity to herself. This is to be accomplished by approaching the enemy under water, and when his keel becomes visible to the pilot of *Le Plongeur* the latter rises from underneath and discharges its terrible gun at the bottom of the unsuspecting ship, which, of course, immediately after goes down with all hands, while *Le Plongeur* dives again and screws away in search of another vessel.[2]

The French officers gave the British the impression that they considered it no more than an expensive toy, though Jules Verne is likely to have seen it as the prototype of his science fiction creation, the *Nautilus*, whose adventures were first published in 1870. Not quite so toy-like was the searchlight demonstrated on the *Magenta*, as well as on the paddle aviso *Dauphin*. Observers noted how it lit up the other ships in the dark, with a light powerful enough to read a newspaper by. It was hoped that this light could be a predecessor of underwater illumination for war purposes – something else for Jules Verne to ponder. Lastly there was on show a replica Roman trireme of 130 oars. It would be of interest to see whether its construction was more true to the original than more recent efforts in Greece.

Next day it was the turn of the British ironclads to receive French guests. M. Chasseloup-Laubat and Dupuy de Lôme took particular interest in the *Royal Sovereign*, going through her from the keelson upwards. The feeling was expressed that this ship, with her heavy guns in four Coles turrets, would be a match for any of the French ironclads in smooth water. She mounted five 10.5in guns, the sort of weapon which had demonstrated such smashing power in the recent American Civil War, and which would be guaranteed to penetrate the armour of any French ironclad. Her commander, Captain Herbert, stated, 'As she now stands she is the most formidable vessel of war I have ever been aboard of; she would easily destroy – if her guns were rifled – any of our ironclads.' The French, it seems, would certainly have agreed. Of the other ships, the French praised construction in iron as superior to that of wood with an iron carapace. Built for utility rather than beauty (especially since the removal of her foremost mast and bowsprit), the *Achilles* boasted sixteen 100pdr, six 68pdr and four 7in guns, all smooth

HM Paddle Yacht Fire Queen *from an old photograph taken in 1847. (CPL)*

bores. The superiority of the British ironclads was self-evident to the British observers, but on the French side, it was understood that Dupuy de Lôme was very contented with the comparative strength and power of his own creations.

The day was rounded off, in squally rain, with a ball at the Hôtel de Ville. If there had been a prize for the most striking costume, it would have gone to Dr John Urquart, a veteran of Copenhagen and other battles of past wars, who wore the official dress uniform of fifty years before. For the senior British officers, it was a chance to dance off some of those heavy meals of truffles.

The next day was one of dispersal, as many ships, including the *Urgent* with her contingent of journalists, returned directly to England. The *Constance*, rerigged and smart again, came into Portsmouth under sail in company with the *Octavia*, and as it was her first time in this port for her current commission, exchanged salutes with the *Victory*. The *Fire Queen* brought back Admirals Seymour and Wellesley, who rehoisted their flags aboard the *Victory* and *Asia* respectively. The *Royal Sovereign* also returned to Portsmouth via Portland as, despite the impression she had made, she was not rigged for sail in the manner of the main ironclad squadron, and her range of action was perceived to be small. She had bunkers for only three days' steaming. Meanwhile, back in Cherbourg, the flagships *Magenta* and *Edgar* exchanged salutes as the British ironclad squadron got under way for Brest. Before arriving at that port, they lay to in the lee of Jersey to repair damage to two of the ships, so that they should make a good showing.

There were those who, only a few years before, had predicted that the naval race between Britain and France would inevitably lead to war. Richard Cobden, writing at the end of 1861, had stated that 'the greatest evil connected with these rival armaments is that they destroy the strongest motive for peace'. He considered that permanent war expenditure without the outlet of war itself, with 'its usual excitements and honours', would not be tolerated by ordinary people. That it never came to war has been attributed variously to the sensible statesmanship and similar policies of both countries, as well as the general self confidence in the efficacy of their naval armaments which was emerging on both sides. Those who saw the celebrations of the ordinary people, both in France and in England, were able to report that there was nothing but the most cordial feeling extended on either side. First there had been exchanges between the monarchs, then between naval notables. The fleet visits on this occasion were seen as sealing the bond between the two peoples at the most basic level. One writer noted that between 1690 and 1815 there had been 56 years of war between Britain and France, and another 30 years in which danger and anxiety had been the norm. Now, the two nations could celebrate 50 years during which neither had raised sword against the other.

> The continued subsidence of the ancient animosities between the two nations, the corresponding growth of a more appreciative feeling, which overflows the accident of repeated changes of the form of Government in France and the idiosyncrasies of individual statesmen in Britain, the widening perception of the interests the two peoples have in keeping peace with each other, the increasing consciousness of common duties to be performed in defence and promotion of Western civilisation, present solid grounds for a firm confidence in the continuance of peace.

Brest, like Cherbourg, was packed with sightseers and holiday makers, whose enthusiasm was rewarded by the arrival of the British fleet under full sail on Monday 21 August. The French Mediterranean fleet had made port the previous Wednesday and were now drawn up in a very smart line at their moorings, with room for the British ships to anchor between them. There was a frisson of excitement as the British consul put out to meet his compatriots in *Gunboat No.5*, and then the *Edgar* saluted the forts on Spanish Point as one by one the black battleships followed her in, under their white clouds of canvas. Admiral Dacres, for one, was proud of the efficient and pretty evolutions of the fleet, though he smarted at the absence of commendation from his superiors.

The arsenal displayed the full pride of the French navy, the ship of the line *Bretagne*, ironclads *Solferino*, *Couronne*, *Provence*, *Normandie* and *Invincible*, ships of the line *Louis XIV*, *Ville de Lyon* and *Jean Bart*, and corvette *Reine Hortense*, acting on this occasion as official yacht. It was the ironclads which were important. There were also a large number of small cruisers, and the *Meuse* and *Allier*, transports, the latter in quarantine after its return from Mexico. As much as anything, these were the major representatives of the fleet that Napoleon III had built to challenge the maritime hegemony of Great Britain. Now, here were the two fleets lying peacefully together. The commander of the Mediterranean fleet was Vice Admiral Count Bouët Willaumez, a veteran of Mexico and the war against Russia.[3]

Once again, the weather was not kind to the French. There was cold and fog, and the first day of the regatta was held in heavy rain. Nevertheless, there were the usual visits, inspections and banquets. The second day of the regatta had too little wind for sailing, but there were some exciting rowing races, and in the evening, banquets aboard the *Solferino*, *Couronne* and *Invincible*. The highest ranking were aboard the flagship, and the middies whose affair was reported to be far the most enjoyable and noisy, were aboard the *Invincible*. The serious toasts were to the respective monarchs and armed forces. The middies were reported to have toasted specially the ladies of France and England, and the hope that the ladies of Portsmouth would be equally welcoming.

> What we can positively affirm is that when, towards 9 o'clock, the guests went on shore the two navies, as represented by their midshipmen, had the strongest need to afford each other mutual support.

On the Wednesday there was a dinner at the Marine Prefecture and a ball aboard a suitably transformed *Ville de Lyon*. Those who saw it were much taken by the gravel paths, fountains and trees which adorned the decks of the French battleship. In the background, as a reminder of

The French fleet arrives at Portsmouth on 29 August 1865, as the Solferino *salutes the British flag. The* Magenta *and* Solferino, *which can both be seen in the picture, were the only two-decked ironclads in the world. The* Solferino *is without her eagle figurehead.*

the old ways now past, lay the training ship *Borda* which until the previous year had been the largest sailing battleship in the world, the *Valmy*.

Next day, Thursday 24 August, both ironclad fleets steamed out to sea, the British to return directly to Portsmouth, and the French to engage in evolutions, including the gathering together of their principal forces, the better to show their power and might on arrival at the principal British naval base in a few days' time.

Portsmouth in its turn was absolutely full of visitors, and the fleet lay in its lines out at Spithead – *Achilles, Black Prince, Hector, Royal Sovereign, Defence, Edgar, Liverpool, Research* (which joined late at night on 28 August) and

Salamis. There were also ten gunboats, to act as tenders to the French ships when they arrived. As soon as a foreign sail was seen, there was a rush to all points of vantage. The first was a false alarm. It was the Austrian corvette *Erzherzog Friedrich*. She was the last of the Austrian fleet in the North Sea which had been operating against the Danes, and for this reason she would be accepted, but not welcomed as the French would be. Britain and Denmark were close friends. The next year she was to be part of the fleet which defeated the Italians at the Battle of Lissa.

Then at 10.30 the *Osborne, Enchantress* and *Black Eagle* steamed out with the Lords of the Admiralty to welcome the French fleet as, with thunder of salute and surrounded

Mutual courtesies between the corvette Reine Hortense, *yacht of the French Minister of Marine, and the* Osborne, *with the Lords of the Admiralty at Spit Buoy. In the background, the* Solferino, *which has just dropped anchor, and the other French ironclads are firing a salute to the* Victory.

by yachts, the black hulls came up to their anchorages in a place of honour opposite Southsea – nine ironclads – *Solferino, Magenta, Héroïne, Couronne, Flandre, Provence, Normandie, Invincible* and *Gloire*, accompanied by the corvettes *Caton* and *Reine Hortense*, and the avisos *Ariel* and *Faon*. The *Pigmy* had taken out officers to board each of the French vessels to bring them safely to their moorings. Along with the British fleet of six ironclads, one ship of the line, one frigate, the despatch vessel and the gunboats, it was a grand sight. On both sides, evolutions were smart, and in contrast to the French celebrations, the weather was fine. It was a day to remember. As Chasseloup-Laubat put it, it demonstrated a giant's strength.

That evening there was a dinner aboard the *Duke of Wellington*, and reporters did not fail to note how the passage of time had rendered her obsolete, but still a symbol of the way in which the British and French fleets had operated as allies against the Russians ten years before. Admirals and cabinet ministers were lavish in their praise of the allies, for the welcome that had been extended on both sides of the Channel, the times they had fought side by side and for the strength of the forces here assembled. They were sure that those present would remember these days with warmth in the years ahead. Taking note among

the guests in his own way, no doubt, was the Russian Admiral Boutahoff.

In the days following, there were visits to the dockyard installations, and to the ships. In particular, there was the new *Minotaur* lying in dock where she was fitting out – a ship of great power and presence. Also present were the new ironclads *Royal Alfred* and *Valiant* and the two ex-Confederate ironclads, *Scorpion* and *Wyvern*. The *Wyvern* was still to be supplied with her 300 pounder guns.[4] The shape of the new paddle despatch vessel *Helicon* seemed to observers to echo the ram bows of the French ironclads. The big frigate *Mersey* was laid up in Portsmouth, and the *Warrior*, perfection of ironclad construction in the public eye, was stripped and gutted as part of a major refit.

It all went very well. Palmerston was to write of the events, that 'all old sentiments of rivalship and antagonism as between Englishmen and Frenchmen are on our part extinguished'.

Another observer gave a rather more basic version of the same thing, as he noted in his diary, 'crowds, taverns, French and English sailors drunk together, some arm-in-arm, mutually friendly and unintelligible'.

Much more lavish than a banquet aboard a battleship was the provision for the guests at the Royal Naval

The French ironclad Magenta *is illuminated at night on 30 August as part of the naval celebrations, while in the background, rockets are fired from the Portsmouth forts.*

College, which hosted a banquet, and later a ball for over 2,000 guests. At night the fleets were illuminated and gave firework displays, and these even extended to the old *St Vincent* and *Victory*. There was also a military review on Southsea Common, though the British would have been the first to admit that it was a small thing compared with what would be normal on the Continent. It was the illuminations which struck the strongest chord.

> As if by magic, every ship in the allied fleets was illuminated. A salute of 21 guns was fired from the fleets, and as the echo of the last shot died away every ship in the two squadrons was so illuminated, by means of red, white and blue lights placed in every port, at both broadsides, and both yardarms, that the object which only a few moments before looked, even at a short distance, so grim and shadowy became at once transformed into a ship of light, revealing to view the outline of her slenderest spar.

Rockets were then sent up in clusters from the whole of the fleet, which, as they burst in the heavens, expanded into bouquets of red, white, and blue, and then gradually melted away in the still air, but only to be followed at short intervals by other clusters of rockets bursting and descending in an equally brilliant shower.

During the period of the celebrations, while the characteristics of broadside ironclad and turret ship had been so much in everyone's mind, there were published some ideas which were straws in the wind for the future. An anonymous author, believed to be a thinly disguised Prince de Joinville, expressed the opinion that what the fleet needed now was fast gunboats armed with heavy guns.

> The *Magenta* herself and her sister ships, beautiful and excellent sea boats as they are admitted to be, are no

The French ironclads leave Spithead to return to Cherbourg on 2 September 1865 at the end of the celebrations. The Gloire *brings up the rear, accompanied by yachts large and small. To the left, the* Enchantress *flies the Admiralty flag.*

longer the formidable war instruments provided with the irresistible power they were supposed to possess when they were first fitted out. The progress of artillery has dethroned them.

He went on to enunciate an ideal which could have been drawn directly from the experience of the American Civil War.

The great advantages to be sought above all others are swiftness and heavy guns; the protection of the iron-casing is but secondary. Swiftness is essential in almost all the circumstances of war, either to compel the enemy to fight, or to evade his pursuit; to keep up a blockade against blockade-runners, or to chase steam cruisers or privateers.

It was not just academic. Britain and France had been in danger for some time of being drawn into the recently concluded American conflict, and even now the United States was building steam cruisers of great speed specifically to operate against their commerce.

The Prince also noted the general malaise of the French officer corps, that so much of their time was taken up merely running a transport service for the army. The abil-

ity to smash through the armour of contemporary ironclads while staying clear of their own guns was an idea, realistic or not, which was to prove seductive for several generations. Even in 1865 the Armstrong company was working towards the production of the first Rendel gunboat – the poor navy's 'battleship-killer'. Nevertheless, expert British opinion, as expressed in *The Times*, was still in favour of the current scheme of things. Would a wooden vessel armed with heavy guns necessarily be faster than an ironclad such as the *Warrior*? Would it withstand the shell-fire of an ironclad if it tried to close to effective range? Contemporary rifled guns were capable of a maximum range of about 2,000 yards. Experience in America indicated that even a weak ironclad could withstand heavy weapons at much less than that. The ideas of the Prince, however, were not to go unheard. Captain Louis Grivel, who was at Portsmouth in command of the corvette *Caton*, would soon be considering the extent to which France should be trying to emulate Britain in the building of battleships, and in his publications, would label it as an illusion. The *jeune école* was just around the corner. A young Lieutenant Jacky Fisher, though in between assignments and courting a wife, was thinking about speed and big guns. He would go on to be one of the great reformers of the British naval service.

The events all came to an end, again in bright sunshine, on the morning of Saturday 2 September. Just five hours after the end of the ball, the visiting warships were under steam. The yacht *Sprightly* carried members of the corporation, and the *Enchantress*, the Lords of the Admiralty, as the ships saluted and manned their yards. Then with ponderous splendour, the French ironclads got under way and sailed for the open sea and home at Cherbourg. There, the Mediterranean fleet would coal before going on. For everyone concerned, it had been a great success. Frenchman and Briton had shown off the best they had, in amity and without accident. When asked what had impressed them most, the answer that the French gave ensured that the British hearts beat proudly with the knowledge that they were, in their blood, a seafaring nation. What had impressed them most? Why, the immense number of yachts!

Sources

The Times
Admiral Sir G. Phipps Hornby GCB (1896)
Parkes, *British Battleships*, 1956
The Three Panics (reprint of 1885)

C. I. Hamilton, *Anglo French Naval Rivalry 1840–1870*, Oxford, 1993
The *Illustrated London News*
K. Bourne, *The Foreign Policy of Victorian England 1830-1902*, Oxford, 1970
H. Allingham & D. Radford, eds, *William Allingham: A Diary*, London, 1985

Illustrations

The engravings are by E. Weedon and F. J. Smyth and are from the *Illustrated London News*, courtesy of Ballieu Library, University of Melbourne. The photograph of the *Fire Queen* is from the Conway Picture Library.

Footnotes

[1] These were likely to have been the cruising ironclad *Jeanne d'Arc* and the ram *Belier*.
[2] The vessel was in fact 146 feet long. Perhaps the reporter mistook metres for feet.
[3] Bouët Willaumez was to command the French fleet in the war against Prussia in 1870, though without distinction.
[4] She was eventually armed with 9in MLR.

PRELUDE TO DISASTER:

E-Boat Operations in the Western Channel 1942–44

The German Navy's *Schnellboote* (E-Boats) remained dangerous right up to the end of the Second World War. **Ian W Skinner** looks at the problems encountered by Plymouth Command, culminating in the disastrous attack on a force of American landing ships exercising for D-Day.

On 28 April 1944, tragedy struck American preparations for D-Day when over 700 servicemen were killed during a German E-Boat attack on Exercise 'Tiger', an amphibious training exercise off Slapton Sands on the Devon coast. Although several studies in recent years have traced the appalling sequence of errors and communications failures that left the fated exercise convoy so hopelessly exposed to attack, it has not been evident to date that similar shortcomings had been exposed in several previous E-Boat successes against convoys plying the coastal route between the Bristol Channel and Portsmouth.

The German E-Boat Command first targeted the Western Channel convoy route in the summer of 1942 and transferred two E-Boat Flotillas from the North Sea to Cherbourg. Their arrival was reported by Admiralty Intelligence but the regional naval authority, Plymouth Command, took no precautions against the threat and the Germans achieved the surprise for which they had hoped. On 8 July, a Luftwaffe reconnaissance aircraft located convoy WP183 and eight boats of the 2nd Flotilla were sent to lie in wait on its anticipated course through Lyme Bay. The E-Boats were led to the convoy by flares dropped from the shadowing aircraft and sank the armed trawler HMS *Manor* and five merchant ships in a devastating onslaught. Luftwaffe fighter-bombers then attacked the remnants of WP183 at dawn and sank one of the three surviving merchantmen.

Plymouth Command responded to this reverse by altering convoy schedules to ensure that no convoys crossed Lyme Bay at night. This represented a significant concession to the E-Boat threat as the reduced turnaround of convoys restricted the amount of cargo carried by coastal trade. Nevertheless, the WP183 action had demonstrated the consequences of E-Boats closing a convoy undetected and Plymouth Command was conscious of the lack of coastal radar stations providing adequate coverage to seaward of the convoy route, particularly in the Lyme Bay area.

Improvements to the local radar network in the South West were taken in hand after the WP183 action but better equipment would only help combat the E-Boat menace if the Plymouth Command could make efficient use of its limited but expanding chain of radar stations in directing an E-Boat battle from the shore. Plots from these stations were passed to the Central Operations Room at the Plymouth Area Combined Headquarters (ACHQ) where they were assimilated with other information compiled from sailing orders, position reports, visual sightings and plots from the Operations Rooms in the local Sub-Commands. A well-organised and proficient shore control could then provide shipping with precise information concerning the movements of unidentified plots. Thus forewarned, a threatened convoy could head for port or at least be alert to an incoming attack. In practice, vital information could be delayed because spurious echoes or inadequate plotting confused the shore control's picture of events. In this respect, the efficiency of the Command's fledgling radar network must have given cause for concern. A report from the Dartmouth Sub-Command stated that 'although sometimes ships are picked up and plotted accurately at considerable distances, there are still occasions when large vessels cross right across our front doorstep without being detected'.

Efficient shore control was also essential to the effectiveness of another countermeasure adopted by Plymouth Command in response to the new threat. On 10 July, the Command instituted anti-E-Boat patrols to the seaward of the convoy route using motor launches (MLs) of the 7th and 10th ML Flotillas from Dartmouth and Falmouth. Although Plymouth Command was following the practice adopted in countering E-Boat activity in the North Sea, it was open to question whether the strategy was viable in the Western Channel. A study of Coastal Forces interception patrols by the Directorate of Naval Operational Studies (DNOS) in 1942 concluded that, 'even with the best arrangements, it seemed unlikely that Coastal Forces can intercept any large proportion of attacks and past experience suggests that the destroyer escorts of convoys are their chief defence'. This study had included the Nore Command area in the North Sea where the Germans were limited by shoals, minefields and time to a restricted area of attack. By comparison, the Plymouth Command coastal route was exposed to attack over a far greater distance and fewer forces of less suitable type were available for patrol.

In the last resort, the onus lay with the convoy escort to fend off an E-Boat attack. The mainstay of the PW/WP convoy escorts in 1942 was provided by the 'Hunt' Class destroyers of the 1st and 15th Destroyer Flotillas, based at Portsmouth and Plymouth respectively, although operational demands were such that only one destroyer could usually be assigned to each convoy. Whilst a well-handled destroyer could successfully break up an E-Boat attack, there was also a serious risk of the principal escort being drawn out of position or overwhelmed by sheer weight of numbers. At this time, the 'Hunts' were equipped with radar that only had an effective range on an E-Boat of 4–7000 yards so unless adequate warning was forthcoming from the shore, an attack could develop before the destroyer could intervene effectively. Once the E-Boats had closed within 2000 yards, radar was rendered ineffective by interference from the sea surface and back echoes from the convoy itself.

In addition to the destroyer, each escort included about four armed trawlers. These were primarily intended for anti-submarine (A/S) defence and had also been equipped with additional light armament in response to the aerial threat. They served a useful purpose in marshalling the convoy and defending its perimeters and, with experience, their A/S hydrophone operators could also detect E-Boat and torpedo propeller noises. Essentially, however, the trawlers were totally outclassed by the E-Boats and lacked the speed and acceleration necessary to close gaps in the escort screen. Nor was their main armament designed for fast-moving surface actions.

On 12 July, the 8th MGB Flotilla was transferred from the Nore Command to Dartmouth to enable the Plymouth Command to retaliate against the E-Boat offensive. This MGB unit had considerable experience of E-Boat warfare in the North Sea and was deployed on cross-Channel sweeps with the intention of intercepting E-Boats as they returned to their bases. These operations had a definite impact on E-Boat activity as the principal diversion from offensive operations for the E-Boats was the commitment to provide cover for important shipping and defensive minelaying operations. E-Boats were called upon to fulfil this function because of the shortage of suitable warships, and the appearance of MGBs in French coastal waters led to constant demands for E-Boats to reinforce the defences. Thus, although the MGBs mistook

The Plymouth-based armed trawler HMS Ruby *regularly operated on the Western Channel convoy route. (IWM, A8013)*

'There was nothing to indicate from which direction the enemy was attacking except the sound of motor engines which changed bearing rapidly.' Captain P. Allan, M.V. Gripfast, WP183. (CPL)

two minesweepers damaged in an action off Cherbourg on 2 August for E-Boats, they had already indirectly served their purpose by causing a German torpedo operation to be cancelled so that the E-Boats could provide cover for those same minesweepers.

Convoy PW196

By the end of July 1942, the Germans had assembled three E-Boat Flotillas in the Western Channel in preparation for another torpedo operation which took place on 4 August. The Luftwaffe again played a key role, locating convoy PW196 and then damaging a tanker in a torpedo-bomber attack. The shadowing aircraft again dropped flares to attract the 18 waiting E-Boats to the convoy but the few attacks that developed were thwarted by HMS *Cleveland* as her charges headed for the safety of Plymouth.

The PW196 action persuaded the Plymouth Command to take the drastic measure of altering the PW convoy schedule to ensure that no convoys were at sea between Land's End and Portsmouth at night. Ironically, the Germans had already decided that 'repetition of the torpedo attacks on the West Channel convoys no longer promises success, the element of surprise being lost' and transferred two flotillas back to the North Sea. Nevertheless, the Western Channel had been established as

a worthwhile target area and the Germans would exploit the potential to use seasonal weather and light conditions to their advantage and so keep British defences tied down by switching forces between the two areas.

The 5th E-Boat Flotilla was retained at Cherbourg to provide defence against MGB incursions into French coastal waters and to carry out a minelaying offensive across the Channel. The minelaying operations never achieved the same rate of success as direct attacks on convoys in the Western Channel because the Plymouth Command enjoyed plenty scope for diverting endangered shipping, assisted by careful plotting of radar contacts and E-Boat signals to locate the minefields. Additional minesweeping forces were deployed in the Command and the only mine victim was a trawler sunk off Berry Head in October 1942.

Convoy PW226

The convoy schedule alterations introduced at the beginning of August had such an impact on the volume of coastal trade that the threat of intermittent E-Boat attacks could not justify the loss in capacity and, on 3 September, night sailings were resumed. This change coincided with a resumption of E-Boat operations as the longer winter nights set in. Henceforth, however, the E-Boat Command was to be increasingly frustrated by the paucity of reliable reconnaissance information from the Luftwaffe.

The Hunt Class destroyer HMS Albrighton *of the Portsmouth-based 1st Destroyer Flotilla. Note the bowchaser fitted specifically for use against E-Boats. (IWM, FL374)*

Commitments in other theatres had led to a significant decline in Luftwaffe activity and the German aerial effort in the Western Channel now consisted largely of fighter-bomber attacks on coastal towns. These low level sweeps yielded little information of value to the E-Boats, which were forced to engage in many fruitless searches for targets along the convoy route.

On 18 September, HMS *Cleveland* beat off an attack by four 5th Flotilla E-Boats on PW219 but the Germans enjoyed more success on their next foray into the Plymouth Command on 1 October, thanks to shortcomings in the shore control of the British defences. An anti-E-Boat patrol of three MLs from Dartmouth was inadvertently routed so that it would run into convoy PW226. Neither the patrol nor the convoy was informed of the other's movements and the two forces met and engaged each other in the darkness. Both an ML and the destroyer ORP *Krakowiak* were damaged and E-Boats then attacked the convoy and sank the armed trawler HMS *Lord Stonehaven*. Admiral Forbes, the Plymouth Commander-in-Chief, blamed the duty officers at the Plymouth ACHQ for 'unpardonable sins of omission' and warned the Admiralty that 'the standard of staff officers in my Headquarters is low; they are mostly retired officers,

untrained as staff officers, who know little of the art of naval warfare and appear to be slow to learn. I am aware of the great shortage of officers but it is necessary to realize that in an operation such as this, in which the enemy is attacking, and which takes place suddenly, the standard of staff work is liable to be low.'

Convoy PW250

Further evidence of the urgent need to improve the efficiency of the Plymouth Command was soon forthcoming. On 18 November, an ML patrol was ordered by the Plymouth ACHQ to investigate some unidentified radar plots. The instruction was so worded that the destroyer HMS *Brocklesby* left convoy PW250 and joined the search, leaving the convoy exposed to an attack by eight 5th Flotilla E-Boats lying in wait off the Eddystone. The armed trawler HMS *Ullswater* and three merchant ships were sunk. Another patrol was directed to cut off the retiring E-Boats but the instruction from Plymouth was wrongly decoded and the opportunity was lost. An Admiralty report blamed the fact that the convoy had been attacked and that the E-Boats had escaped unscathed on 'the far reaching results of comparatively small though inexcusable errors in handling signals by the communications staff'.

The action also provided further evidence of the inadequacy of ML patrols in the anti-E-Boat role. Between 10 July and 30 November, the MLs had been on patrol on 59 occasions but had made no interceptions. Admiral Forbes reluctantly acknowledged that, by reason of their lack of speed and poor navigational and look-out facilities, MLs were useless for offensive counter patrols against E-Boats and redeployed the 7th and 10th ML Flotillas on close escort duties. This change strengthened the convoy escort in each direction between Falmouth and Portland by at least three MLs but the general consensus amongst seagoing officers was that they were more of a liability than an asset because of the difficulty in establishing the identity of a small craft during an E-Boat attack.

Convoys PW256 and PW257

At 0250 on 1 December, an unidentified plot was detected by shore radar and convoy PW256 was warned within five minutes. Further unidentified contacts were then plotted approaching the convoy but this information was not conveyed to the escort until 0358. In the meantime, the Norwegian destroyer *Glaisdale* had left the convoy to engage the first group of E-Boats, unaware of the presence of the others which sank the armed trawler HMS *Jasper* in the ensuing attack. The Admiralty's docket on the action contained strong criticisms of Plymouth Command. The Director of the Tactical, Torpedoes and Staff Duties Division [DTSD] considered that communications left 'much to be desired and in the case of PW256 insufficient information was passed to the escorts in the early stages of the attack'. The Director of the Operations Division (Home) [DOD(H)] concurred that the PW256 engagement was 'generally an example of poor communications and bad drill' although he acknowledged that the many operational demands placed upon the available destroyers made it difficult to improve teamwork. Nevertheless, it was evident from the findings of the Board of Inquiry that at least one escort captain had received no instructions as to what to do in the event of an E-Boat attack.

The E-Boats that attacked PW257 were first detected by shore radar at 0325 on 3 December and were being continuously plotted by 0405. Just one badly-worded signal referring to unidentified plots was sent to the convoy at 0437 because the Plymouth ACHQ staff were unsure as to whether the contacts were hostile as an ML was known to be somewhere in the area. This unjustified reluctance to issue warnings was to cost PW257 dear for a surprise attack by E-Boats of the 5th Flotilla sank the destroyer HMS *Penylan* and a merchant ship. This further debacle caused the Deputy Director of Operations (Coastal) [DDOD(C)] to comment that 'this incident, though possibly small in itself, is regarded as a typical example of a serious weakness – the way in which we have faced up to the defence of our south and east coast convoys . . . it has been a matter of amazement that the enemy has been so

unenterprising and, taken by and large, so unsuccessful in exploiting our weakness. It does not follow that he will continue to let us off so lightly. Although it is probably unfair on Plymouth to select this particular incident for a showdown . . . an analysis will almost certainly bring to light many weaknesses which are not being rectified, chiefly because the staffs of our Home Commands consist in the main of passed over officers who are lacking in initiative.'

An analysis of the statistics indicates that the Plymouth Command represented a particular problem. In 1942, E-Boats torpedoed and sank 23 ships in all operational areas. Seven attacks on convoys in the Western Channel had accounted for 13 ships, over half the total losses, in a period of less than five months. Inadequate shore control had been identified as a crucial factor on four of the five occasions on which losses had been sustained, placing generally inexperienced escorts at an even greater disadvantage. This was reflected in the heavy losses sustained by the armed trawlers in their exposed positions on the convoy flanks.

There were, however, two significant factors militating against a thorough external review of the Plymouth Command defences. First, the bureaucratic process in the Admiralty precluded swift remedial action. The docket on the PW256 action went between Admiralty departments until 28 April 1943, when it was decided that the paper had been 'gathering moss for four months and had become so far out of date that an out letter of criticism would be blatantly inappropriate.' Furthermore, the delays made it difficult to justify an encroachment into the domain of the local Commander-in-Chief in the face of assurances that matters had been taken in hand. The intermittent nature of E-Boat attacks in the Western Channel made the accumulation of evidence to the contrary a slow process and an investigation into the organisation of Plymouth Command's defences would have to wait until they had been found wanting in further attacks on the convoy route.

Convoy WP300

Bereft of aerial support and restricted by bad weather, the 5th Flotilla had few opportunities to go on the offensive at the beginning of 1943 and an encounter on 6 January, when the Norwegian destroyer *Glaisdale* drove off an attack on PW274, was the only incursion into Plymouth Command for nearly two months. On 26 February, the fruitless search for targets brought the E-Boats so close inshore that they were taken under fire by the Falmouth coastal batteries. The following night, however, the Germans scored another striking success in the Western Channel.

On this occasion, convoys PW300 and WP300 were closing each other in Lyme Bay when shore radar detected the approach of four E-Boats. Plymouth ACHQ sent a comprehensive report to the convoy but a half-hour elapsed between the shore plot being read and the warning signal being received aboard the escorts. Further delay ensued as the signal was decoded and WP300 was attacked before the escorts could respond to the danger.

One merchant ship, two armed trawlers and *LCT381* were sunk, 11 seamen being taken prisoner from the latter by a German boarding party.

One of the factors identified in causing lengthy delays in communications was congestion of wireless traffic on the Plymouth Port Wave and measures were introduced to ensure that other signal traffic ceased in the event of an E-Boat attack. The Board of Inquiry even proposed that warning signals be transmitted in plain language to save time, particularly as decoding and plotting facilities were poor aboard the armed trawlers, but this recommendation was never implemented.

The Board also identified a lack of cooperation between the WP300 escorts during the attack and suggested that closer teamwork would be facilitated if the escorts were fully rehearsed in R/T communications. It was then revealed that the Plymouth Command's armed trawlers were neither equipped nor manned to operate both wireless and R/T systems simultaneously and that the former was given priority to ensure that a constant listening watch was maintained on Plymouth Port Wave. The Admiralty insisted on the introduction of 'this well-tried normal arrangement' to enable more efficient inter-communication between escorts but eight months elapsed before the Command was supplied with receivers to equip its 33 armed trawlers.

The lack of proper communications facilities was just one of the factors that hindered effective teamwork between escorts in the event of an E-Boat attack. One escort captain commented on the 'obstacles to close cooperation amongst the heterogeneous collection of warships. We are based at different ports, we work constantly with different ships and we can seldom get together to work as an effective team.' The Board of Inquiry acknowledged these difficulties and recommended that the PW/WP convoy escorts should, as far as practicable, always work and train together as a team.

Despite its undoubted advantages, the escort group system was, in practice, a far more complicated and resource-hungry method of providing escorts than that of simply detailing individual ships from the available forces. It was also seldom practicable to release enough escorts simultaneously to train as a group, and the system could easily break down as ships withdrew for repairs and refits. The problem was exacerbated by the fact that both Portsmouth and Plymouth destroyers had to be used, and those from Plymouth were continually required for other service outside the Channel. Nevertheless, Plymouth Command sought to at least facilitate improved cooperation by introducing a monthly meeting for merchant and naval officers working on the PW convoy route.

The E-Boats returned to Lyme Bay on 5 March but were thwarted in their attack on WP303 by the destroyer escort. The growing threat persuaded Plymouth Command to suspend night sailings through the area once more, although it was acknowledged by the Admiralty that the policy was so uneconomical that the aggregate number of ship hours lost outweighed the risk of losses by enemy action.

Convoy PW323

On 31 March, Admiral Forbes informed the Admiralty that 'the whole subject of the efficient employment of the RDF warnings has been overhauled and steps have been taken to ensure that full use is made of information gained and that it is passed to ships at sea without delay'. The purported improvements were not in evidence when, two weeks later, the Admiralty again had cause to issue the now familiar refrain 'that the delay between E-Boats being detected by shore radar and the receipt of this information on the bridges of the escorts was a contributory cause of the losses' suffered by PW323. On this occasion, unidentified plots were picked up by shore radar at 0004 but a report was not sent out from Plymouth until 0027, 11 minutes after they had been identified as E-Boats. Decoding and plotting caused a further 18-minute delay aboard the escorts, by which time the attack by six E-Boats was underway. The Norwegian destroyer *Eskdale* and a merchant ship were torpedoed and sunk.

The losses sustained by WP300 and PW323 led Admiral Forbes to advise the Admiralty that the Germans were attempting a 'systematic attack of torpedoing and mining on the traffic routes in Plymouth Command'. He pressed for an early reinforcement of the Coastal Forces in his Command as an urgent requirement and argued that, until such forces were available, 'the chances of inflicting a decisive defeat on the enemy's E-Boats is remote'.

This proposal received support from the DDOD(H) following an analysis of the relative threat posed by E-Boats to the convoy routes in the Nore, Portsmouth and Plymouth Commands in April 1943. The report concluded that there had 'been no occasion in the last six months when E-Boats have actually attacked a convoy without inflicting damage. There have, however, been many contacts between patrols and E-Boats which undoubtedly have saved convoys. From this it would appear that the combination of RDF warning, air patrols and surface patrols is of greater importance than escort strength. Tactically, close escorts will always be at a serious disadvantage when attacked by E-Boats at night unless it is possible to provide them on the same lavish scale as the enemy'. This analysis ignored the fact that convoys in the Western Channel had usually sustained losses because the shore authorities had failed to provide adequate warning of impending attacks. E-Boats had therefore been able to close their targets undetected and had achieved a fairly high degree of effectiveness in their attacks. Where escorts were forewarned, they had invariably prevented the majority of the E-Boats in contact from reaching an attacking position. Once an E-Boat was in action with the escorts and forced to take evasive action, the chances of launching a successful torpedo attack were reduced.

The report's conclusions also stood in stark contrast with those of a review of anti-E-Boat patrols by Coastal Forces in the Nore Command. This noted that E-Boats were usually first detected by shore radar, listening stations or destroyers. This meant that the Coastal Forces invariably had to be vectored onto the E-Boats and, owing to the slower speed of the MGBs, this usually resulted in opportunities being missed or interceptions only being effected during the E-Boats' withdrawal. The report concluded that up to September 1943, 'Coastal Forces had only once detected and engaged E-Boats before the latter had reached the convoy route or had been detected by destroyers or shore radar . . . E-Boats were usually driven off by the convoy escort so the Coastal Forces defensive function was only indirect'. If this was the case on the East Coast, where the defences were superior to those in the Western Channel, then clearly the system stood even less chance of success in the Plymouth Command, where the shore control network had repeatedly been exposed as unreliable. Operational experience seemed to bear out the theory since only one interception had been achieved in the Plymouth Command since the introduction of anti-E-Boat patrols in July 1942. This occurred on the night of 26 March 1943 when two MGBs briefly engaged six E-Boats off Prawle Point. The Germans used their superior speed to escape after a brief action.

Nevertheless, the defensive strategy pursued by Plymouth Command continued to place the emphasis on anti-E-Boat patrols. By mid-June of 1943, three MGB Flotillas were operational in the area and confidence in their prospects of success was engendered by the installation of improved radar facilities in the South West. The fact remained, however, that there was little prospect of Plymouth Command's Coastal Forces inflicting a 'decisive defeat' on their counterparts. Deducing from signals intercepts that shore radar was providing more extensive cover in April 1943, the Germans decided that an undetected approach to within 20 miles of the convoy route was impossible and that only concerted attacks by at least 15 boats were likely to succeed. Massed attacks helped confuse radar and ensured that, whilst a proportion of the attacking force might be intercepted, the remainder would get through. Indeed, on occasion, some E-Boats would deliberately serve as decoys to draw interception patrols away from the main force.

The E-Boats also benefited from German *B-Dienst* reports of interceptors being vectored onto them and carried a basic form of radar interception equipment. Thus, the MGB patrols faced a daunting task in intercepting, let alone inflicting fatal damage on fast, manoeuvrable adversaries that were heavily armed, better protected, used less flammable fuel and often operated in larger groups. Gunfire was usually only effective within 600 yards in such engagements but the disparity in speed between rival craft meant that the E-Boats, invariably intent on avoiding action, were able to disengage when attacked.

Coastal Forces could not achieve the required ascendancy over the E-Boats through fleeting engagements in which no decisive result was achieved. To deploy them in penny packets on fruitless patrols for which they were ill-suited and in which they consistently failed to achieve results was a waste of resources. MGBs and MTBs were designed as strike craft and their retention in an unaccustomed defensive role worked against the successful prosecution of an offensive against German coastal trade. Indeed, it clearly suited the Germans' purpose if British Coastal Forces were tied up in anti-E-Boat patrols in their own coastal waters. This effectively released E-Boats from defensive commitments and enabled the Germans to maintain a level of offensive activity that was disproportionate to their comparative naval strength.

Far greater success was enjoyed by aircraft patrols, introduced at the end of 1942 as a means of detecting incoming E-Boats in the most vulnerable sectors of the convoy route. Whilst an MGB had to be brought within 1.5 miles of an E-Boat to bring it within radar range and enjoyed no speed advantage to close the remaining distance, aircraft radar could locate an E-Boat at a range of eight miles. The slow speed of the Swordfish aircraft used

An E-Boat at 30 knots alongside an MTB after the German surrender in May 1945. The larger wake produced by the MTBs could easily betray their approach at night, so making interception of the faster E-Boats even more difficult. (IWM, A29321)

on the patrols, whilst easily sufficient to overhaul the E-Boat, was also an asset in manoeuvring to engage their agile target. Although bombs were not an effective weapon against an E-Boat planing across the water unless they scored a direct hit, damage and casualties caused by strafing attacks had a significant impact on German policy. On 15 April, the E-Boat Command declared that the 5th Flotilla could no longer operate on moonlit nights because of the aerial threat. Compared to that posed by Coastal Forces, the threat was very real – during three operations at the end of May, E-Boats were subjected to 16 attacks by aircraft despite bad visibility. The E-Boat Command even requested Luftwaffe nightfighter support without success and had to withdraw E-Boats from operations during the summer in order to install additional bridge armour to protect personnel against air attacks.

Through convoys between Portsmouth and South Wales resumed on 22 May but the threat posed by the build-up of E-Boat Flotillas across the Channel ensured that measures were also taken to bolster the convoy defences. Four destroyers were temporarily transferred from the Nore Command to reinforce Plymouth and Portsmouth from May to August 1943 and destroyer escort was generally discontinued beyond Trevose Head in the Bristol Channel to enable a greater concentration of strength on the south coast. Thereafter, convoys sailed with two destroyers in their escort on this most vulnerable sector of the route.

The threatened onslaught failed to materialise in May 1943 as bad weather forced the Germans to abandon two torpedo operations. With the hours of darkness growing shorter, E-Boats could no longer search for convoy targets and be sure of regaining their bases before being caught at sea by the RAF fighter-bombers that swept the French coast at dawn. The Germans turned to minelaying as an alternative but, despite four Flotillas being deployed, the campaign proved no more successful than that of 1942. Some 16 minefields were successfully swept by Plymouth Command forces between 1 March and 30 June and no mine casualties were sustained during this period.

Plymouth Command's dismal communications record was again exposed on the night of 28 May when three separate forces were directed to intercept E-Boats heading into Lyme Bay. Three MLs from Portland, two MGBs from Dartmouth and two destroyers converged on the E-Boats but were not kept adequately informed of each others' movements. The British forces ran into one another just as night recognition signals were being changed and, in the resulting confusion, engaged each other causing damage and casualties. Again, the Admiralty blamed 'an inefficient communications system in the Command, involving long delays and/or corruption in the receipt of important signals, and consequent failure to act on such signals'.

A number of factors combined to ensure that the Germans failed to capitalise upon the continued shortcomings in the Plymouth Command's anti-E-Boat defences in the summer of 1943. On 11 August, two Flotillas were moving to a temporary base at L'Abervrache in preparation for a torpedo operation against shipping off Falmouth when they were attacked by RAF fighter-bombers. One E-Boat was sunk and the remainder all damaged, putting a temporary halt to offensive activity. E-Boat strength at Cherbourg then diminished as three Flotillas were redeployed eastward in response to the increased level of Allied offensive activity in the Dover Command and North Sea, which gave rise to the expectation of an invasion attempt. The shortage of warships for escort and patrol work increasingly forced the Germans to deploy their E-Boats on defensive duties, although they were as unsuited to this role as their Allied counterparts. The E-Boat Command pressed for an early resumption of its offensive as it argued that 'attacks by E-Boats tie down the enemy and relieve the German defences because activity by enemy MTBs in German coastal waters ceases whenever the E-Boats are on the offensive'.

Although bad weather, full moon periods and German defensive commitments all combined to afford Plymouth Command a temporary respite in the winter of 1943, the lingering menace continued to exert an overriding influence on the deployment of the resources available to the Command. The E-Boat Command would no doubt have taken some satisfaction from the fact that Plymouth Command's Coastal Forces went on the offensive on just 15 occasions between 15 September and 31 December 1943, whereas anti-E-Boat patrols were sent out on 43 nights.

This considerable defensive effort was wasted since the Germans did not resume torpedo operations in the Western Channel until 23 December, when the 5th Flotilla was driven off by WP450 in Portsmouth Command waters. The action demonstrated the value of having two destroyers in the escort as they were able to frustrate German attempts to mount simultaneous attacks from different bearings by small groups of E-Boats.

Convoy WP457

The next attack brought renewed criticism upon Plymouth Command. The lack of E-Boat activity on the convoy route beyond the Lizard had persuaded the Command to discontinue destroyer escort in the area to release destroyers for other duties. WP457 paid the penalty on 6 January when seven E-Boats of the 5th Flotilla discovered the convoy straggling badly off Mount's Bay. The escort of four armed trawlers was swiftly overwhelmed and HMS *Wallasea* and three merchant ships were sunk. The shore radar plot was confused by the presence of numerous fishing boats and a virtually complete lack of communications between the convoy and the shore authorities meant that the fate of WP457 was only established when HMS *Talybont* arrived at the scene the following morning. Rescue arrangements were described in the Admiralty's report as 'inadequate and dilatory' and 72 lives were lost.

In view of the impending tragedy in April, the findings of the DTSD in the Admiralty docket on WP457 are of some note. He commented that, if the various shortcomings identified as a result of the WP457 action were not rectified, it 'might lead to a much greater disaster. The disquieting feature is that apart from extending the destroyer escort and a brief criticism of Falmouth, the

Commander-in-Chief, Plymouth, does not appear dissatisfied.' There was nothing new either in the criticism of Plymouth Command's handling of the E-Boat problem or the speed with which the Admiralty reached its conclusions. The paper was dated 2 June 1944.

Plymouth Command was reinforced in the aftermath of WP457 to release destroyers for escort as far as Trevose Head once more. Thus, when the 5th Flotilla returned to the Lizard on 17 January, it was driven off PW462 by two destroyers.

Throughout this period, the Plymouth Command remained committed to the notion that 'the most efficient method of protecting our coastal convoys is by destroying the E-Boats' and even reverted to the discredited practice of deploying MLs on interception duties. At the same time, the new Commander-in-Chief, Admiral Leatham, was bemoaning the shortage of 'coastal craft of suitable type' and acknowledging that the 'best that happens with our MTBs is that they get in fleeting touch with the enemy, only to be rapidly outdistanced as he takes alarm and heads for home at full speed.'

In the spring of 1944, the Admiralty conducted a review of radar plotting and communications arrangements in force along the south coast to assess their efficiency in preparation for the forthcoming invasion operations. The system that had evolved in the Plymouth Command allowed for the control of anti-E-Boat operations from outlying stations under the general supervision of the Plymouth ACHQ. The Admiralty report commented that shore control of an anti-E-Boat battle required a plot that was efficiently arranged and supplied with all information, adequately manned with experienced personnel. It questioned how instant and correct decisions could be made with control decentralised and actually handled by any duty officer who might, eventually, be available. The report recommended a thorough reorganisation of the Plymouth Command's plotting rooms and communications on a centralised system and warned that 'forthcoming operations will throw a far greater strain on shore plots. If they are inefficient now, they will be chaotic when the real test comes'. The recommendations were rejected by the Plymouth Command on the grounds that the ACHQ had little space to accommodate the staff and equipment required to operate a centralised system.

Dealing with the threat of E-Boat attacks on the coastal convoy route was but one of many demands placed upon the Plymouth ACHQ, which was recognized as having a greater range of responsibilities than any of the other British Home Commands. The Command was concerned not only with the organization and defence of local trade but was also required to provide escorts and support for shipping in the South-West Approaches. The Command also had extensive offensive commitments, ranging from destroyer and MTB sweeps and minelaying operations across the Channel to the prosecution of a sustained campaign against U-Boats on passage to and from their bases in the Bay of Biscay. These wide-ranging commitments placed a heavy burden on the ACHQ, thereby giving rise to the policy of handing over anti-E-Boat operations to outlying stations.

Given the demands placed upon the existing resources of the Plymouth Command, it is surprising that it was not until March 1944 that a Captain, Coastal Forces (Channel) was appointed to support and advise both Plymouth and Portsmouth Commands in organizing and deploying their Coastal Forces. Such an appointment had first been advocated after the PW256 action and a comparable officer had overseen tactics and training of Coastal forces in the North Sea since 1942. Although a lack of training and the inexperience of their crews had been considered to be a factor that contributed to the lack of success in anti-E-Boat operations by Coastal Forces in the Plymouth Command, it was the requirements of the forthcoming invasion operations that finally provided the incentive to review the situation.

Given the commitment to the concept of interception patrols, it was almost inevitable that Plymouth Command would look to use destroyers as a means of strengthening its anti-E-Boat patrols during the programme of amphibious invasion exercises off Slapton Sands in the spring of 1944. Such deployment began during Exercise FOX on 10 March when no less than 10 destroyers were used in providing distant cover to the training forces.

On 12 March, Plymouth Command received advance warning from ULTRA decrypts that the Germans intended to carry out an E-Boat operation off Land's End. Three days later, a chance intercept enabled the Command to prepare and execute a planned interception. WP492 was diverted to safety and two destroyers were homed onto the attacking force of 10 E-Boats by a shadowing aircraft. One E-Boat was claimed sunk but, in fact, the Germans were able to disengage after having only suffered damage to one boat. This was the second occasion on which Plymouth Command destroyers operating independently had intercepted E-Boats, the first being a brief and ineffective skirmish in early September 1943, and the outcome of these actions gave little ground for optimism that destroyer patrols would represent a significant counter to E-Boat operations.

It is interesting to note that the Germans did not regard the presence of interception patrols as a critical factor in a lean spell that persisted from the unsuccessful attack on PW462 through to the end of April 1944. The failure to even locate a single convoy during this period was attributed rather to bad weather and the lack of Luftwaffe support. In addition, the E-Boat Command acknowledged that, owing to the superior radar, strong escorts and air patrols of the enemy, and the German dependence on good visibility, each success had to be paid for by many fruitless attacks'.

On 16 March, E-Boats again ventured so close to Falmouth that they were fired at by the coastal defences but the MTB and destroyer patrols sent to intercept failed to make contact. Three more unsuccessful torpedo operations followed until, on 21 April, two MTBs were vectored onto five E-Boats in Lyme Bay in the first enemy interception by Plymouth Command Coastal Forces for 13 months. Despite initially closing to within 50 yards of their opponents the MTBs soon lost contact with the faster German boats, though not before damage had been inflicted by both sides.

Exercise 'Tiger'

The American amphibious exercises off Slapton Sands entered their final stages in April 1944 having thus far escaped the attentions of the E-Boats and the Luftwaffe. Forces began assembling for the biggest exercise to date, codenamed 'Tiger', on 22 April and put to sea on the evening of 26 April. In order to provide as realistic a simulation as possible, both for the troops engaged in the landings and the naval forces charged with their defence, the transports spent a night at sea prior to disembarkation off Slapton Sands. The main beach assault using service ammunition, accompanied by naval gunfire support and air strikes, was scheduled to take place on the morning of 27 April, followed by an advance inland. Build-up convoys would then follow the same circuitous route through swept channels in Lyme Bay to bring troops and equipment to secure the beachhead at Slapton.

The arrangements for the defence of this shipping had been in operation since the first exercise in January 1944. The American exercise commander retained tactical control of the amphibious forces and their close escort but was dependent upon Plymouth Command to provide advance warning of E-Boat attacks. The Command retained the capacity to provide an immediate response to E-Boat incursions by deploying Coastal Forces on anti-E-Boat patrols to seaward of the exercise forces. Four destroyers that might otherwise have been made available for escort purposes were retained under the direct control of the Plymouth Command as covering forces. This dilution of the available escort forces ignored past experience in the Western Channel, which had shown the importance of a strong convoy escort and the limitations of patrols as a means of preventing E-Boats from reaching their objectives. The DDOD(H) later wrote that 'the system of patrol lines which looks so solid and comforting on a chart is in fact an ensnaring myth of security in which a sublime faith is invariably put. Naval history abounds with examples of attacking forces slipping through these thin almost skeleton, lines but scarcely an instance of patrols intercepting and completely driving off and breaking up the attackers. Even when contact is made . . . it can hardly be regarded as more than a general warning for it invariably transpires that another group has slipped through from a different bearing.'

One of the convoys scheduled to arrive off the exercise beachhead on the morning of 28 April was T4, comprising eight LSTs carrying the troops and equipment of the 1st Engineer Special Brigade. The escort allocated to T4 comprised the old destroyer HMS *Scimitar* and the corvette HMS *Azalea*. This compared unfavourably with the protection accorded to a typical PW convoy of up to 15 merchantmen, which would be escorted by two destroyers and five armed trawlers. Experience had already shown the importance of having two destroyers to contend with multiple E-Boat attacks and one sixteen-knot corvette could hardly fulfil the same function as the trawlers in marshalling the convoy and defending its perimeters.

The escort allocated to T4 also suffered from a further disadvantage in that neither warship had any previous experience of E-Boat warfare. This was an inevitable consequence of the gradual build-up of escort forces in the Channel as many of these ships came directly from the Atlantic convoys and were accustomed to the tactics and doctrine of anti-submarine warfare.

At 0445 on 27 April, HMS *Scimitar* was inadvertently rammed by a landing craft and holed above the waterline whilst participating in the exercise. The destroyer returned to Plymouth to refuel and effect temporary repairs and her captain signalled to the ACHQ that his ship remained seaworthy in the current weather conditions. This message was received at the ACHQ at 1015, by which time the dockyard had refused to allow the destroyer to put to sea. This decision was taken without reference to the ACHQ but the destroyer captain remained under the erroneous impression that the senior commanders responsible for Exercise 'Tiger' had been informed of the situation. This confusion meant that no destroyer joined the Plymouth section of T4 when it put to sea at 0950 that morning. Neither Lieutenant Commander G.C. Geddes, commanding HMS *Azalea*, nor the convoy's senior officer, Commander B.J. Skahill, queried the absence of the principal escort.

Some nine hours later, at 1930, the Duty Officer at Plymouth realised that something was amiss and began checking which escorts were in company with T4. At this time, the convoy was off Berry Head and three LSTs from Brixham had not yet joined up. No signal was sent to the convoy, which was allowed to head out into Lyme Bay despite the doubts concerning the composition of the escort. Indeed, it was not until 2306 that Plymouth ACHQ sent a signal informing the senior escort commander aboard HMS *Tanatside* in Start Bay that HMS *Scimitar* had been detained in Plymouth and requesting that a replacement be detailed to escort T4.

In the meantime, nine E-Boats of the 5th and 9th Flotillas had set out from Cherbourg on a cross-Channel sortie at 2200. They would not arrive in the vicinity of T4 until 0200 the following morning, which meant that there were still three hours in which to reinforce the convoy escort. Communications delays proved to be a critical factor as the vital message to HMS *Tanatside* was not decoded and read until 0045. Another hour was lost before HMS *Saladin* finally left Start Bay and began the thirty-mile passage to join T4.

The organisational and communications failures that had left T4 bereft of adequate protection meant that the fate of the convoy depended on the effectiveness of the covering forces deployed by the Plymouth Command and the tactical control exercised by the shore authorities. The first line of these defences had already been breached as three MTBs (Force 114) lying in wait off Cherbourg had failed to intercept the E-Boats. There remained two MGBs (Force 113) off Start Point and four destroyers (Forces 27 and 28) disposed on two patrol lines on the edge of Lyme Bay.

Unidentified plots were first picked up by Plymouth and Portland at midnight and their positions were relayed to all ships on Plymouth Port Wave at 0007. Four minutes later, one of the covering destroyers, HMS *Onslow*, reported contact with two E-Boats. The German craft, which had already fired torpedoes at the destroyer before

Defending the invasion convoys required an enormous influx of escort vessels which, like the Flower class corvette HMS Azalea, had no experience of anti-E-Boat warfare. (IWM FL1300)

being spotted, were easily able to shake off their pursuer. This fleeting engagement with two of the nine E-Boats heading into Lyme Bay was the only inward-bound interception achieved by the covering patrols in which such unwarranted faith had been placed. Plymouth Command attributed this failure to 'the confused situation, the time factor and a continuance of contacts and unidentified plots near their patrol lines which prevented Force 27 or 28 being sent into the scene of the action'. Force 113 was successfully vectored onto an unidentified contact in their vicinity which turned out to be friendly.

At 0039, 28 minutes after HMS *Onslow*'s report confirmed the identity of the unidentified plots, Plymouth Command repeated this information to all ships engaged in Exercise 'Tiger'. Subsequent plotted positions were broadcast at frequent intervals until 0129 but the supply of information then ceased for 40 minutes. Admiral Leatham later explained that 'although the analysis when completed shows the E-Boat tracks fairly clearly, it was very different as the radar plot developed; there were a number of friendly craft in the area, and the E-Boats appeared to have steered a number of courses while searching the middle of Lyme Bay.' The earlier warning that, unless improvements were made to the organisation of the plotting system, it could be left in chaos under a real test had proved to be provident.

The one course of action that might still have saved T4 as these events unfolded was for the convoy to have made for the shore. In the subsequent Admiralty investigation,

Geddes was criticised for a lack of initiative in continuing to lead T4 'in line ahead at 3.5 knots towards an enemy for nearly two hours after the initial enemy reports'. Geddes is reported to have stated, however, that the E-Boat reports were being studied when the attack started. The implication that HMS *Azalea* was only just becoming aware of the content of the warnings issued by the Plymouth Command some two hours after they were first transmitted is corroborated by other examples of serious communications delays. The 2306 message from Plymouth ACHQ to HMS *Tanatside* was not received on the destroyer's bridge until 0045. HMS *Saladin* was to report that HMS *Onslow*'s E-Boat report was not picked up until 0130, some 79 minutes after its time of origin, The communications and plotting facilities available to these destroyers were far superior to those aboard HMS *Azalea* and yet substantial delays were experienced in receiving vital information. The LSTs in T4 never even received the E-Boat warnings because they were monitoring the wrong frequencies. Nor had any arrangements been made for radio communication with their escort and Geddes and Skahill had no contact other than brief interchanges of routine nature by visual signal. Thus, the convoy remained unaware of the impending danger.

Even if Geddes had been aware of the E-Boat activity, his orders were to head for shore if the convoy came under attack. He might reasonably have expected any instruction to deviate from his course to come from the exercise commander or Plymouth ACHQ, who should have had a far better appreciation of the overall situation and were better placed than he to assess the correct course of action. The fate of T4 was sealed by Plymouth ACHQ's failure to send any such signal, although it was known that the convoy was missing its principal escort. This omission becomes even more incomprehensible in the knowledge that another exercise convoy, codenamed 'Obstacle', was ordered to reverse course off Start Point at 0059. The breakdown in communications arrangements is further highlighted by the fact that the 'Obstacle' convoy never received the recall signal and continued to head into the danger area.

HMS *Azalea* had assumed a station a mile ahead of the convoy, a position more accustomed to her customary anti-submarine role than for defence against an E-Boat attack. Without any trawlers to help maintain a close formation the convoy, arranged in line ahead as opposed to the more compact double column employed by the PW convoys, had also straggled over a considerable distance. The E-Boats were therefore able to close unhindered on the exposed flanks of T4 to launch their attacks and, at 0203, LST507 was torpedoed and burst into flames. The stricken LST was the last ship in the line and the convoy had straggled to such an extent that neither Skahill nor Geddes associated this conflagration with a ship from their convoy. The reality of the situation soon became readily apparent when LST531 was torpedoed at the centre of the convoy. The LST blew up in a spectacular ball of flame, capsized and sank. The convoy then disintegrated in confusion as the burning ships and gunfire attracted more E-Boats to the scene. Return fire from the convoy was wild as the only indication of the E-Boats' presence was the roar of their engines on rapidly changing bearings, bursts of tracer fire and the torpedo tracks racing between the milling LSTs. HMS *Azalea* came under fire from the LSTs as she turned back to defend her charges but could do little as the LSTs scattered. LST511 suffered casualties as she was inadvertently raked by fire from LST496 and LST296 was hit by a torpedo which blew her stern off. Had the Germans not initially failed to recognise their targets as shallow-draughted vessels, more hits might have been scored as a number of torpedoes ran too deep to hit their targets.

As the E-Boats disengaged and headed back out to sea, they had to pass the alerted interception patrols once more. At 0240, HMS *Offa* and HMS *Orwell* clashed briefly with one group but could not maintain contact. Another group of E-Boats were soon encountered but this engagement was broken off when both forces ran into the four American patrol boats escorting the 'Obstacle' convoy that had not received its recall orders and had found itself to seaward of the destroyers' patrol line! An exchange of friendly fire was only narrowly averted and in the confusion the E-Boats escaped, having only just missed the opportunity to attack a second valuable LST convoy. These two brief encounters were the only interceptions achieved by the waiting naval patrols and it remained for aircraft to make the only successful intervention, attacking seven of the E-Boats during their withdrawal and damaging one of them.

At the scene of the action, it was several hours before the survivors from the two sunken LSTs were rescued. Most of the surviving LSTs, shepherded by HMS *Azalea*, made for the shore in accordance with their instructions and the corvette did not return until her charges were safely assembled in West Bay. The first ship to arrive in the area was HMS *Saladin* but, after rescuing about 50 survivors from the wreck of LST507, the destroyer moved off in search of E-Boats. Most of the survivors were picked up by LST515, which turned back to the scene of the attack at 0415 after a debate aboard as to whether the security of the ship and its cargo should take precedence over rescue work. Most of the vessels dispatched by the shore authorities arrived after dawn and, although a few survivors were retrieved from the water at this time, the delay proved fatal for many. 287 men were rescued but an estimated 749 died, mainly succumbing to hypothermia or exhaustion.

For a time, the disaster placed the whole future of the Allied invasion plans in jeopardy. A major operation was mounted to recover the bodies of ten officers who knew the location of the landing beaches in France in case any of them had been retrieved from the water by the Germans. By chance, all ten bodies were found and this threat to the security of the invasion plans was eliminated. The Germans failed to place any great significance on the action but their success in sinking two LSTs and damaging a third reduced the reserves of these vital transports to nil.

Notwithstanding the difficulties faced by the Plymouth Command in defending a long and exposed convoy route against intermittent attacks by a determined and resourceful enemy, there are a number of sobering parallels between the fate of T4 and earlier convoy actions in the Western Channel. The Plymouth Command's communications and plotting arrangements, which had been repeatedly criticised in the past, failed the test of action once more in the early hours of 28 April 1944. Given the Command's poor record in this respect, the arrangements for the naval defence of the exercises invited disaster since the close escort allocated to each of the exercise convoys was well below the strength recognised as necessary to protect even a routine coastal convoy against an E-Boat attack. Furthermore, the exercise escorts faced many of the obstacles to effective cooperation and teamwork that had previously undermined the effectiveness of the coastal convoy defences. These factors meant that the security of the exercise forces in the event of an E-Boat attack was largely dependent upon the outlying interception patrols, notwithstanding the fact that this defensive strategy had consistently proved incapable of preventing E-Boats from pressing through to their objective.

Sources

Public Record Office, Kew:
    ADM1/16068
    ADM179/260
    ADM199/536, 541, 261, 784, 785
    ADM219/13, 121, 220
    ADM223/28

EMILE BERTIN

Fast Minelaying Cruiser

Emile Bertin was the prototype for the second generation of French interwar cruisers. She was also one of the fastest ships of her day. **John Jordan** examines the rationale behind the construction of this unique vessel.

Naval planning during the 1920s continued to focus on Germany as France's most likely antagonist in any future conflict. Geostrategic realities and the lessons of history combined to suggest a strategy based on the blockade of Germany's major North Sea ports and coastline by mining operations, enforced by a well-balanced French battle fleet to prevent any major excursions into open waters. The generation of naval vessels laid down between 1922 and 1925 was heavily specialised in order to implement this strategy.

The battle fleet, which in the almost total absence of surface construction since 1914, had become seriously unbalanced in favour of capital ships, was the first priority. The 1922 Programme saw the authorisation of the three fast scout cruisers of the *Duguay-Trouin* class, the twelve fleet torpedo boats of the *Bourrasque* class, and the six *contre-torpilleurs* of the *Jaguar* class, a new intermediate large flotilla type capable of independent operations. These

would be followed in 1924 by the first two 10,000-ton 'Treaty' cruisers (*Tourville* class), and the first two of a series of 1,500-tonne 'fleet' submarines (*Redoutable* class).

Once these programmes were well-established the *Marine Nationale* turned its attention to the 'blockade' element of the strategy. The twelve 600-tonne submarines building as part of the 1922 Programme were designed with a dual mission in view: the defence of French coastal waters and the imposition of a coastal blockade in enemy-dominated waters. This mission had already been performed with some degree of success by French submarines during the First World War in the Adriatic, and the *600 tonnes* and their successors would subsequently see similar deployment in the confined waters of the North Sea during 1939–40.

The programme of specialist minelaying ships began in 1925, which saw the authorisation of both the minelaying cruiser *Pluton* and the first two submarines of the *Saphir*

The minelayer Pluton, *photographed off Toulon in October 1936. The mine rails, which extended from the break in the forecastle to the stern, could accommodate 290 Sautter-Harlé mines.* Pluton *was the first and last purpose-built surface minelayer built for the Marine Nationale between the wars.*

Table 1: *EMILE BERTIN*

Name	Builder	Laid down	Launched	In service
1930 Programme				
Emile Bertin	Penhoët	18.08.31	09.05.33	17.05.34

Characteristics (as completed)

Displacement:	5,886 tons standard
	6,530 tonnes normal
	8,480 tonnes full load
Length:	167m pp (548ft), 177m oa (581ft)
Beam:	15.84m (52ft)
Draught:	5.33m (17ft 6in)
Machinery:	Six Penhoët small-tube boilers, 27kg/cm^2 (330°); four-shaft Parsons geared steam turbines for 102,000shp; speed 34kts (designed)
Oil fuel:	1,360 tonnes; radius 6,000nm at 15kts, 1,100nm at 33kts
Armament:	Nine 152mm/55 Model 1930 in triple mountings Model 1930 (1,300 rounds); four 90mm/50 Model 1926 HA in one twin mounting Model 1930 and two single mountings Model 1926 (1,000 rounds + 200 starshell); four 37mm/50 Model 1925 AA in single mountings (2,500 rounds per gun); eight 13.2mm/76 Model 1929 Hotchkiss MG in twin mountings Model 1931 (2,500 rounds per gun); six tubes for 550mm torpedoes Model 1923D in two triple 1928T mountings; two racks each for three 52kg depth charges (+15 reloads); 84 Bréguet B4 mines
Aircraft:	Two Gourdou-Leseurre 832 floatplanes
Protection:	*magazines:* 30mm
	deck: 20mm
	CT: 30mm sides, 20mm roof
	turrets: none
Complement:	553 peace (+24 as flagship), 675 war

class, a further four boats being authorised in successive programmes, 1926–1929.

The submarines, which carried 32 Sautter-Harlé mines in saddle tanks, were intended for covert mining off ports and in river estuaries. However, the French strategy envisaged the laying of larger minefields, probably in conjunction with the British Royal Navy, farther out into the North Sea. Hence the configuration of *Pluton*, a specialist minelaying cruiser with mine-rails running along either side of her upper deck from the break in the forecastle. Although she displaced 6,500 tonnes fully loaded, the topweight implicit in accommodating up to 290 mines at upper-deck level meant that she could be only lightly armed. She carried four single 138.6mm mountings of the type fitted in the latest *contre-torpilleurs* for self defence against enemy flotilla craft, together with a few AA weapons; the extent of the mine rails precluded fitting torpedo tubes. Her relatively low maximum speed of 30 knots suggests that minelaying operations would have been carried either at night or in low-visibility conditions.

By 1925 the minelaying strategy had been further refined, and the length of the proposed off-shore minefields established at 7½ miles. At the maximum spacing of 40m this implied a field of 350 mines. These estimates led to a request by the *Conseil Supérieur* for an enlarged *Pluton* (a study by the *Service Technique* indicated a displacement of 7500 tonnes), which was considered in committee on 10 March 1925. However, there was much discussion regarding the practical utility of such a vessel,

and this line of thinking was eventually to be overtaken by other considerations. By the time *Pluton* finally entered service in April 1931 the concept of the specialised minelaying cruiser had been abandoned by the *Marine Nationale*. The ship served as a gunnery training ship at Toulon throughout the 1930s, and in 1939 was converted as an officer cadet training cruiser, the sides between the hull and the shelter deck being plated in to provide additional accommodation. She was renamed *La Tour d'Auvergne*.

The second generation of postwar cruisers

By the late 1920s the pattern of international cruiser construction was becoming well-established. For all the major naval powers this effectively meant building up to the Washington Treaty limits of 10,000 tons and 8in (205mm) guns. In effect a new naval arms race was developing in the cruiser category which the European powers could ill afford, given the difficult economic situation prevailing.

For France and Great Britain the 'Treaty' cruiser presented a further problem. It was fundamentally unsuited to commerce protection because it could not be built in the requisite numbers, and both Britain and France were colonial powers with world-wide interests to defend. On the other hand, Britain felt unable to revert to the cheaper 6in gun 'B'-type cruisers it would have preferred as long as the Imperial Japanese Navy continued to build fast, powerful 8in gun cruisers which threatened its trade routes in the Far East. Pressure was therefore building for further treaty limitations on cruiser size and capabilities, and it was with these considerations in view that the *Marine Nationale* undertook its review of new cruiser contsruction in 1927–8, following the entry into service of the first cruisers of the 1922 Programme, the three units of the *Duguay-Trouin* class.

In 1928 the *Etat-Major* established three criteria for the new ships: they were to be essentially unprotected, with a maximum displacement of 6,000 tonnes; they would incorporate the newly-available superheated steam turbines in order to maximize power; and they would be armed with 6in (152mm) guns in order to conform to the anticipated new Treaty restrictions.

In the same year it was decided to abandon the construction of specialised surface minelayers. Instead all light ships – cruisers, *contre-torpilleurs* and colonial sloops – would be fitted with removable mine-rails. The first step was the redesign of the last eight *contre-torpilleurs* of the *2400 tonnes* series (*Milan*, *Epervier* and the six *Vauquelins*), which were given a reconfigured stern to enable them to carry 50 Bréguet mines on quarterdeck rails. The second was to incorporate this latter feature into the prototype for the new 6in gun cruisers, which by 1929 was being referred to as a *croiseur mouilleur de mines* (the same designation as *Pluton*, despite the fundamental differences in conception).

Emile Bertin

The first studies for the new cruiser were commissioned from the STCN in December 1928. Characteristics were quickly established as follows: displacement 5,980 tons, length overall 177m, propulsive power 102,000shp for 34kts, and range 3,000nm at 18kts. These characteristics were to remain essentially unchanged between the drawing board and the slipway.

The ship was authorised under the 1930 Programme with the number CL1, and was designated *croiseur de 2e classe* in accordance with the classification system adopted by the *Marine Nationale* following the London Treaty. The name *Emile Bertin*, which honoured the name of one of France's greatest naval constructors, was allocated in December 1930, and the contract with Chantiers et Ateliers de St Nazaire signed on 26 August 1931. The contract specified acceptance of the completed ship at Brest on 30 June 1934.

In the event the ship was delivered two days early, a performance which reflects great credit on the shipbuilders, given the radical innovations in the construction of the ship's hull and the design of the propulsion machinery. Only the late delivery and installation of the main and secondary artillery and their related control systems, all of which were newly developed, delayed the ship's entry into service until 17 May of the following year. In the interim, as the prototype of a new generation of cruisers, *Emile Bertin* underwent extensive sea trials to assess the performance of the new superheated propulsion machinery, achieving remarkable results in the process.

Hull and superstructures

The requirement for high speed necessitated careful design of the hull. A relatively high length-to-beam ratio of 10.5:1 was adopted. The raised forecastle combined gentle sheer with a pronounced flare at the bow, so that the fore-deck was dry in a moderate sea. The cruiser stern, *'en cul de poule'*, was similar to that adopted for the contemporary *contre-torpilleurs* of the *Vauquelin* class, being designed to ensure that mines were laid well clear of the ship's hull. It had the additional effect of conserving the trim of the ship at high speed, when the four propellers exerted powerful downward forces on the stern.

Major efforts were made to minimise the weight of the hull and superstructures. Longitudinal construction was employed, as in contemporary flotilla craft, and extensive use was made of welding (the first time this technique had been applied to a major French surface vessel). The hull was of standard 50kg/mm^2 shipyard steel, riveting being employed only for the 'strength' elements of the ship's framing. Duralumin was used extensively for external and internal fittings. The total weight of the hull, including protection, accounted for only 46.3% of Washington displacement.

Protection was minimal. Only the conning tower and the sides of the magazines were armoured; the plating comprised two thicknesses each of 15mm hardened steel with a resistance of 60kg/mm^2. The turrets were virtually unprotected (the weight of each triple turret was 112 tonnes, as compared with 172t for the *La Galissonnière* class, which had 40-50mm armour on the turret sides and roof with 100mm on the faces). The total weight of armour was a mere 123.8 tonnes, representing 4.5% of the displacement.

However, particular care was taken over the compartmentation of the ship. There were 13 transverse bulkheads extending from the keel to the upper deck, and these were fully watertight with no access route below the main deck. The 14 watertight compartments thereby created were served by nine 30-tonne pumps, one of which was located in each of the five main machinery spaces.

Emile Bertin proved to be a remarkably seaworthy ship in service, although the light construction of the hull resulted in some problems. There was some distortion of the bow section in a heavy head sea, enforcing a reduction in speed, and the hull structure beneath the turrets had to be reinforced following trials, in order to permit salvo firing. On the other hand, the *Emile Bertin* was a good seaboat, and the roll period of 12 seconds coincided almost exactly with the rate of fire of the main artillery, making her a remarkably steady gunnery platform. The only significant negative feature was her large turning circle (800m with the single axial rudder at 32°); this was a common defect with other contemporary French surface construction, particularly the *contre-torpilleurs*.

Propulsion

The advanced propulsion plant occupied almost 50% of the ship's length, yet accounted for only 23% of the ship's

Profile and Plan Views:
The profile and plan views are based on official plans dated 21 June 1935. Note that they show the projected twin 37mm Model 1933 abeam the bridge structure rather than the single Model 1925 fitted on completion. Note also the location of the forward 13.2mm Hotchkiss MG in their original exposed position on the forecastle. They would subsequently be relocated to the after end of the bridge wings. The mine rails, which were removable, extended from the stern to just forward of the single 90mm/50 AA guns. (Drawn by the author)

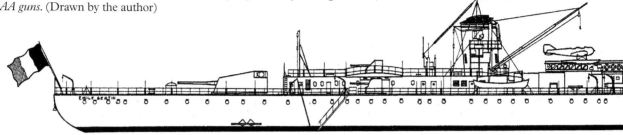

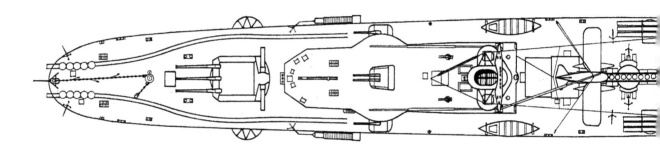

displacement. It comprised six small watertube Penhoët boilers with superheating, and four sets of Parsons single-reduction turbines, disposed in a unit arrangement. The six Penhoët boilers were located on the ship's axis in three boiler rooms, two of which (compartments G and H) had their uptakes combined into the broad fore funnel, with the narrower after funnel combining the uptakes from the third (compartment J). The boilers operated at a pressure of 27kg/cm², with superheated steam at 330°.

The forward machinery room (compartment I), which housed the two sets of turbines driving the wing shafts, was located between the second and third boiler rooms. The after machinery room (compartment K), housing the turbines driving the centre shafts, was located abaft the third boiler room (see inboard profile). Each set of turbines comprised HP, MP and LP turbines operating in series, with the reversing turbine on the LP turbine and a separate cruise turbine. The four three-bladed Brard propellers were 3.6m in diameter, and rotated outwards with the engines running ahead.

Four turbo-generators each of 200kW, distributed between the fore and after machinery rooms, provided the ship's electrical power while underway. There were also three groups of 100kW diesel generators for use in emergency and when alongside.

Remarkable figures were achieved on trials. During her eight-hour trial on 1 August 1934, *Emile Bertin* averaged 36.33 knots with 108,026shp. Much of her heavy equip-

ment, including the main guns and fire control directors, had yet to be embarked; on the other hand these trials were conducted in difficult sea conditions, with 3–4-metre waves. On 8 August, at Washington displacement, a full-speed trial resulted in an average of 39.67 knots with 137,908shp. In service *Emile Bertin* could comfortably maintain 33 knots. Fuel consumption was in line with expectations, giving a projected range of 6,000nm at 15kts on cruise turbines alone, and 2,800nm at 20kts / 1,100nm at 33kts on the main turbines.

High performance was not to be without its cost, however. The ship's first post-trials docking at Brest on 15 August revealed serious erosion and deformation of the Brard propellers, which were returned to the manufacturer for repair. At a further docking in Brest the following January similar damage was found, and a new set of propellers was subsequently ordered. These were installed in July 1936 but on 13 August, during a 35-knot sortie, there were horrendous vibrations aft, causing a breakdown in 'X' turret. A further inspection in dry dock revealed that the propellers had again suffered serious deformations and erosion from cavitation. In order to minimise disruption to the ship's programme, a major refit was brought forward during which the propellers were repaired. Meanwhile, a new set of propellers with a modified configuration were ordered from Brard. These were fitted in 1938–9, after which *Emile Bertin* appears to have suffered no serious problems.

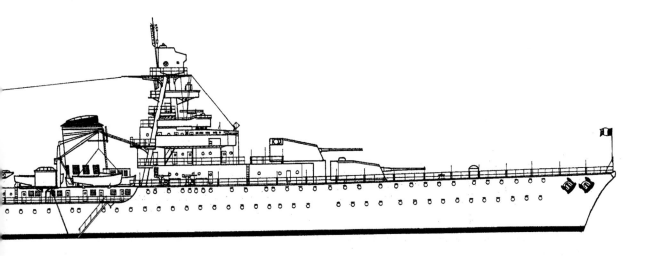

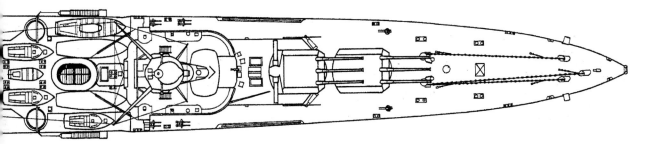

Main armament

The 152mm/55 Model 1930 was specially developed for the second generation of interwar cruisers. Derived from the 138.6mm/50 Model 1929 fitted in the *contre-torpilleurs* of the *Le Fantasque* class, it proved just as successful in service. The semi-automatic sliding breech mechanism featured a power-operated rotating loading tray and a catapult rammer with electromagnetic firing, resulting in the relatively high firing rate of 5/6 rounds per minute.

The two standard projectiles were the OPF Model 1930 armour-piercing shell, and the OEA Model 1930 high-explosive shell, which could be fired against either surface or aerial targets (a Schneider time fuze was fitted in the latter rôle). Both weighed approximately 54kg. Using a C1 combat charge and the OPF Model 1930, maximum range was 21,500m against surface targets with a muzzle velocity of 870m/s.

The three Marine-Homécourt turrets were the first multi-gun turrets to enter service with the Marine Nationale. They were constructed of riveted steel, and each weighed 112 tonnes. The guns were in individual cradles, and were powered in training and elevation by Janney electric motors. Although maximum elevation for firing was 45°, the guns could be loaded only between −5° and +15°. There were separate magazines for shells and cartridges for each turret with a maximum total capacity of 1,315 rounds. Seven ready-use rounds could be accommodated in each of the turrets' distribution chambers. Each turret was served by three electrically-driven shell hoists and two double cartridge hoists.

Full remote power control was planned, but was not installed until the ship's refit in 1938 due to development delays. The main director control tower (DCT), located atop the tripod foremast, was initially fitted with a 5m base coincidence rangefinder (SOM 50 Model 1926). This proved inadequate and was later replaced by an 8m stereoscopic model (OPL Model 1937). The transmitting station, which was located beneath the main deck, was identical to that fitted in the 10,000-tonne 'Treaty' cruisers.

The DCT proved to be the weak link in the fire control system. It was incapable of making successive turns in the same direction, and its training rate was significantly slower than that of the turrets (a full turn took 70 seconds). In rapid combat manoeuvres the DCT was often temporarily 'disconnected' and the turrets fired under local control, for which purpose 'B' and 'X' turrets were provided with the excellent OPL Model 1932 8m stereoscopic rangefinder.

For night firing three searchlight projectors were provided, of which one was located on the tripod foremast and the other two atop platforms on either side of the second funnel. Originally all were to have been Bréguet 75cm models, but it was subsequently decided (May 1930) to fit the more powerful Sautter-Harlé 120cm projector abeam

Inboard Profile:
Inboard profile of Emile Bertin. *The machinery spaces
occupied 50% of the ship's length; in consequence 'X' gun
mounting was located relatively close to the stern. The
six Penhoët small-tube boilers were disposed in three
compartments, of which two were forward of the first
machinery room which served the wing shafts.*
(Drawn by the author)

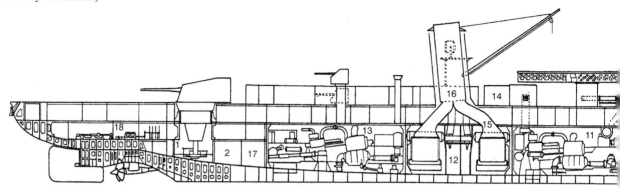

Table 2: *CHARACTERISTICS OF ARTILLERY*

	152.4mm/55 Model 1930	90mm/50 Model 1926
Gun Data		
muzzle velocity	870m/s	850m/s
max. range at 45°	21,500m	15,600m
weight of projectile	54.17kg	9.5kg (+3.1kg BM5 charge)
		18kg (fixed round)
Mounting Data		
weight of turret /mounting	112 tonnes	*twin:* 13.7 tonnes
		single: 7 tonnes
protection	light plating	5mm plating
elevation of guns	−10°/45°	−10°/80°
max elevating speed	8°/sec	
max training speed	12°/sec	
firing cycle	5/6 rounds per minute	13/14 rounds per minute

	37mm/50 Model 1925 (CAS) and 1933 (CAD)	13.2mm/76 Model 1929
Gun Data		
muzzle velocity	810–840m/s	800m/s
ceiling at 80°	5,000m	1,500m
weight of projectile	0.750kg (OEA)	0.052kg (0.122kg cartridge)
	0.755kg (tracer)	
rate of fire	*CAS M1925:* 20 rpm	450 rpm
	CAD M1933: 30 rpm	
Mounting Data		
weight of mounting	*CAS M1925:* ?	350kg
	CAD M1933: ?	
elevation of guns	−15°/80°	−15°/90°

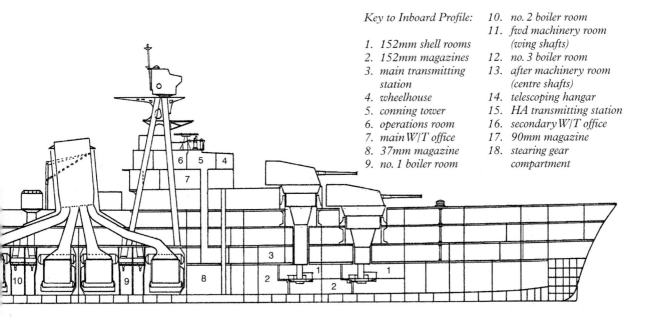

Key to Inboard Profile:

1. 152mm shell rooms
2. 152mm magazines
3. main transmitting station
4. wheelhouse
5. conning tower
6. operations room
7. main W/T office
8. 37mm magazine
9. no. 1 boiler room
10. no. 2 boiler room
11. fwd machinery room (wing shafts)
12. no. 3 boiler room
13. after machinery room (centre shafts)
14. telescoping hangar
15. HA transmitting station
16. secondary W/T office
17. 90mm magazine
18. stearing gear compartment

the second funnel. The six tonnes of additional topweight implicit in this decision had to be compensated for by the suppression of the original mainmast, thereby contributing to the ship's distinctive, racy appearance.

Secondary armament

The secondary armament, based on the 90mm/50 Model 1926 gun about to enter service in the 'Treaty' cruisers *Colbert*, *Foch* and *Dupleix*, was intended to provide defence against torpedo boats as well as aircraft. Like the 152mm Model 1930, it was a modern semi-automatic weapon with a sliding breech. Maximum elevation in the anti-aircraft rôle was 80°, and the use of fixed ammunition resulted in a high rate of fire (theoretically 13/14rpm, although the gun proved difficult to load above 60°). The standard OEA Model 1925 HE shell was fitted with an impact fuze for surface targets and a time fuze for aerial targets; starshell Model 1926 and tracer Model 1927 could also be fired.

According to the original design plans *Emile Bertin* was to have had only a single centre-line twin mounting (Model 1930) atop the after deckhouse, but in November 1930 it was decided to fit additional single mountings (Model 1926) on either side of the twin mounting at upper-deck level. The reason for this unusual disposition was that all three mountings had to be served by the single centre-line magazine originally provided for the twin mounting. Although this magazine had a capacity of 1,422 rounds (the standard combat loading was 1,000 plus 200 starshell for the twin mounting), and was therefore just about adequate for the task, the capacity of the single Sautter-Harlé hoist was unaltered. This provided 10 buckets each with two rounds per minute – insufficient even to supply the axial twin mounting at its maximum rate of fire! Moreover, the hoist exited onto the upper deck,

whence the rounds had to be distributed to the mountings by hand.

The centre-line mounting enjoyed excellent all-round arcs (320°), while those of the single mountings were inevitably more restricted (75° fore and aft of either beam). Both single and twin mountings were provided with 5mm splinter shields.

All three mountings had full remote power control, Janney again supplying the electric motors. Fire control was provided by two circular DCTs located at the edge of the shelter deck immediately abaft the fore-funnel. Each incorporated a 3m stereoscopic range-finder (SOM Model 1932), replaced in late 1939 by the 4m OPL Model 1933. The fire control calculating position Model 1930, which was located on the main deck abeam the second funnel, proved to be the weak link in the system. Intended to operate in conjunction with the twin mounting originally envisaged, it could handle only one target at a time. A target on the opposite beam could be engaged only by using the local control sights fitted on the mountings.

Anti-aircraft weapons

It was originally envisaged that the *Emile Bertin* would be fitted with the new twin 37mm mounting currently under development. Four were to be installed at forecastle deck level abeam the bridge structure. In the event development of this weapon was delayed, and on completion the ship was given an interim outfit of four single 37mm Model 1925, a robust and reliable weapon which nevertheless suffered from an inadequate rate of fire (20rpm). The twin mountings Model 1933 were fitted in their place only in late 1939. Single Sautter-Harlé hoists were provided port and starboard, each with a capacity of 10 buckets of 7 rounds per minute, and provision was 2,500 rounds per gun.

Emile Bertin *at Royan in May 1936, 12 months after her entry into service with the Atlantic Squadron. She is flying the flag of Rear-Admiral Duplat, commanding the* groupe des contre-torpilleurs. *(Marius Bar)*

Emile Bertin *leaves Toulon on 28 October 1938, shortly after joining the Mediterranean Squadron. The small tricolore flying from the mast immediately forward of 'X' turret is the flag of Admiral Darlan, who had embarked with the Chief of Staff, General Gamelin, for a review of the fleet off Brégançon. Note the distinctive configuration of the stern, and the identification colours on 'B' turret. Contrary to the regulations these were never applied to 'X' turret. (Marius Bar)*

Table 3: *UNDERWATER WEAPONS*

	550mm torpedo Model 1923D
Torpedo Data	
length	8.575m
weight	2,120kg
warhead	AG-326: 310t tolite
propulsion	Brotherhood type fuelled by alcohol
range	14,000m at 35 kts
	20,000m at 29 kts
deviation	+/– 250m at 14,000m
Mounting Data	
designation	1928 T
firing mechanism	compressed air
training arc	20°–160°

	Bréguet B4 mine
Mine Data	
dimensions	*height:* 1.400m
	width: 0.850m
	length: 1.065m
weight	*mine:* 159.5kg
	cable: 22.5m
	base: 353.0kg
charge	80kg tolite
immersion settings	0–90m

The 37mm mountings were complemented by four of the new twin 13.2mm Hotchkiss MG Model 1929, of which two were mounted abeam 'A' turret at forecastle deck level, and the other pair on the after deckhouse. These had a high rate of fire (450rpm) but insufficient range to be truly effective, and the reloading arrangements proved less than satisfactory.

For fire control purposes the light AA guns were divided into three groups: the 37mm and forward 13.2mm port and starboard; and the after 13.2mm mountings. Each group was provided with its own 1m rangefinder (OPL Model 1930) on a light pedestal, target data being transmitted by telephone to the individual mountings. The forward rangefinders were located immediately abaft 'B' turret to port and to starboard.

During a major refit in 1938 the forward 13.2mm Hotchkiss mountings were moved from their exposed position on the forecastle deck to the after end of the bridge wings. At the same time they were fitted with splinter-proof shields.

Underwater weapons

Triple 550mm tubes Model 1928T were mounted port and starboard between the funnels at upper deck level. The tubes had arcs of 20°-160° on either beam, and fired the powerful Type 1923D torpedo, which had a maximum range of 14,000m at its top speed of 35kts (see table). The torpedo fire control position was located in the armoured conning tower, and was served by its own 3m base rangefinder atop the bridge structure. Two auxiliary torpedo FC positions were installed in the bridge wings, and there were local on-mount sights for use in the event of a breakdown in centralised control. In 1938 the torpedo mountings were fitted with spray deflectors.

The mine rails, manufactured by Decauville, were 50 metres long and were removable. The sections were normally stowed between decks, and could be assembled by the ship's crew when required. The Bréguet Type B4 mines, which were specifically designed to be carried by the *contre-torpilleurs* and had an 80kg charge, were embarked using special davits fitted on either side of the stern. The maximum combat load was 84 mines, and the additional 45 tonnes of topweight had to be compensated by the disembarkation of the catapult and floatplanes.

During her entire (and otherwise eventful) career, the only occasion on which *Emile Bertin* laid mines was during her acceptance trials in 1934, eight exercise mines being embarked for the purpose.

Two small DC racks, each with a capacity of three 52kg depth charges, were located above the stern. These were reloaded by hand, and fifteen reloads were stowed close to the racks. The ship could also sweep mines at up to 25kts with her two Type C4 paravanes. A G-32 passive acoustic array comprising 16 hydrophones was installed at Toulon at the end of 1939.

Aircraft

By the time *Emile Bertin* was designed, embarked aircraft for reconnaissance and spotting were well-established in the *Marine Nationale*. A single trainable 20m catapult, built by Penhoët and capable of launching aircraft with a take-off weight of two tonnes, was located on the ship's axis between the funnels. Operating by compressed air, the catapult imparted a speed of 95km/h on launch. Practical training arcs were restricted to 30° on either side of the beam.

Two electrically-powered booms, each with a capacity of two tonnes, were installed at the base of the second funnel for aircraft-handling. One of the two aircraft was carried atop the catapult while the other was stowed, partially dismantled, in a telescoping hangar of corrugated steel located beneath the after end of the catapult. There was a fully-fitted workshop, and 2,400 litres of aviation fuel were provided.

The floatplane embarked was the Gourdou-Leseurre Type 832 two-seat float monoplane, which entered service in 1934. It proved to be of limited utility, being capable of landing only in the most favourable sea conditions. A report dated 15 October 1938 by Capitaine de Vaisseau Battet, the ship's C.O., states that he would have preferred the extensive aircraft-handling facilities to be removed in favour of enhanced anti-aircraft provision – a sentiment not uncommon among cruiser captains of the period.

Emile Bertin in August 1939, shortly before the outbreak of war. She has received a number of modifications since completion, including replacement of the original SOM 5m coincidence rangefinder mounted in the main DCT by a stereoscopic OPL 8m model, and the relocation of the forward 13.2mm Hotchkiss MG to the after end of the bridge wings. However, she retains the 37mm single mountings Model 1925 abeam the bridge structure. Note the Gourdou-Leseurre 832 floatplane atop the catapult amidships. (Marius Bar)

Service 1935–1939

By the time *Emile Bertin* was completed, the mine-laying function originally envisaged had been further downgraded in importance. Italy, under the expansionist imperial policies of Benito Mussolini, had emerged as a major threat to the status quo in North Africa, and the deployment of French naval forces would henceforth have to take this into account. It was therefore initially envisaged that *Emile Bertin* would, together with the *La Galissonnière* and *Jean de Vienne*, make up a new cruiser division of the *1re Escadre de la Méditerranée*.

In the event, however, her temporary assignment to the *2e Escadre* at Brest in May 1935 as cruiser flagship *hors rang* of the *contre-torpilleurs* proved so successful that she continued in this rôle until late 1938. The *groupe des contre-torpilleurs* (renamed *2e Escadre Légère* in August 1936) initially comprised:-

4e Division Légère	6e Division Légère
Milan	*Bison*
Epervier	*Lion*
Valmy	*Vauban*

By late 1935 the *Le Fantasque* class had joined the fleet,

and the *groupe des contre-torpilleurs* was organised as follows:-

10e Division Légère (later 10e DCT)	2e Division Légère (later 8e DCT)
Le Fantasque	*L'Indomptable*
L'Audacieux	*Le Triomphant*
Le Terrible	*Le Malin*

The prolonged stay of *Emile Bertin* as flagship of the *contre-torpilleurs* of the Atlantic Squadron prompted Vice-Admiral Darlan, then C-in-C of the *2e Escadre*, to instruct that the rôle of the cruiser *hors rang* be incorporated into the operational orders of the group (April 1936). He further stipulated that the cruiser flagship should be considered to have the offensive capability of a three-ship division of *contre-torpilleurs*, and that the ship should actively participate in the surface action when the latter were engaged, lending her weight wherever it was deemed to be most effective.

Following her refit at Brest in the autumn of 1938, *Emile Bertin* served briefly in a similar rôle in the Mediterranean Squadron. This was dissolved on 1 July 1939 and succeeded by three squadrons. *Emile Bertin* was henceforth to join the *4e Escadre* based at Bizerta, which under the designation *Forces légères d'attaque de la Méditerranée* was to

These impressive bow and quarter views of Emile Bertin *were taken from the contre-torpilleur* Chevalier Paul
while the ship was starring as the fictitious cruiser Austerlitz *in a film by Christian-Jaque entitled* 'Tourelle III' *('X Turret')*
in August 1939. Filming was curtailed by pre-mobilisation measures. The ship is steaming at 35 knots with all guns trained to
port. (Marius Bar)

Emile Bertin *in April 1949, showing her final configuration. During the major rebuild at the Philadelphia Naval Dockyard 1943–44 all the original light AA weapons were removed and replaced by a powerful battery of four quad 40mm Bofors (in the bridge wings and abeam the second funnel), and 20 single 20mm Oerlikon. SA air surveillance and SF surface surveillance radars were also fitted, although fire control radars for the main and secondary armament were added only in 1945, when British Types 284 and 285 were installed. In compensation the aviation facilities and minerail seatings were removed.* Emile Bertin *was to end her career as a gunnery training ship, finally paying off into reserve in 1951.* (Marius Bar)

operate against enemy communications between Sicily and Tripolitania. Besides the 3rd Cruiser Division (*Marseillaise, Jean de Vienne* and *La Galissonnière*), this force would eventually comprise three divisions of *contre-torpilleurs* led by *Emile Bertin*:-

3ᵉ DCT	1ᵉ DCT	11ᵉ DCT (forming)
Guépard	*Vauban*	*Milan*
Verdun	*Lion*	*Epervier*
Valmy	*Aigle*	*Bison*

Service 1939–45

When Italy defied expectations by failing to enter the war on the side of Hitler's Germany, *Emile Bertin* was diverted to other more pressing tasks. In January 1940 she relieved the 10,000t cruiser *Foch* in 'Force X', operating out of Dakar on the northwest coast of Africa, and was subsequently teamed with the 10,000t cruisers *Duquesne* and *Colbert* to form 'Force Y', with the mission of protecting allied sea lines of communication off West Africa in conjunction with British naval units based on Freetown.

In mid-February *Emile Bertin* was transferred to Brest,

where she was to be the flagship of a new grouping designated 'Force Z', commanded by Rear-Admiral Derrien. This force was being prepared for an Allied intervention in Norway with the aim of providing material support for Finland in its war against the USSR. However, when Finnish resistance finally crumbled in March 'Force Z' was disbanded, and *Emile Bertin* was again despatched to the Mediterranean, arriving at Oran on 28 March.

'Force Z' was to be reconstituted little more than a week later, when the decision was again taken to invade Norway, this time to interrupt the supply of iron ore from Sweden. After making the transit to Brest, *Emile Bertin* immediately set sail for Scapa Flow, where she was due to join the *contre-torpilleurs Tartu, Chevalier Paul* and *Maillé Brézé* of the 5ᵉ DCT.

While accompanying the first convoy of French troops to Namsos, *Emile Bertin* was attacked by a single German Ju-88 bomber, which released two 500kg bombs. One fell ten metres off the starboard quarter, causing some splinter damage; the other struck close to the starboard after 13.2mm mounting atop the after deckhouse, and continued its path down through the ship, exiting beneath the waterline on the port side without exploding. *Emile Bertin* was almost certainly saved from more serious damage on this occasion by her light protection, the thin plating failing

Table 4: *AIRCRAFT*

	Gourdou-Leseurre 832 floatplane
Aircraft Data	
length	8.70m
wing span	13.00m
take-off weight	1,700kg
propulsion	Hispano-Suiza type 9 Kb; 230hp
max. speed	195km/h
ceiling	5,000m
armament	7.5mm Darne MG
	2 G2 75kg bombs
Catapult Data	
length	20.00m
capacity	2,000kg aircraft
acceleration	to 95km/h
training arcs	60°–120° on either beam

to detonate the fuze. However, the hole in the ship's hull beneath the waterline was felt to be serious enough to warrant a proper repair, and *Emile Bertin* returned to Brest on 26 April, Admiral Derrien transferring his flag to the *Montcalm*, which had been despatched from Brest as a replacement.

Following repairs *Emile Bertin* undertook two missions to transport the French gold reserves to Halifax, Nova Scotia. The second of these, however, was aborted when it became clear that a French military collapse on the Western Front was imminent, and the ship was ordered from Halifax to Fort-de-France, Martinique, in the French West Indies. The British were opposed to this move, fearing that the ship would return to Brest and be seized by the Germans. They attempted to shadow her using HMS *Devonshire*, but *Emile Bertin* managed to shake off the British cruiser during the night, and made her entry into the harbour at Fort-de-France unaccompanied.

The next day the Armistice came into force and, following disembarkation of the gold reserves, the ship was immobilised. She would remain tied up, with the guns of 'B' turret trained on the harbour entrance, for the best part of the next three years. Although she was fully manned, only a handful of training sorties were to be possible, due to the effectiveness of the US blockade, which meant that the ship would have insufficient fuel to make the journey back to Europe or North Africa. When relations between the USA and the Vichy Government deteriorated sharply following the Allied landings in North Africa in November 1942, the captain was ordered to sabotage the ship, but he resisted the instruction on the grounds of practical difficulties until it was withdrawn in July 1943.

On 25 August, following the resolution of the political situation, *Emile Bertin* finally sailed for the Philadelphia Naval Dockyard, where she was to be completely rebuilt in preparation for the final campaign of the war on the side of the Allies. In 1944 she would return to the Mediterranean, deploying in support of the landings in Provence, and subsequently operating with 'Flank Force' against enemy shipping in the Gulf of Genoa. A projected deployment to the Far East, together with the four *Croiseurs légers* of the *Le Fantasque* class, was pre-empted by the Japanese surrender on 15 August 1945, and following a brief campaign in Indochina in 1945–46 *Emile Bertin* became a gunnery training ship. She was placed in reserve in October 1951, and was finally stricken in 1959.

Sources

Jean Lassaque, *Le croiseur Emile Bertin*, Marines (Bourg-en-Bresse, 1993)

C.F. Caroffe, *La campagne de Norvège 1940* (Service Historique de la Marine, 1955)

Official plans of *Emile Bertin*, Centre d'Archives de l'Armement

John Campbell, *Naval Weapons of World War Two*, Conway Maritime Press (London, 1988)

THE RUSSO-JAPANESE WAR

Technical Lessons as Perceived by the Royal Navy

The Russo-Japanese War of 1904–05 was the first naval conflict involving all modern ship-types since 1815. **David K Brown RCNC** looks at the implications for the Royal Navy, which had equipped and trained the victors, and had observers present at the conflict.

Introduction

The Russo-Japanese war was fought at a time when great technical changes were taking place in the Royal Navy such as the introduction of the *Dreadnought* and the fire control revolution. In consequence, there was a tendency in the Admiralty to regard the war as old fashioned, fought between ships of an earlier generation, using obsolete tactics. On the other hand, detailed reports were closely studied and, in most cases, action was taken swiftly when thought necessary. Japan was allied to Britain and the RN had a team of observers with the Japanese fleet, led by Capt Pakenham.

The real lessons of the war as perceived by the RN are obscured by the utterances of the First Sea Lord, 'Jackie' Fisher, who tended to quote the war as evidence in support of his current ideas and, since these changed rapidly, so did the lessons he read. For example, his proposals to scrap a large number of obsolescent ships (to achieve financial savings from which the new building programme) could be funded was said to be a lesson of the war, though it had been put forward in detail before the war began.

The Value of Speed

In 1902 Captain H J May had argued on a basis of war games at the War College that speed was of little value in a fight between battle fleets. He thought that the slower fleet could turn on a smaller radius to keep the faster fleet on the broadside. A paper written by his successor, Captain Slade, in 1906 is frequently quoted, and clearly tried to bring out the lessons of the war. Slade pointed out that May's manoeuvres were possible only in open water and when neither fleet had a pre-determined destination. When the slower fleet was constrained in manoeuvre, as at Tsushima, and had to reach a specific port the situation was changed. Slade added detail, pointing out that there

would never be enough ships to position them for interception of a faster fleet, that the faster fleet can force or decline action and that time could be won by the faster fleet so that victory could be achieved before nightfall. He pointed out that, tactically, speed enables the fleet to bring the whole broadside to bear quickly and keep it bearing. He also said that Togo used his speed advantage at Tsushima to chose a position and course which would minimise interference from spray. Mahan took a different line, suggesting that it was undesirable to build a new ship with higher speed as it would have to operate in company with slower ships.

Jellicoe (advised by Phillip Watts) took a pragmatic view; the cost of speed increases rapidly and that selected should be just below that at which the cost becomes 'excessive'[1]. It does not seem to have been brought out that the cost of individual ships was effectively limited by politicians and that any increase of speed would mean sacrifices elsewhere. *Dreadnought* evaded this restriction by the introduction of turbine machinery, helped by changes to the hull form.

On 10 August 1904, in the Yellow Sea, the Japanese had only a small advantage in speed and were unable, perhaps unwilling, to press the action to a decisive conclusion. At Tsushima the Japanese had a big advantage in speed and were able to control the action. Sims, quoting Lt White, USN, suggests that the speed of the Russian fleet at Tsushima did not exceed 9 knots. This seems quite probable, considering the number of old ships in poor condition whilst the extent of fouling during their voyage and long stay at Madagascar would lead to a loss of about 3 knots on all ships.

Guns and Shells

The following section deals with gunnery issues: – did they hit, what with and with what effect? – leaning heavily on a report prepared in DNO department in 1906, almost

The Japanese protected cruiser Kasagi. *Built by Cramp in Philadelphia and wrecked in 1916*

certainly by Captain E W Harding, RMA, an expert on fire control.

There is strong evidence that both the rate of fire by Japanese ships and the effect of that fire was significantly different between the battles of 10 August 1904 and Tsushima in 1905. Semenoff wrote of the latter battle 'I had not only never witnessed such a fire before, but I had never imagined anything like it. Shells seemed to be pouring upon us incessantly, one after another.' This statement relates to rate of fire and is supported by evidence that the Japanese were concerned about a shortage of shells, particularly armour-piercing, in 1904.

Fire Control

Harding wrote that the war '. . . has been rich in lessons on the employment of naval artillery, the more so, perhaps, because it marks the highest achievement of a system of gunnery which is rapidly passing away;'. True fire control was extremely primitive in Japanese ships and virtually non existent in the Russian fleet.

Direction of fire was by voice pipe or local control. Japanese ships had Barr & Stroud 4ft 6in rangefinders which were inaccurate at the ranges used and liable to go out of adjustment. The chief RN observer, Pakenham, wrote that even a perfect rangefinder would be of little value since individual guns varied so much in performance. He thought a rangefinder might be of value in obtaining an approximation to the opening range but, after

that, gunlayers would have to rely on spotting the fall of shot. It is likely that Pakenham's views, though wrong, were widely held; indeed, Sims, the USN's gunnery expert, makes very much the same point based on USN target practice in 1905. It is likely that spotting would be very difficult, even in ideal conditions, at over about 7,000 yards, particularly if also out for line and would be virtually impossible if two or more ships were firing on the same target. Spotting with two calibres close in size would always be impossible.

Commander Sims, using a track chart prepared by Lieutenant White and Ensign Henderson from notes by a Russian constructor, shows that hits on the Russian ships only occurred when the rate of change of range was low. Electrical range transmitters were used and worked well except in *Nisshin*, where they were said to be unreliable.

The Japanese believed that fatigue had a major influence on accuracy of firing. They took great pains to rest gunlayers whenever possible – 'husbanded eyesight and nervous energy'. Their fire discipline was very good, guns under local control firing only when they had a clear target. Sims believed that Russian crews were trained for close-range action; however, their initial shots at long range were quite accurate, particularly at 10 August (Russian ships at this battle did not have telescopic sights, making their performance more remarkable – perhaps it was luck). Russian gunners tended to fire rapidly, even when they could not see.

Telescopic sights were fitted to the Baltic ships just before departure with Krilov sights on the later ships. Barr

& Stroud rangefinders were also fitted before departure but in a trial off Madagascar, ranges on a target varied from 7,300 to 11,000 metres. No corrections were applied! There is also a suggestion that there were defects in many Russian guns or mounts.

Sims suggests short funnels are needed to get control tops above the smoke. This may have contributed to Fisher's desire to abolish or reduce funnels and hence to the unfortunate short funnels of *Invincible*.

Shells and Fuzes

At the outbreak of war, Japanese shells were filled with 'shimose' (picric acid, similar to Lyddite), the AP shell (base fuzed) having about a 5% burster and the HE (high capacity, DA fuze) about 10%. The Shimose filling was very sensitive and violent, the high-capacity shell, in particular, breaking the casing into innumerable tiny fragments. It was noted that even the base, which was usually blown off intact from powder-filled shells, was shattered by Shimose[2]. At 10 August, it was thought that the fuzes were too sensitive, causing premature explosions which destroyed three of the 12in guns.

Changes before Tsushima

The prematures were blamed on the Ijuin base fuze of the Mk II AP shells and the protection of the fuze against the

flame and shock of discharge was redesigned before Tsushima. These precautions seem to have been fairly successful as at Tsushima there were no prematures from 12in AP. *Mikasa* did have a common shell, burst in the muzzle of the right gun of the fore turret without damage. Two hours later, the 28th round, a common shell burst and wrecked the barrel[3]. *Nisshin* had failures in both 8in at the same point, suggesting that they were the result of prematures. Even if modifications to the fuzes had reduced the chance of prematures, they had done little to improve performance on impact.

Accounts differ widely on what shells were used at Tsushima. It is not well known that a number of high capacity, powder-filled shells were issued to Japanese ships before Tsushima but the number of such shells was unknown though it may have been up to three quarters of the outfit. The effects observed suggests that such shells formed a large proportion of shells fired at Tsushima.

Due partly to the deep draught of the over-loaded Russian ships there were few hits on armour but there were no penetrations on surviving Russian ships and nor are penetrations mentioned by survivors of those sunk. All Russian accounts of Tsushima mention that Japanese shells burst on the least contact. Semenoff also says of Tsushima 'They [Japanese shells] burst as soon as they touched anything – the moment they encountered the least impediment to their flight. Hand rails, funnel guys, topping lifts of the boats' derricks, were quite sufficient to cause a thoroughly efficient burst'. He continues 'In

Mikasa, Togo's British built flagship throughout the war. Though hit frequently, damage was not severe. She is preserved today as a museum.

addition to this, there was the unusual high temperature and liquid fire of the explosion which seemed to spread over everything . . . No! It was different to the 10th August!' Again, there is confirmation of Semenoff's opinions. The lack of penetration could be due to sensitive fuzes, detonation of the Shimose filling on impact or the fact that few AP were fired.

Russian Shells

Russian fuzes did not do well on 10th August when 2 out of the 16 shells hitting Japanese ships failed to explode and at Ulsan (14 Aug 1904) 4 out of 15 hits failed. At Tsushima, 8 out of 24 12in shells which hit failed to explode as did 28 out of 81 smaller shells which hit. A German account says that in the engagement between torpedo boats on 3 March 1904, Russian shells frequently failed to explode. Novikoff-Priboy offers a possible explanation for the failure of the Russian shells. He says that someone at the Ministry of Marine thought that the pyroxylin filling (wet gun cotton) would dry out in the tropics and ordered the moisture content to be increased from 10% to 20–30%. A year later, in 1906, when the fortress of Sveaborg was in revolt it was bombarded by the *Slava* with these wet shells. When the fortress surrendered it was found that few of the shells had exploded. The much higher proportion of duds at Tsushima gives some credence to this story.

It does not seem that the poor performance of shells of both navies was appreciated either in the UK or in the USA; almost certainly the most serious failure to learn from the war. The *Edinburgh* trials of 1910 may have been partly inspired by a suspicion that all was not well.

Penetration of armour

It does not seem likely that any Japanese shell penetrated armour of 6in thickness or more. On 10 August there were at least 10 verified hits on Russian armour of 6in or more and there were no penetrations. The Japanese fired 279 AP shells that day. Because many Russian ships were sunk, the evidence is less complete for Tsushima. There were no penetrations of *Orel*'s armour belt though one 12in had burst on 5¾in armour of the forward belt. Semenoff's incomplete account suggests that there were no penetrations of *Suvarov*'s belt or, if there were, they caused little damage or flooding. The even more incomplete accounts from other ships suggest that there were few, if any, penetrations of thick armour. For some ships there are survivors' accounts, for *Orel* a post-battle inspection, and these not only fail to mention any penetration but emphasise that every shell burst on contact. One may see further confirmation of this in the number of prematures, less than in 1904.

There were problems with the support to armour; on 10 August *Tsessarevitch* had a 10in plate forced in causing flooding. At Tsushima, *Osliabia* had a plate dislodged due to failure of the fastenings and *Orel* had 5 of the 8 fastenings on one plate broken. White describes how a 6in plate

on *Orel* was forced to pivot, the outer edge being forced out.

Russian shells were less sensitive and hence somewhat better at penetration. A 12in shell penetrated 6in armour on *Shikishima* and burst some distance behind, possibly the only AP shell of the war to function properly, though causing little damage. There were at least six other hits by 12in shells on 6in armour which pierced to some extent, though in these cases the shell seems to have burst while passing through the plate.

Damage to Orel

The damage to this ship is well documented both from official inspections after the battle and from a fascinating, highly coloured but generally accurate account of the battle by a survivor:

> The *Orel* was hit many times, and large numbers of shells struck the near-by water, drenching us with spray. The sea appeared to form a wall, barring our progress. Vomits of black and brown smoke, jets of flame, fountains of spray thrown up by the bursting shell, created an elemental tempest.

The attaches' reports after surrender and inspection of photos show that the *Orel* was probably hit by five 12in, two 10in, nine 8in, thirty nine 6in and twenty-one smaller on both port and starboard sides. The slide shows that the few 12in hits account for most of the weight of shell and burster hitting the ship.

Hits on Orel

Calibre (in)	No.	HITS Wt Shells (lbs)	Wt Burster (lbs)
12	5	4,200	405
10	2	980	96
8	9	2,250	207
6	39	3,400	351

Conning Towers

Damage to conning towers or bridge is of interest. On 10 August, *Tsessarevitch* was hit by two 12in shells at about 1837 hrs. The first hit the foremast and wrecked the bridge, killing Admiral Vitgeft and some of his staff who were standing there outside the conning tower. The second burst against the projecting roof of the conning tower; blast and splinters entering through the viewing slit killed or wounded everyone inside. In some ships a shelf was fitted below the slit to stop splinters coming through and ricocheting off the roof. At Tsushima, Novikoff-Priboy refers to a hit on the conning tower of *Orel* causing casualties from splinters inside whilst early in the battle *Suvarov* had heavy casualties, including Admiral Rojestvensky, from a hit on her conning tower. It would seem that the protection afforded by conning towers was

Damage to the after end of Orel *seen after her surrender at Tsushima.*

illusory, whilst loss of vision was real. The RN continued to fit heavy conning towers up to World War I but they were little used. Alone among major navies, the RN did not fit armoured conning towers in their battleships of the 1930s.

Fire

At Tsushima, most Russian battleships were disabled as a result of serious fires long before they were in danger of sinking. Observers comment on the incendiary effect of Japanese shells, Semenoff, quoted earlier, says that there was a marked difference from 10 August. It is almost certain that this was due to powder-filled shells, which were better firelighters than picric acid. There are specific references to paint catching fire, with flames either spreading along the surface of fire or spreading from dislodged flakes of burning paint. It is said that the red lead primer did not burn.

A single fire is easy to put out if the fire-fighters are unhindered but it is more difficult when they are being fired on and this may be seen as the main contribution of the smaller guns. If there are several fires and fire-fighting is hindered by casualties and cut hoses they will spread and join to a single massive conflagration. Ammunition fires seem fairly common and it is surprising that only the

Borodino blew up; *Iwate* was very close to it. The vulnerability of the lightly armoured ammunition supply routes (and ready use storage) for the secondary armament may be recognised. Casualties in fire parties were severe, due to splinters. Harding suggests that the serious fires at Tsushima and the long time for which they burnt was due to the coal carried high in the ship. The RN had done much to reduce the risk of fire after the Spanish-American war and fires were rare in World War I.

Big Guns or Hail of Fire

Most of the post war debate centred on whether the Russian ships were destroyed or disabled by the effects of 12in shells or by the 'hail of fire' from smaller guns, particularly 6in. Jellicoe in two papers written in justification of the 'all big gun ships' largely ignores the war and bases his arguments for the 12in on the rate of hitting during RN battle practice.

Gun	Rate of fire per minute	
	Gunlayers*	Battle Practice
12in	2	1
9.2in	5	2
6in	12	4

* Starting with gun loaded.

Iwate, *an armoured cruiser built by Armstrong. At the battle of Ulsan (14 Aug 1904) she was hit in the foremost upper 6in casemate and the explosion also wrecked the lower casemate and the next upper one.*

He shows that the rate of fire in battle practice corresponded closely to that achieved by the Japanese. He emphasised the need to make a clear distinction between rate of fire and rate of hitting which became increasingly important as range was increased.

The senior Royal Navy observer, Captain Pakenham, gave his views in the following well known quotation –

> The 10 inch guns of the *Peresviet* and *Pobeida* were of 45 calibres, and may also be of greater range, but the effect of every gun is so much less than that of the next larger size, that when 12in guns are firing, shots from 10 inch pass unnoticed, while, for all the respect they instil, 8in or 6in guns might just as well be pea shooters, and the 12 pounder simply does not count. This must be understood to refer entirely to the moral *(sic)* effect.

It is not clear what Pakenham based this statement on though it seem consistent with accounts by Russian survivors. It should be noted that Pakenham is referring specifically to the effect on morale; a sentence too often omitted.

The *Dreadnought* committee minutes mention briefly the Yellow Sea battle as confirming their views on the value of speed and big guns. In an attempt to decide on the merits of big or medium guns it is necessary to look at fire control and the chance of hitting and on shells for the resulting damage.

Cause of Sinking

From Russian accounts one can see a number of common factors, a gradual breakdown of command due to injuries to senior officers and the difficulty in passing orders as voice pipes were cut, access was obstructed by debris, structural damage and fires together with a hail of splinters on the upper deck.

Splinters also affected the stopping of holes above the water-line; not difficult if unhindered, virtually impossible under fire. Such holes led to a build up of water above the protective deck as the ship rolled in the heavy seas off Tsushima, reducing stability and possibly giving a heeling moment. Fire-fighting water added considerably to the problem. *Suvarov* had quite severe flooding through a lower deck gun port.

The centre of gravity was high in the Russian ships of French style, with towering sides, and a satisfactory intact metacentric height was obtained by inceasing the beam. Much of the benefit of beam is lost when extensive flooding occurs and it is virtually certain that the stability of these ships after damage was very poor. The centre line bulkhead in the machinery spaces would lead to large heeling moments whilst the righting moment would be seriously reduced if hits had made the upperworks nonwatertight and the tumble home would further reduce the righting moment. It was a combination of a high centre of gravity, asymetric flooding and reduced righting moment which led to capsize, though in the case of *Alexander III* and *Osliabia*, flooding of the lightly protected ends was a contributory factor.

Pakenham drew attention to the dangers of centre line bulkheads in several of his reports. No attention seems to have been paid to this point, which was probably the prime cause of capsize. At the time, capsize was blamed on tumblehome which was used only to a small extent in British ships prior to World War I. He also pointed out the need for unpierced bulkheads and, quite reasonably, it was

Russian ships resting on the bottom after the surrender of Port Arthur.

felt that efforts already in hand, eg *Lord Nelson* and *Dreadnought*, were adequate.

Due to failure of the shells, there was no clear guidance on 'all big gun' versus 'hail of fire'. Indeed, the big gun enthusiasts, such as Jellicoe, only referred to the Russo-Japanese war in most general terms. At the short ranges of Tsushima there does seem to be some support for the hail of fire theory as splinters inhibited leak-stopping and fire-fighting.

Armour

British policy was to fit a fairly thick and deep belt between the turrets with a thinner, upper belt which would keep out all HE shells. The Japanese ships were all of this style, *Mikasa* was generally similar to the *Formidable* but with thicker turret protection. *Mikasa* received 12 heavy hits at Tsushima but was little damaged; a tribute to ineffective shells rather than to her armour. There was little change in philosophy in either navy after the war, though the upper belt was omitted in *Dreadnought* to save weight and cost since there was no secondary armament to protect.

The Russians, in their first post-war design, the *Gangut* class, adopted a scheme with thinner armour, spread over a larger area which may be seen as consistent with their view that the serious damage was inflicted by medium calibre, high capacity, HE shells.

High Angle Fire and Deck Protection

The attack on Russian ships at Port Arthur by Japanese Army 280mm howitzers appeared, according to some accounts, to show a weakness in deck protection. Accounts differ greatly as to the cause of sinking of the Russian ships at Port Arthur; it is variously claimed that they were scuttled before they came under fire, that they were sunk by gunfire or that they were damaged and finally scuttled. The most likely explanation is that all explanations were true for different ships. There is also conflict on the nature of damage caused by gunfire.

On 4 December, the day before the Japanese finally captured 203 Metre Hill, they established an observation post on the slopes. Fire began from eighteen 11in howitzers and ten 4.7in naval guns, *Retvizan* suffering most. The howitzers used were made at Osaka, and fired a 480lbs projectile for 12,242 yards. On 5 December the *Poltava* was sunk following a magazine explosion and *Retvizan* hit again; she was sunk the next day. On 7 December the *Pobeida* and *Pallada* were sunk by gunfire and *Peresviet* scuttled after damage. It is quite possible that other ships were scuttled in shallow water, early on, suffering damage from gunfire whilst resting on the bottom. Inspection of the wrecks showed the following hits (Table 1).

Of the 30 big shells hitting the decks, just over half reached the protective deck. The British account suggests

Table 1: *280MM HITS ON RUSSIAN SHIPS AT PORT ARTHUR*

Ship	Hits on deck	Number penetrated	Hits on side
Bayan	7	5	5
Pallada	6	0	2
Pobyeda	3	1	6
Peresvyet	9	8	2
Poltava	3	2	2
Retvizan	2	1	4
TOTAL	30	17	21

that most shells did explode but caused little damage but a German account says that many shells failed to explode; those which did burst on the deck making a hole in so doing. Damage below the deck was local and not severe. The German account instances *Peresvyet* saying that 12 shells hit the upper deck of which 11 passed through to hit the main deck. Six of these went through and hit the armour deck of which 4 penetrated. Those which burst on the armour deck dished it slightly, while there was very little damage from those which burst below. This seems broadly in accordance with the British account of the hits on *Bayan* where 4 burst before reaching the protective deck and 3 burst on it causing only slight damage.

The towering hulls of the Russian ships helped to protect them from high angle fire and the thin protective decks (1¾–2in) were sufficient to prevent serious damage under these conditions. Some ships had put extra steel plates or sandbags on the upper deck but these were not well thought out and were ineffective. The British report says that some shells listed as hitting the side exploded in the water and led to flooding. However, the German report says that divers who examined the wrecks said that they were sunk by scuttling charges. This is confirmed by Rear Admiral Wiren who says 6 to 8 torpedo warheads were placed round each ship and exploded just before the surrender on 2 January but there was little time and most of the crews were fighting ashore so that the work was not well done and some charges failed to detonate.[4]

The British view was that high angle fire against ships at sea was unlikely as the long time of flight would make hits unlikely. The protective deck was intended to prevent damage below from shells bursting above it; the deck was not expected to be hit directly by a shell. At the ranges used in 1905, this was a reasonable line to take.

Armoured Cruisers or Second Class Battleships

Once Togo had lost two of his six battleships to mines, he was forced to use his powerful armoured cruisers in the battle line and, since the Russian fleet had many second rate (or worse) ships at Tsushima, their value was overrated. It does seem as though *Osliabia* was sunk mainly as

Russian protected cruiser Aurora *which took part in the battle of Tsushima. Russian protected cruisers had inadequate shields to their guns where crews suffered heavy casualties.*

a result of fire from cruisers, but she was a strange ship. Her main armament was four 10in, barely more than the latest cruisers, and she was fast for the day. She had a fairly thick belt (9in Harvey) but it was very shallow and her towering sides made her a fine target for cruiser guns. If an armoured cruiser is to double as a second class battleship, the arguments for an all 12in armament apply.

Scouts The Japanese seem to have relied on destroyers for scouting, based on the Elliot islands though they were always supported by cruisers. This policy was used by Fisher in arguing that nothing was needed between a big destroyer and a battle cruiser.

Torpedoes – Japanese Equipment

The pre-war Japanese torpedo boats came from Schichau and Normand and their destroyers from Yarrow and Thornycroft. The first home design, *Harusame*, was said to be a mixture of the British designs. The only wartime change was to fit an extra 12pdr in place of a 6pdr. The Japanese torpedo force consisted of 22 destroyers (2 mined during the war), 38 first class TBs, 35 second class and a few third class (of which 4 were sunk in action) and some used as minesweepers. All destroyers were fitted with W/T with a range of about 60 miles. The Russians had 25 destroyers at Port Arthur of which 6 escaped; 20 torpedo boats at Vladivostock (4 mined) and 9 destroyers with the Baltic Fleet of which 2 escaped.

It is uncertain what torpedoes were used by the Japanese Fleet. Older ships carried Schwartzkopff, described by the IJN as Types 84 and 88, believed to be Schwartzkopff models C/84 and C/84A of 35.6 cms (approx 14in). A British report gives the following data on Whiteheads supplied to Japan.

Diameter (in)	Length	Weight (lbs)	Range Yds	Kts	Charge (lbs)
14	15	747	656	26	110
18	12′1	864	800	26.3	110 Submerged tubes
18	16′5	1,188	1,093	27.8	198

In 1904, Japanese torpedoes were not fitted with gyros. In 1905 only a few were so fitted. There was a reserve of 226 torpedoes in store on 1 December 1904.

Opening Actions

Up to the start of this war there had been no effective torpedo attacks on moving ships. Three divisions of Japanese destroyers were already on the way from their base at Round Island, some 60 miles away when the Declaration of War was handed to the governor at about 10pm on the 8th. The Russian ships lay outside the harbour with their nets out but otherwise unprepared to fight. The first division of four destroyers fired two torpedoes each (one from one boat) while steaming 'dead slow', scoring three hits. They thought that they had fired at 500 yards but it is likely that the range was at least 800 yards. It is possible that the fourth boat closed to 400 yards hitting both

Retvizan and *Pallada*. The second division had been thrown into confusion by a near collision with the first division followed by a near encounter with a Russian guard ship and the third division had also been confused by the Russian patrol and no more hits were scored.

Altogether 10 destroyers fired 19 torpedoes for 3 hits against an unready force at anchor. Japanese doctrine called for ships to attack individually, the risk of collision being too high in mass attacks. They also had too much faith in the accuracy of the torpedo, attacking at too great a range – often greater than they realised.

The three ships hit were not sunk but damage from the 18in warhead was severe. The most interesting is *Tsessarevitch* which had strong longitudinal bulkheads protecting her magazines from underwater explosions. She was probably hit abaft the magazine, 80 feet from the stern, but the British believed she had been saved by the bulkhead and fitted similar protection in the *Dreadnought*. *Retvizan* was hit on the port side 80 feet from the stem and completed repairs on 28 May, *Tsessarevitch* on 8 June and *Pallada*, hit amidships abreast a boiler room, completed on 16 June.[49] Watertight doors were said to be shut, but flooding spread through ventilation trunks.

There was an inconclusive encounter between the fleets on 23–24 June 1904 when Japanese torpedo craft attacked as the Russians were re-entering Port Arthur. It was a bright, moonlit night; 67 torpedoes were fired and there were three hits, that in *Sevastopol* took six weeks to repair. *Pobeida* and a cruiser were also hit. The Japanese claimed that they fired at between 440 yards and 1600 yards but it is likely that the true range was greater, though less than the three miles given in Russian accounts. There were several other minor encounters in which torpedoes were fired but no hits were scored.

10 August 1904 – Battle of the Yellow Sea

During the main action the fleets were never within torpedo range of each other but there were numerous torpedo attacks on the Russian fleet as it returned to Port Arthur. The night was quite favourable for attackers; no moon but mostly clear and starlit but with a little haze. Good eyesight could detect a battleship at a mile and a half and a destroyer at about 1,000 yards. There was enough swell to slow the attacking force which consisted of 17 destroyers and 29 torpedo boats. Between them they fired 74 torpedoes (which suggests that most boats fired) and scored no hits. Most claimed to have fired at 400-600 yards but, again, this was probably an under estimate. The Russians seem to have avoided the use of searchlights and only fired occasionally.

Sevastopol

Following the Japanese capture of 203 metre Hill at Port Arthur the *Sevastopol* left the harbour on 9 December 1904 and moored out of sight of the Japanese howitzers, protected by nets. By 16 December the Japanese had launched six gallant attacks on her involving 30 torpedo boats (of which two were lost), two mine launches and three picket boats. Japanese reports show that 124 torpedoes were fired of which one hit and at least two exploded in the nets close enough to cause damage. Captain von Essen's defence was well planned and bravely carried out but it was not a conspicuous success for the torpedo. *Sevastopol* was scuttled in deep water at the surrender.

Tsushima – 27 May 1905

Daytime. About 20 torpedoes were fired by the Japanese during the daytime phases, mostly at *Suvorov* after she was disabled. Of the battleships, *Mikasa* fired four single shots against various targets and *Shikishima* fired two. These six torpedoes were the only ones fired during the war by the large number of torpedo tubes in the big ships of both sides. Even the close range at which gunnery actions were then fought was too great for torpedoes prior to the introduction of the heater and gyro. *Iwate* fired four torpedoes, probably the only ones of the war fitted with gyros, at a Russian cruiser at a range of 2000 yards, but failed to hit. The torpedoes were set for 26 knots and 1000 yards! These torpedoes were the only ones fired in battle from the numerous submerged tubes in both fleets.

The despatch vessel *Chihaya* fired two 14in at *Borodino* at 1505hrs at a range of about 2,750 yards and two more at *Suvorov* at 1539hrs – at 1,800 yards (another stuck in the bow tube). The 5th Destroyer Division fired five against *Suvorov* about 1540hrs, probably no hits (2 claimed). At about 1600hrs the 4th Division carried out a brave attack – brave since each of the attacking destroyers also carried eight 100lb mines on deck – They fired four torpedoes for no hits. Finally, the 11th Torpedo Boat Division (2nd class, 88 tons) was called on to despatch the battered *Suvorov*. Steaming at 20 knots, they fired 7 torpedoes for three hits at about 800 yards which caused the disabled battleship to capsize and sink within ten minutes.

Night attacks. The sea was rough during the battle and the crews of the destroyers in company were exhausted whilst the commanding officers had very little idea of the progress of the battle or where they were. The torpedo boats had been ordered to shelter at Miura or Kosaki but at about 1450hrs they sailed to join the fleet. The sea was on the beam and it was reported that they rolled 50-60°, straining the hulls. 'Telescopes and glasses were so drenched with spray and spume that nothing could be seen through them, and the men in the torpedo craft had been blinded all day with spray and spume till their eyes were suffused with blood and their sight much impaired.'

The Russian ships were picked up using their searchlights at 2000hrs and the action was inevitably confused. Altogether, 21 destroyers and 32 torpedo boats were available in the area at night of which 14 were unable to fire. A total of 87 torpedoes were fired, 50 by destroyers, 37 by torpedo boats, mostly at close range – 400–500 yards[5]. Four hits are known to have been made, one on the small armoured cruiser *Monomakh*; low in the water, she was scuttled the next morning when more Japanese ships approached. The other hits were on ships already disabled;

Nakhimoff was torpedoed forward and was scuttled off Tsushima the next morning to avoid capture. *Sissoi* was hit in the stern disabling the rudder and one propeller and sank off Tsushima next day. *Navarin* was sunk by the explosion of two mines dropped ahead of her by the gallant 4th Division.

This meagre success cost the Japanese two torpedo boats sunk by gun fire, one by collision besides three destroyers completely disabled by collision and one by gun fire with 32 killed and 86 wounded. The effect on the morale of the Russian Fleet was considerable and was a factor in the surrender on 28 May.

It would seem that the Japanese planned to use divisional attacks of about four boats but, in the confusion of a night action – particularly in such bad weather – even this degree of concentration was not possible. The danger of collision was high as was that of formations breaking up to avoid collision. Most of these problems were unsolved at Jutland and, indeed, it is likely that they were insoluble until the introduction of radar and TBS radio. Torpedo attack from destroyers was not effective, day or night, in 1905. The value of torpedoes in battleships and cruisers was zero and only represented an additional hazard.

The total number of Japanese torpedoes fired during the war is in doubt but the following table is of the right order.

February 1904	35	
June 1904	56	
August 1904	48	
December 1904	124	
Tsushima	87	(Assumed)
TOTAL	350	

The three hits on the night of Tsushima seem to be the only ones on moving ships.

Mine Warfare

There were heavy casualties on both sides from mines; the Japanese lost a third of their six battleships in one day whilst the sinking of *Petropavlovsk* off Port Arthur on 13 April 1904, killing Admiral Makarov, deprived the Russians of their only competent leader; *Pobeida* was damaged on the same occasion.

In all, the Japanese lost to mines the *Hatsuse* and *Yashima* (battleships). *Hei-Yen*, *Takasago*, *Miyako* and *Sai-Yen* (cruisers) and five smaller ships. The Russians lost *Petropavlosk*[6] while the *Sevastopol* was mined twice without being sunk. *Navarin* was sunk by floating mines dropped ahead during the night after Tsushima – a form of attack much feared by Jellicoe.

Lessons: (a) Protection

The most immediate task was to improve the protection of the *Dreadnought* (whose design was almost complete) against underwater explosions. Several papers mention the *Tsessarevitch*, and her survival after a torpedo hit which was attributed to her thick, inboard, longitudinal bulkhead and it was decided to try a similar scheme. In fact, the hit was abaft the protection. A test section was built into a merchant ship, the *Ridsdale*, for trial. The trial was conducted with unusual secrecy and no full account has been located.

The British observers with the Japanese fleet frequently pointed out the value of unpierced transverse bulkheads in surviving underwater explosions. *Yakumo* was the only Japanese ship with unpierced bulkheads and it was noted that these caused little inconvenience once one was used to them. Pakenham also pointed out that doors to coal bunkers could rarely be shut properly, something already well known. In fact, there had been a gradual reduction in the number of doors below the water line following the loss of the *Victoria*, and *Lord Nelson* was designed as the first ship with unpierced main bulkheads.

(b) Minesweeping

There is very little published information on RN work on minesweeping as a result of the war but many hints show that such work was extensive, effective and implemented. By January 1908, Fisher told a sub-committee of the Committee for Imperial Defence that mines could easily be cleared but he would not explain the technique as this would 'throw away one of the deepest secrets' possessed by the Navy. That year the conversion began of 13 torpedo gunboats to carry the new sweeping gear. The nature of the sweep is not known but it is likely that it was a wire sweep between two ships using kites to depress the wire. By 1913 it was reported that sufficient gear had been stock piled to equip 82 trawlers and that a special reserve force trained to sweep mines was ready.

(c) Mines

In May 1905 Fisher set up a committee to decide on the number of mines required for war. They decided on 10,000 of which 3,000 were to be laid off the Elbe, Weser and Jade. An initial order was placed for 1,000 of the naval spherical type – which subsequently proved almost useless. In 1906 the old cruiser *Iphigenia* was converted into a minelayer, followed by six sister ships.

Enthusiasm then waned, presumably because of the effectiveness of sweeping. By 1914 there were 4,000 mines and though trials of foreign, Herz horn mines had been carried out, none had been ordered. It is likely that there was no direct decision to abandon minelaying but other material was higher priority.

Conclusions on mine warfare

The lessons of the Russo-Japanese war as regards mine warfare were read and acted upon, though the scale of the threat was underestimated and it is likely that the success of sweeping gear was over-estimated. Perhaps it was still

thought that the Germans would only lay in accordance with international law. Goodall, visiting the cross channel passenger steamer, *Konigin Luise*, in May 1914 noted that she already had sponsons fitted for minelaying. She was sunk laying mines off Harwich on the first night of the war. Fisher's unusual emphasis on secrecy has led to an incorrect belief that the RN did little about MCM before 1914.

General Conclusions

The RN was generally correct in seeing the war as an old-fashioned one from which few lessons could be drawn. However, it is clear that the war was studied very carefully, that some lessons were drawn and, in most cases, swift and effective action was taken to implement necessary changes. The war was seen as confirming many existing ideas and was used to support much of the Fisher revolution. Poor Nebogatov's Third Squadron showed that obsolete ships were a hindrance of no value and the value of speed was reconsidered.

The main debate after the war was between supporters of the 'all big gun' ship and the 'hail of fire' enthusiasts (including White, the former DNC) both of whom claimed that the war supported their views. With hindsight, it seems clear that 10 August demonstrated the possibility of long-range fire – over 12,000 yards – which made a considerable number of 12in essential for salvo firing. Tsushima was fought at closer range and the evidence seems less clear. However, closer examination of the damage, such as the table of damage to *Orel*, demonstrate the destructive power of the larger shell. The value of the hail of fire in disrupting fire fighting and leak stopping is often neglected, even by supporters of the 6in.

The RN was concerned over the destructive power of the big, high-capacity shell, probably as a result of the *Belleisle* trial. It was this which led them to retain a lighter upper belt and light protection to the water-line rather than an all or nothing scheme as in USS *Nevada*. It was probably the same reasoning which led British designers to pay a lot of attention to protection and duplication of *Dreadnought's* fire control communications.

The Admiralty were satisfied with their fire precautions and World War I largely justified their confidence. They were also satisfied with subdivision and this was not entirely justified. Pakenham had warned of the dangers of longitudinal bulkheads but these were to topple many ships in the coming war. Spread of flooding through vent trunks etc remained a problem. Unpierced bulkheads had already been introduced in *Lord Nelson*. Mines took a terrible toll of ships in 1904-5 and the British actions were prompt and sensible though not entirely adequate.

The one serious failure was in not recognising that Japanese problems with over-sensitive fillings of picric acid (Shimose or Lyddite) and AP fuzes which detonated before penetration applied to the RN as well. New shells were being introduced at this time and it is probable that it was thought that any such problems had been overcome. Most tests of penetration were with unfuzed shell (often inert-filled) and these failings were not apparent.

Footnotes

[1] Resistance and hence power for a given speed increase very rapidly as a speed given by V kts $= Sq\ rt(L\ ft)$ is approached, close to that selected for *Dreadnought*.

[2] In some cases, where an AP shell hit light structure, there were two holes, one of entry and the other from the base being blown back.

[3] Note *Mikasa*'s rate of fire; 28 rounds in 2 hours, and she was probably the most heavily engaged Japanese ship.

[4] It is said that the machinery of some ships was greased before scuttling so that they would be undamaged when re-floated by a Russian relieving force.

[5] Corbett's text implies that 87 torpedoes were fired at night. However, the night attacks which he records only account for about half that figure; I suspect 87 refers to the whole battle.

[6] *Hatsuse* was mined at 1050hrs on 15 May 1904 about 10 miles off Liau-ti-shan (Amur). Mines were laid 50-100ft apart. At 1130hrs stern well under water, heel 4° when another mine exploded below funnel and the magazine exploded, sank in 1½ minutes. *Yashima* hit two mines in the same field at 1050hrs, sank 1230hrs.

Acknowledgements

I must thank the following for supplying information, papers, ideas and criticism. Messrs:- J Brooks, J Campbell, Dr A Lambert, S A Lilliman, I McCallum, Admiral R Morris, Dr J R Reckner, J Roberts, P Sims, A Smith, Prof J Sumida.

Sources

Reports of Naval Attachés, MoD Library
PRO ADM1/7597
Tweedmouth Papers, MoD Library
CB47
Semenoff, Cdr V, *Rasplata*, 1906
Battle of Tsushima, 1908
Narkoff-Priboy, A, *Tsushima, Grave of a Floating City*, 1937
White, R D, 'With the Baltic Fleet at Tsushima', published in *USNI Proceedings*, 1906
Westwood, J N, *Russian Naval Construction 1905–45*, 1904
Moniteur de la Flotte, 1905
Official History of the Russo-Japanese War, HMSO, 1912
Corbett, J S *Maritime Operations in the Russo-Japanese War*, reprint, 1994.

THE ROYAL NAVY'S 1944 CRUISER

The existence of a 1944 cruiser programme for the Royal Navy has been known for many years, but few details were known. **George L Moore** unravels the complex background to the RN's last big gun cruiser-designs.

At the outbreak of the Second World War nine *Fiji* and ten *Dido* class cruisers were under construction for the Royal Navy. A further batch of four *Fiji* class ships was about to be ordered whilst a new 10,000 ton heavy cruiser was in the early design stage. Immediately after the outbreak of war an additional six *Dido* class and two of the 1939 Programme *Fiji* class ships were ordered but the second pair of *Fiji* class vessels, which were to be built in Portsmouth and Devonport Dockyards, were cancelled. The latter decision resulted from production considerations as the smaller ships would take less time to build.

All design effort in the Cruiser Section of the Admiralty's Design department was soon concentrated on heavy cruisers. Treaty limits were abandoned and with them the constrained 1939 heavy cruiser design. Initially, designs of 12,500 tons, 15,500 tons and 21,500 tons were considered, the latter idea inspired by the new First Lord of the Admiralty, Winston Churchill. The 15,500 ton design was selected for development and it was intended to order four similar ships under the 1940 Supplementary Programme but other priorities intervened.

In late 1940/early 1941, cruiser requirements were again considered, the choice lying between an 8,650 ton improved *Fiji* with nine 6in guns, a 14,000 ton design with twelve 6in guns and 15,000 ton heavy cruiser with nine 8in guns. Clearly the Staff found this a difficult choice for the diary of Sir Stanley Goodall records that the Controller was pressing to get a decision made. The urgent need for new ships resulted in the improved *Fiji* design being chosen and three ships, *Swiftsure* (Vickers Armstrongs – Tyne), *Bellerophon* (John Brown) and *Minotaur* (Harland and Wolff), were ordered in May. However, design work on new 8in gun cruisers proceeded, the intention being to order ships of this class in the Autumn of 1941. When the 1941 Supplementary Programme was considered in November the construction of a further three improved *Fiji*'s was authorised and the *Defence* (Scotts), *Superb* (Swan Hunter) and *Tiger* (Vickers Armstrongs – Tyne) were ordered in December. The armament for one heavy cruiser was also authorised but the contract was suspended in February 1942 and finally cancelled in June 1943.

The 1942 programme provided for six cruisers and again saw the perpetuation of the improved *Fiji* design, two of which were ordered – *J1496* from Stephens on 7 April 1942 and *Blake* from Fairfield on 13 May 1942, The plan was to order the other four ships from Fairfield, Hawthorn Leslie, Vickers Armstrongs (Barrow) and Cammell Laird but the decision to order nine intermediate (light fleet) carriers in August 1942 resulted in the cancellation of *J1496* and the Fairfield, Hawthorn Leslie and Vickers Armstrongs vessels, while the planned order for Cammell Laird was put back six months. This revised plan was modified in September 1942 following a decision to repair and construct large ships at Royal Dockyards on the south coast where improved air defences had substantially reduced the vulnerability of the yards to aircraft attack. One cancelled ship, the *Hawke*, was reinstated and ordered from Portsmouth Dockyard on 14 October 1942. The proposed Cammell Laird ship was not abandoned until March 1943 by which time more advanced designs were in prospect.

The 1943 Programme

The urgent need for new cruisers meant that the *Fiji* was chosen for the 1942 Programme, in spite of known weaknesses, there being no time to produce a new design. The principle problem areas were (a) endurance, where 6000 miles at 20kts was required; (b) the 6in low angle mountings were unsatisfactory and there was no separate HA director; (c) the close-range armament was insufficient and not properly distributed; (d) the general layout was too cramped. The alternative was the *Dido* class, some of which were still under construction, but here endurance was far too low, an improved 5.25in mounting – capable of a higher rate of fire was required and the close-range armament was insufficient.

Work on considering the characteristics of the 1943 Cruiser commenced in May 1942. It was anticipated that the ships would mount 6in guns but all requirements were the subject of debate and the views of several Heads of Departments were sought. The ACNS (W) (Assistant Chief of Naval Staff (Weapons)) raised the following questions:

Are separate low angle and high angle [LA/HA] armaments required? Is 6in the best low angle or is 5.25in acceptable? Can weight be saved by not making guns fully high angle? Is any simplification of gun mountings and control possible to save weight? Are aircraft required?

He also commented that displacement should not exceed 10,000 tons and that ten low-angle guns were desirable. The DTSD (Director of Training and Staff Duties Division) went back to basics with his summary of the functions of a cruiser: 'ability to fight; ability to protect herself and ability to obtain information and report it'. He pointed out that cruisers might have to operate without large scale air support and it was therefore considered imperative to have a good AA armament. However, aircraft carriers were expected to be available for trade route protection thus eliminating the need to carry aircraft on cruisers. Four torpedo-tubes on each side and two searchlights bearing on each side were requirements, as well as substantially improved endurance due to the spread of the war to the Far East.

The DGAAW (Director of Gunnery and AA Warfare) argued for a ship with three triple 6in HA/LA mountings with 80deg elevation – the gun being developed from the existing 5.25in design – and a close-range armament in a four cornered arrangement on the superstructure, well clear of the main armament. He wanted the funnel low and as far aft as possible, the directors on the centre-line and before the funnel if possible, and one searchlight forward of the bridge and one on each side amidships. Significantly, he asked for a re-definition of the functions of a cruiser before a logical case was made for her armament as, in his view, the aircraft carrier could carry out many cruiser functions more effectively.

The DNO (Director of Naval Ordnance) did not consider a 5.25in gun acceptable for the main armament. On a long term basis he felt it was possible to produce a HA 6in gun mounting with 80deg elevation. Weight would, however, be saved if elevation was limited to 55deg and he considered this restriction acceptable providing intermediate weapons with a greater range than the 40mm gun (he suggested 3½pdr) were developed. He also mentioned that the 1943 Cruiser could have a 6in mounting modified to give 60deg elevation and, despite his dislike of it, suggested that a 5.25in main armament could be fitted – as faster training and elevation speeds were already under investigation for this mounting.

The DNAD (Director of Naval Air Division) took the view that the time had now arrived when a general decision on the carrying of catapult aircraft should be taken. The point being that cruiser duties could now be more effectively undertaken by the aircraft carrier, the cruiser only being needed to provide gun protection.

The D of P (Director of Plans) believed that the main function of cruisers from 1945 onward would be to act in conjunction with aircraft carriers and to protect them on minor operations and when escorting convoys. They would also provide surface reconnaissance for either the main fleet or on patrol when bad weather reduced the effectiveness of aircraft for this task. To discharge these duties the cruiser should be able to neutralise ships of a similar class and destroy inferior vessels such as destroyers and armed merchant raiders. He considered an AA battery on the most ample scale was needed. To achieve these aims, his suggested requirements were for an efficient HA 6in gun armament, endurance equal to aircraft carriers and speed a little in excess of capital ships and aircraft carriers. Catapults and 4in guns could be eliminated with the space saved being used for better close-range weapons.

1943 Staff Requirements

With the benefit of the various departmental comments, the DTSD set out his view of the Staff Requirements for the 1943 Cruiser as follows:
Guns: nine 6in (3 × 3) HA/LA (80deg elevation).
Fire-control: three directors, one per turret, two being HA/LA, one HA only.
Close-range weapons: to be as powerful as possible and arranged as suggested by the DGAAW. Type of weapon must depend on developments.
Torpedoes: four tubes per side.
Searchlights: one on centre line, two sided 44in.
Speed: 32kts.
Endurance: to correspond with the 6000 miles at 24kts of the 1942 aircraft carrier.
Although an 80deg elevation was specified for the ship the DNO stated that the weapon could not be produced in time for the 1943 Cruiser. It was known that the USA were developing a fully HA/LA 6in gun mounting.

The papers containing the views of the Heads of Departments were now passed to the DNC (Director of Naval Construction), Sir Stanley Goodall, and on 27 August 1942 he produced the following comments on the requirments as formulated up to this point.
Main armament: 6in HA/LA (80deg elevation) would simplify arrangements but the weight of the mounting and the space for ammunition would be considerable. He accepted doubts about the availability of this mounting but pointed out that the ship could not be laid down before 1944, for completion by about the end of 1946, and this delay would give time for new weapons to be developed.
Endurance: He regarded this requirement as severe.
Protection: No requirement had been stated but the DNC stated that the lessons of war experience would apply to underwater protection. It was, however, accepted that a ship of normal cruiser size might have two important compartments flooded by a torpedo hit and would therefore be put out of action. Against gunfire, the protection of the *Tiger* class was specified. It was regarded as hopeless to provide deck protection against heavy AP bombs but a very high standard of defence against AA attack would mitigate the weakness.

Preliminary characteristics were soon produced (see Table 1). The prominent feature was the displacement which Sir Stanley Goodall felt was heavy for a ship mounting nine 6in guns according to comments in his diary. The size of the vessel was also a disappointment to the DGAAW who pointed out tha the ship displaced

3–4,000 tons more than *Fiji* after the surrender of three 6in guns, eight 4in guns and two LA directors and with no increase in armour. He also felt that detection by RDF would be a considerable handicap in the effective use of torpedoes and noted the requirement with interest. The DTSD, however, whilst concurring with the view of the DNC, felt the results of the study to be reasonable. The ACNS(W), who had initiated the debate in May, felt the result to be disappointing in some ways. He considered that the endurance requirement might be too high whilst the torpedo armament was perhaps a bit of a luxury. He suggested that if a fully HA/LA 6in gun could not be produced, then one with elevation limited to 60deg might be acceptable in view of the twin Bofors and twin Oerlikons included in the design.

Clearly there was no consensus on the design of the new cruiser and the requirements were ambitious; the problem was turned over to the newly formed FBC (Future Building Committee) for an early decision on the way to progress.

The Future Building Committee

When the FBC discussed the 1943 Cruiser at the end of September 1942 the merits of 6in and 5.25in guns were among the first matters to be considered. The DNO felt that the weight of broadside from four triple 5.25in would be much the same as that from three triple 6in. The rate-of-fire of the new 6in mounting, said to be under development, was not known but it was felt unlikely that it would be markedly inferior to the 5.25in gun. To reduce vulnerability it was stated that the staggering of the main machinery and the fitting of forward traction motors were under consideration. It was decided that the characteristics of three potential designs should be investigated:

1. three triple 6in, endurance 6000 miles at 20kts.
2. four triple 5.25in, endurance 6000 miles at 20kts.
3. four triple 5.25in, endurance 6000 miles at 24kts.

These seem to have led nowhere as, when cruisers for the 1943 Programme were next discussed by the FBC, opinion swung in favour of a smaller 5.25in gun ship, the DNC being asked to prepare two designs, one with three triple 5.25in and one with three twin 5.25in. The guns were to have 80deg elevation, each turret having a director, while Bofors were to provide short-range defence and required endurance was 6000 miles at 20kts.

The cruiser programme was again considered early in November, in conjunction with the initial draft for the 1943 Programme. Only one cruiser was planned at this stage which was not considered right by the Controller who wanted three ships ordered so that design work on the new class could be spread over three firms. In reality, taking account of other commitments, the capacity to design these new ships just did not exist which meant that an existing design would have to be perpetuated. This option was not one that the committee wished to follow and it was concluded that no cruisers should be included in the forthcoming programme.

The Size Problem

This recommendation did not mean that future cruiser plans stopped at this point. On 16 November the DNC produced outline designs of two small cruisers – 1 6,800 tons ship with six 5.25in (twin) and a 10,500 tons ship with nine 5.25in (triple) – (see Table 1). It was agreed that for escort work with a carrier the smaller type was preferred whilst for front line fighting the potential for larger numbers again favoured the smaller ship. Sir Stanley Goodall mentions the designs in his diary; he did not like either of them, particularly the big one!

The 6in Cruiser still had its advocates for a week later the issue was raised again. There was some support for the larger vessel as a heavy escort ship, for combined land and sea operations and as a decisive factor in the ultimate engagement when aircraft on both sides had been destroyed. It was, nevertheless, decided that the gap between the 6in and 5.25in guns might be too small and that the 5.25in design should be pressed forward with the larger type left for future consideration.

Although the concept for a 1943 6in cruiser was thus discarded by this point, work did not entirely cease on technical aspects. In June 1943 the Admiralty Experiment Works at Haslar tested two cruiser designs – Design E of 12,150 tons standard with triple screws, all aft, for 32¾kts and Design F of 12,300 tons standard with quadruple screws, two fwd two aft, for 31¼kts. Dimensions for both were 630ft × 70ft 6in × 19ft. The aim was to test the feasibility of bow propellers (the term quoted was forward traction) so that all power would not be lost from a hit aft – the *Bismarck* episode being in the forefront of the minds of the Naval Staff. Unfortunately, the system was inherently inefficient and soon proved to be not worth pursuing.

On 25 November 1942 the views on future cruiser construction were passed to the First Sea Lord in a detailed memorandum. The weakness in existing designs, particularly in the main armament of 6in cruisers, were highlighted while essential features of a new design were seen as improved 5.25in or 6in mountings, adequate and well spread close-range armament and greatly increased endurance. It was stated that providing the design was started at once the first modified 5.25in mounting could be ready for the ship at the end of 1944. A new 6in mounting could not be ready for installation in a ship before mid 1945 if all effort was concentrated on the design and manufacture of this gun but, if the 5.25in mounting proceeded then the 6in gun would not be ready until mid 1946. Details of new sketch designs for small and large 5.25in cruisers K and L were set out together with sketch designs H (nine 6in) and J (twelve 5.25in) for comparison (see Table 1). In both K and L, engines and boiler rooms were alternated with the machinery units separated by oil fuel tanks. The larger ship had better sub-division but similar armour protection to *Tiger*. The smaller vessel had better sub-division but similar armour protection to *Dido*. The smaller design was preferred because:

a) It was in all respects suitable to fulfil its primary duty which was to act as escort for the carrier force.
b) It was the best type for operations with light forces in confined waters.
c) More building slips would take the small cruiser.
d) The building time would be appreciably less.

Programme Limitations

It was pointed out that, if it was decided to proceed, the design could be ready and orders placed in May 1943. The Controller's views on the subject of orders were highlighted. Additionally, it was predicted that deficiencies by 1947 in other types would be – fleet carriers 18, intermediate (light fleet) carriers +2 (note: one fleet carrier was assumed equal to two intermediate carriers and would thus partially make up the fleet carrier deficiency), fleet destroyers 25 – were all worse than the cruiser deficiency (8 ships) which would arise assuming no cruisers were ordered under the 1943 Programme. The ideal fleet requirements at this time were ambitious being 22 fleet carriers, 19 intermediate carriers, 50 cruisers and 191 fleet destroyers. Sixteen cruisers were then building or ordered and they were expected to complete for service at the following rate: five in 1943, four in 1944, four in 1945 and three in 1946. If small 5.25in gun cruisers were included in the 1944 Programme they were expected to enter service in 1947. The inclusion of the ships in the 1943 Programme would displace three fleet destroyers and two intermediate carriers.

It was confirmed that no cruisers should be included in the 1943 Programme and that designs should be prepared for a 5.25in gun cruiser of 6,800 tons for inclusion in the 1944 Programme. In addition it was decided that the DNC should get on with an entirely new design of larger cruiser, for which the FBC was said to be considering Staff Requirements, so that it could be considered, at the latest, in the 1945 Programme. The FBC subsequently concluded that there was no need to include a 6in ship in the programme for a couple of years. The recommendation for the larger cruiser proved prophetic in the light of subsequent history.

Development of a new design did not start immediately for there were still some design uncertainties. The DTSD had prepared a memorandum on 'Speed and Protection in Cruisers' in which he highlighted the vulnerability of the *Dido* class to a single torpedo hit, which, in his view, made the design unbalanced. The three factors to be weighed were armament, speed and protection. To achieve adequate protection he felt that a maximum speed of 27/28kts should be accepted if the cruisers security was to be greatly enhanced. By this means the size of engines and boilers could be reduced. (It was pointed out that horsepower nearly doubled in a *Dido* type when speed was increased from 28kts to 32kts.) As a carrier support ship the reduced speed was expected to be adequate on passage where 26kts was felt to be needed. A problem was, however, envisaged in providing AA support to carriers in calm weather where maximum speed would have to be used by the carrier possibly resulting in the two ships becoming widely separated. Clearly this risk needed to be

Swiftsure. The 1943 Cruiser was probably of similar appearance to Design 'H' but with funnels of equal height. The 1941 Heavy Cruiser had this feature, the policy being for large warships to look similar to the battleship King George V. *(CMP)*

considered. For supporting 'advanced forces' in actions similar to those at Tunis and Guadalcanal, speed was felt to be of lesser importance. By reducing the space needed for engines and boilers, subdivision could be improved thus giving better protection against a torpedo hit. On balance DTSD felt that a maximum speed of 28kts should be accepted, giving 27kts in ships out of dock for six months in tropical waters.

Opinion was now moving away from a 6in HA/LA mounting partly because it was felt to be little better than a new 5.25in mounting and also because it was considered likely that it would be difficult to design. At the end of the year the Sea Lords accepted the 5.25in gun as the main armament of the next class of cruisers and after some debate, they also accepted the reduction in speed. On 28 December the FBC agreed that the DNC should provide sketch designs for cruisers with three twin 5.25in and four twin 5.25in mountings. Both designs were to have a speed of 28kts (acceleration rather than speed was wanted) and an endurance of 6000 miles at 18kts. Development of the 1944 Cruiser now commenced but there were soon problems to be solved – Sir Stanley Goodall's diary records a meeting with constructors Hickey and Andrew in which turret loading, which was proving very difficult was discussed and during which they were instructed to bring in drastic schemes for better underwater arrangements.

In March 1943, four sketch designs designated K4, M1, N1 and P1 were submitted to the FBC (see Table 2). In the discussions which followed a preference was expressed for N1, a four turret ship, which gave four cornered AA fire in addition to increased LA fire. The question of speed was again raised, for it was felt there could be some difficulty in operating at night with fleet carriers, and it was decided to investigate the effect of increasing speed to 30kts. What was needed now was to crystallise the future programme as early as possible in order that development of appropriate mountings could proceed.

The Question Re-examined

The question of building a larger type of cruiser was also resurrected in March, the alternatives according to one Sea Lord being a 6in gun cruiser of about 14,000 tons or a 7.5in/8in gun cruiser of up to 20,000 tons. It was agreed that a series of papers should be produced so that the issues could be fully appreciated. In mid April four papers were presented to the FBC namely: 'The case against the large Cruiser', 'The Case for a Large Cruiser', 'The Case for and against the Large Cruiser' and 'Cruisers Heavy and Light – an Historic Analysis'. A large cruiser was defined as a ship of 15,000 tons with eight 8in guns and the small cruiser was of 7–8,000 tons with six or eight 5.25in guns. The conclusions are interesting; the case against the large cruiser pointed out that since the days of the sailing navy these had always been built to counter large cruisers developed by a potential enemy, a point confirmed in the 'Cruisers Heavy and Light' study. The record of the heavy ships was described as poor and it was felt that such ships would be at a marked disadvantage as aircraft played an increasing role in naval warfare. No case

could be seen for building a vessel between the 7–8,000 ton class and the fast, heavily armed and protected battleship. The historical study on the other hand concluded that the RN should have large cruisers but with numbers strictly limited to those possessed by opposing navies.

'The Case for the Large Cruiser' study predictably said there was a requirement for a ship with 'A main armament of size greater than 6in. An adequate high-angle long-range armament. A formidable close-range armament. Speed to keep up with a Fleet Carrier or to shadow enemy. A high cruising speed. Long endurance without refuelling. The ability to maintain high speed in bad weather. A speed high enough to give tactical initiative. A good measure of protection.' Nothing was said about the cost of achieving these ideals.

The 'Case for and against the Large Cruiser' study considered the two main purposes of the cruiser to be attendance on the fleet and commerce protection. In the first case the argument was for numbers rather than size, the impact of air power and the growth of the destroyer being noted. In the second case the need was described as doubtful with the growth in carrier numbers. It was considered that, in certain waters, the ships need not have a heavy armament or excessive speed but should possess some protection, good seakeeping, habitability and high endurance.

When these papers were discussed it was concluded that the 5.25in gun cruiser was a well-balanced design and that a heavier cruiser would probably evolve into a small battleship rather than a large cruiser. It may well be that as a result of this analysis, plans for heavy cruisers finally died in June 1943.

The 5.25in Gun Cruiser

Design of the 5.25in gun cruiser continued and in May 1943 the development of the new mounting was proceeding. Significantly in the same month it was learnt that the USA were considering a new 13–14,000 ton cruiser armed with 6in HA/LA guns.

The design of the four twin 5.25in turret cruisers of 28kts for the 1944 Programme came before a meeting of the Sea Lords on 25 June 1943 – the First Sea Lord at this time was Admiral of the Fleet Sir Dudley Pound. Design N2 was presented (see Table 2) but Designs M1 and N1 were also set out for comparative purposes. Design N2 had a different machinery layout from N1, with a shorter after boiler room and consequently better underwater protection. The forward boiler room was abaft the forward engine room and gearing rooms so that the funnels were closer together and further away from the bridge than usual. The feature was expected to reduce smoke interference. Combining the funnels into a single stack had been considered but was ruled out. The boilers had to be raised to allow the shafts from the forward engine room to pass underneath them, thus raising the centre of gravity of the machinery and so necessitating an increase in beam. The design was debated but virtually all the issues raised had been considered earlier: weakness of *Dido* design to torpedo hits, composition of main armament (both 8in and 6in guns were wanted by some Sea Lords), speed and triple mountings were among the features discussed. Comparison with US designs were also made where so much more seemed to be achieved on the displacement. The Controller dismissed this criticism as unfair pointing out that where standards had been reduced such as in the *Tribal* class destroyers and in the cruiser *London*, vessels had to be strengthened. He also doubted the US weight figures. David K Brown, RCNC points out that machinery and electrical equipment fitted in US naval ships weighed much less than similar equipment used in RN ships at this time and the Controller's doubts were therefore unfounded. All answers to all issues were satisfactory and the meeting concluded that design N2 was the best balanced ship which could be produced as an AA cruiser to replace the *Dido* class.

The sketch designs were placed before the Board of Admiralty five days later. The statement included the effect of raising speed from 28kts to 30kts – an increase in displacement from 8,650 tons to 9,750 tons. This was not thought to be worthwhile and Design N2 was approved without modification.

A Sea Lords' meeting on 25 June, however, had another significant item on the agenda; the necessity or otherwise of building a heavier type of cruiser. The consensus was that nothing should be built between the small cruiser and the battleship, anything between being regarded as illogical. The size of gun in a small cruiser was also considered. It was pointed out that the destructive power of a 120lb 6in projectile was far higher than of the 85lb 5.25in shell and the Controller said that if there was a requirement for a larger HA/LA gun than the 5.25in it must be produced. It was therefore agreed to look into the design of a new HA/LA mounting carrying a gun as near as possible to 6in calibre.

The 5.25in gun project progressed further in July 1943 when Treasury approval was obtained for the placing of orders with Vickers Armstrongs for two 'pilot' 5.25in mountings, one with electro-hydraulic power and the other all-electric, in anticipation of the new class being included in the 1944 Programme.

By October 1943 the Admiralty Experiment Works, Haslar, were carrying out tests on unpropelled models. The only modification in the basic design at this stage would seem to be a slight increase in the displacement by 20 tons to 8,670 tons.

Return to the 6in Gun

Meanwhile, in July 1943, the Sea Lords decision that there should be a preliminary investigation into the design of a 6in HA/LA mounting was discussed by the FBC. It was pointed out that the pressure of work on high priority design and development projects meant that work on the new mounting could not be started for some time to come but it was decided that Staff Requirements for such a mounting should be produced. More details of the new US 6in gun cruiser became available in mid August – the ship's large displacement was remarked upon and the project was described as not in conformity with current British ideas.

The 5.25in gun ship seems to have moved steadily forward, if perhaps rather slowly, and in December 1943 the project came before the FBC for the discussion of detailed design requirements. At the end of the month the 1944 Programme was to come up for consideration. The D of P indicated that four cruisers, including *Tiger* (later *Bellerophon*), could be laid down on available ships by March 1945 and a further two slips for cruisers were

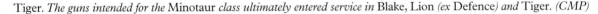

Tiger. *The guns intended for the* Minotaur *class ultimately entered service in* Blake, Lion *(ex* Defence*) and* Tiger. *(CMP)*

expected to be to hand by September 1945. One suggestion made at this late stage was that the ship should have three shafts, an idea which the DNC ruled out.

January 1944 proved a turning point for the 5.25in gun cruiser. On 13 January the First Sea Lord called a meeting to discuss the 1944 Construction Programme. It was decided to ask approval for five new cruisers, the type of cruiser depending on the gun armament that was likely to be available. It was also, however, decided that the cruiser should mount 6in guns. On 17 January, at a meeting of the FBC, the First Sea Lord – now Admiral of the Fleet Sir Andrew Cunningham – said that he did not like the proposed 5.25in gun cruiser and that he preferred the 6in armament. Further, he considered the 1944 fleet destroyer (*Daring* class) was too large and valuable a ship for her functions. He suggested the cruiser design was dropped and that a medium fleet escort was developed in its place. He then went on to say there would be no difficulty in mounting quintuple torpedo-tubes and, in any case, requirements for a small cruiser and a large destroyer could not be considered separately. However, the committee re-affirmed the view that the 5.25in gun cruiser was preferred for reasons previously argued and because increased tonnage would mean a larger air target. Moreover the 6in guns rate of fire was slower so that the weight of broadside per minute was greater for the 5.25in gun than for the 6in weapon. In any case it was doubted if it would be practical to include a 6in gun cruiser in the 1944 Programme. To add to the element of uncertainty that had now been injected into the programme, another suggestion was that a cruiser on the lines of an 'Improved *Belfast*' be built. It was decided that a paper should be prepared on the comparative merits of the 5.25in and 'Improved *Belfast*' designs, the task falling to the DGAAW. His report was produced before the end of January 1944. Comparisons were made between main armaments of eight 5.25in HA/LA guns, nine 6in LA guns and twelve 6in LA guns. The fully HA/LA qualities of the 5.25in mounting were preferred which, combined with its modern design, gave greater offensive qualities for a given weight in a smaller hull. An improved *Belfast* design would need to mount six twin 4.5in as secondary armament to achieve an adequate AA performance. This situation was expected to continue until a modern mounting with a high rate of fire could be developed. The conclusion was that more of the smaller ships could be built for equal effort, and a clear endorsement was given to the 5.25in gun cruiser project.

A Sea Lords' meeting on 6 February, nevertheless, resulted in the demise of the 5.25in gun cruiser. The First Sea Lord wanted an armament of twelve 6in and twelve 4in HA/LA, the equivalent of the *Cleveland* Class cruisers of the USN. Eight torpedo tubes per side were proposed. During the meeting the Controller pointed out that it would take four years to produce a modern 6in mounting.

It is difficult to understand just why the decision to change designs was made, particularly when it was quite clear that the weight of opinion, carefully formulated over many discussions, favoured the 5.25in gun design. However, the Sea Lords were looking beyond the end of the war, as witnessed by the record of discussions on the

Hermes Class carriers which were a contemporary design. Unwritten long term aims may have been the catalyst which caused the demise of the 5.25in gun cruiser.

The 1944 Programme

Meanwhile preparations for the 1944 Programme were progressing and proposed laying down dates were being decided. By 5 February five slips were earmarked for the construction of new cruisers – John Brown (keel-lay February 1945), Hawthorn Leslie (keel-lay December 1944), Vickers Armstrongs, Barrow (keel-lay January 1945), Devonport Dockyard (keel-lay March 1945) and Portsmouth Dockyard (keel-lay April 1945). Later in the month the Devonport cruiser was transferred to Harland and Wolff, the plan being to lay her down in August 1945. The change in design resulted in delays in this tentative schedule and the laying-down dates slipping to the third quarter of 1945. Building time was to be 3½ years. It was felt that the delay would cause production problems as it looked likely that construction of all ships would start at the same time. Another expected problem was a potential work gap at Hawthorn Leslie and John Brown.

The future of the new 5.25in mounting was now in doubt. However, although the gun was no longer needed as the main armament for a cruiser, there was thought that the weapon might serve as the secondary armament for a battleship. It was confirmed in March 1944 that work would continue and development proceeded, albeit slowly, until late 1948, at which stage it was perceived as the main armament for cruisers and destroyers. The gun was finally abandoned when it was decided to try and standardise ammunition with the USN, a new 5in gun being developed instead – but this gun also died later.

The FBC still saw a need for small cruisers and the issue was debated again in August 1944. The old arguments were rehearsed but with more emphasis on offensive use in confined waters. One other development was an enquiry from Australia in the summer of 1944 for a cruiser but nothing came of this.

We must now retrace our steps to March 1944 when the formal authorisation process began. On 14 March, the First Lord of the Admiralty sent a detailed memorandum to the Prime Minister relating to the 1944 Programme. The paragraph on cruisers read as follows:

> In the 1943 Programme the Admiralty were inclined to favour a Cruiser with 5.25in guns to the **exclusion** for the time being of a 6in gun Cruiser. Further investigations of the design problems involved however show that the greater need for the present at least is for a 6in gun. I therefore include five 6in [gun] Cruisers in the programme. I expect that the necessary facilities will become available to lay down these ships in the second and third quarter of 1945. Since these five Cruisers will only replace one years wastage at the rate hitherto experienced, additional Cruiser construction may be needed if we experience reasonably heavy losses this year.

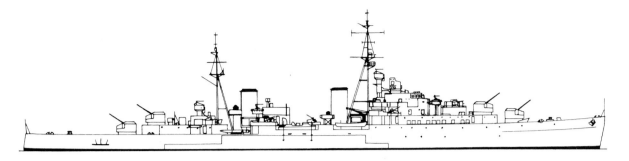

Black Prince. *The modified* Dido *was the starting point of this 1944 5.25in design. Appearance probably similar but the funnels were much slimmer and located close together roughly in the position of the second funnel.*

The estimate of expenditure by Financial Years presented to the War Cabinet on 1 May 1944 stated that the costs of the project would be spread as follows: 1945 – £4.8m, 1946 – £6.25m, 1947 – £6.5m, 1948 – £1.45m = Total £19m.

On 18 May the cruiser project was discussed by the War Cabinet. The Prime Minister said he felt 'a little doubtful about the Admiralty programme of Cruisers. Aircraft Carriers now carried out a good deal of the work of scouting previously carried out by Cruisers'. He also questioned the advisability of the armament not exceeding 6in. The First Lord said that 'the Cruisers proposed would be ships of about 14,000 tons with twelve six inch guns capable of a very rapid rate of fire'. (Note – the main armament at this point was MkXXIII 6in guns; not the rapid fire weapon visualised. The question of fitting a modern gun was addressed in July 1944 as we shall see). The First Sea Lord made several observations: 'the strength of these ships would lie in the hitting power of the twelve guns capable of rapid fire'. 'A 6in Cruiser would not be outranged by an 8in Cruiser since a Cruiser could not hope to engage another Cruiser at a range over 20,000 yds'. 'The United States are building some 6in Cruisers and some 8in Cruisers. The latter were very big ships'. Towards the close of the discussion the Prime Minister said there was something to be said for building a smaller number of rather larger cruisers. The programme proceeded.

The 6in Gun Designs

Work commenced on the new 6in gun cruiser, immediately after the 5.25in gun design was cancelled. On 9 February the DNC received a request for a new sketch design of an 'improved *Belfast*' type cruiser with four triple 6in MkXXIV mountings and 'if possible six twin 4.5in or alternatively four 4.5in provided, displacement to be in the order of 12,000 tons'. The 6in MkXXIV mounting was a development of the MkXXIII but could elevate to 60deg as against 45deg; both mountings carried the MkXXIII 6in gun which dated back to the early 1930s. The MkXXIV mounting had already been specified in March 1943 for the improved *Fiji* class cruisers *Defence*, *Bellerophon*, *Tiger*, *Hawke* and *Blake*. This alteration was

made subject to there being no delay in the completion of the ships. The new group constituted the *Tiger* class.

In mid March 1944 Design 'Q' appeared, a 14,200 ton (standard) ship which was somewhat larger than anticipated (see Table 3). Design 'R', also produced at this time, had the same characteristics but differed in that the directors were sided and the 4.5in magazines were on the centre line while in 'Q' this arrangement was reversed. Completion dates for the ships were now expected to be three in 1948 and two in 1949. Also prepared were designs for two smaller ships ('V' and 'W') which seem to have been much closer to *Belfast* in concept (see Table 3) but these were quickly ruled out. In early May it was decided that 'R' would be the basis of the new design with four triple MkXXIV mountings as the main armament.

However, the delayed completion dates provided a further scope for the main armament debate and in April 1944 three new options were considered, comparisons being made with the existing MkXXIV mounting (see Table 4 – clearly little if any development work had been carried out on new designs). With reference to Table 4, the Director General of Gunnery did not favour option 'A' because it was a half measure. The DNC, whilst agreeing that a new 6in gun design was overdue, pointed out that if either option 'B' or 'C' were adopted it would be four years before any turrets would be available to the shipbuilders. The timescales highlighted led to the Director of Gunnery voicing the thought that at least two ships could be completed with MkXXIV mountings and, at best, three with mountings 'B' or 'C'.

In June 1944 the main armament options were discussed by the Sea Lords. The 6in armament was primarily for LA purposes but was required to have AA capabilities to supplement the AA armament at medium and short ranges. The time factors involved in developing the designs were a problem and only one design could be developed at a time. Under the new completion schedules mounting designs 'B' and 'C' could not be installed in the first three ships. Options were:-

a) Fit all five cruisers with design 'A'. This was felt to be a half measure as the turret was not a completely modern design. Adoption of this option would mean that development of a fully up to date 6in mounting could not start before about 1948.

b) Complete first three ships with MkXXIV and fit designs 'B' or 'C' in last two cruisers only. This would mean commencing new cruisers with an out of date main armament and involve designing two different classes.

c) Accept some delay in the completion of the first three ships and fit all with design 'B' or 'C'.

It was appreciated that the ships would not be completed in time for the war. At this time the displacement of the ships was very approximately 14,200 tons with the MkXXIV mounting, 14,700 tons with the 'A' mounting, 15,100 tons with the 'B' mounting, 15,300 tons with the 'C' mounting and 13,800 tons with the 'C' mounting if the number of turrets was reduced from four to three. By July 1944 design 'B' had been adopted which meant a major re-design and resulted in cruiser design 'Y' which was presented to the Controller in September 1944 (see Table 3). Displacement had risen to 15,350 tons. By November 1944 the names *Neptune*, *Centurion*, *Edgar*, *Mars* and *Minotaur* had been approved for the new ships, the whole group being known as the *Neptune* class.

The Neptune *Class*

With the war obviously nearing an end, the future of the programme was re-considered in January 1945. The merchant shipbuilding programme now had priority so approval was sought by the D of P to lay these ships down 'fitted in with the merchant shipbuilding programme providing their completion was not delayed beyond the year 1950'. A request was also made for the one remaining ship of the *Tiger* class which had not yet been laid down (*Bellerophon*, ex *Tiger*) to be built to the 1944 design bringing the number in the class up to six ships.

In November 1945 the Admiralty Board sought to lay down two ships immediately and the remainder over a longer period so that they could best be fitted in with the merchant shipbuilding programme. A request was also made for approval to proceed with one turret of the new 6in design in advance of construction in order to fit it into one of the new cruisers.

However, by January 1946 questions were being raised about the future of the *Neptune* design as other developments were evolving. The point was made that there seemed little value in proceeding further, and thus incur-

Minotaur. Sketch D: Profile and deck view.

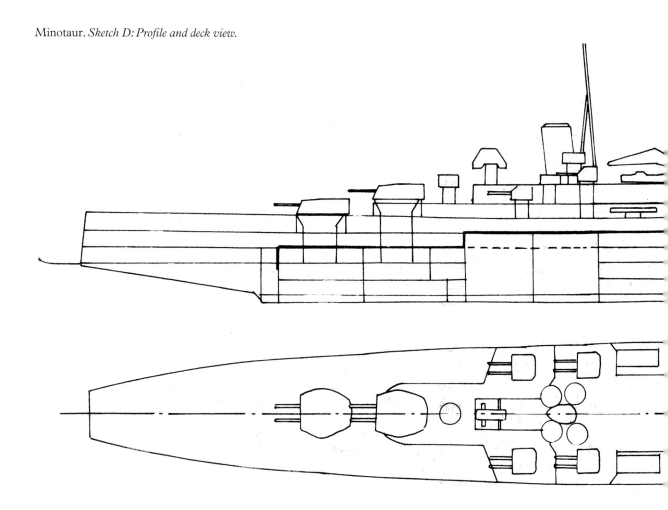

ring unncessary work, until the position on new designs and mountings had been clarified. One month later the Controller confirmed that a new design with five 6in (twin) and a 3in secondary armament was to be considered. Work was duly suspended on the *Neptune* design, apart from an examination of the amenities which were being increased by 25 per cent. This latter improvement would mean that the forecastle would be extended right aft with the result that the ship became flush decked. This revision took displacement up to 15,960 tons and reduced the speed to 31.75kts. It was calculated that if speed was kept to 32kts displacement would rise to 16,300 tons (see Table 3).

The Minotaur *Class*

The design of the new cruiser was built around the new Mk26 twin 6in mounting with 80deg elevation and the new 3in/70dcg gun which was thc main AA armamcnt. Both weapons were in the initial design stages. The US cruiser *Worcester* was the catalyst for the new ship, the Royal Navy having been given full details of the American design. In July 1946 four sketch designs 'A', 'B', 'C' and 'D' (See Table 5) together with *Neptune* were presented to the Board for a decision on which way to progress. Sketch 'A' was a five turret design with sixteen 3in/70 which was slightly smaller than *Neptune*; Sketch 'B' was a four turret design again with sixteen 3in/70, about 1,000 tons lighter than Design 'A'; Sketch 'C' was a five turret design with a revised engine room layout and a reduced length; whilst sketch 'D' was again a five turret design with a revised engine room layout but length the same as 'A'. All were flush-decked ships. No detailed work had been done on either of the new gun mountings; space and weight quoted were the best estimates that could be foreseen. Details of the various engine room layouts were not quoted but were no doubt clearly shown in the sketch's presented to the Board. It was decided to proceed with sketch design 'D' and cancel the *Neptune* design as it was 'now out of date and the ship was now larger than we needed'. However, compared with *Neptune* the new ships were only 10ft shorter in lcngth and of 1ft less bcam. Displacement was reduced by about 1,000 tons but engines were only slightly smaller. The side armour (3.5in) and deck armour (1.5in) aimed to give immunity from destroyer attack (4.5in shell)

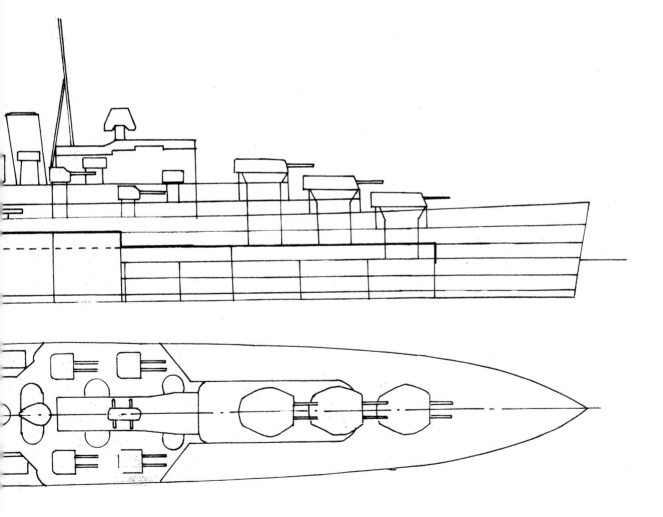

at ranges beyond 6,000yds and 60deg inclination. A torpedo armament was retained, with four quadruple 21in mountings fitted. In December 1946 the names originally allocated to the *Neptune* class were transferred to the new ships, the *Minotaur* becoming the new class name.

There still remained uncertainty for, in March 1947, a further set of designs were drawn up, this time in the P to S and P1 to S1 series (see Table 5). They were essentially concepts to illustrate the effect of various combinations of armaments, including quadruple 3in/70 mountings, and comparisons were made with design 'D'. March 1947 also saw consideration of that year's new construction programme. There was clearly no immediate prospect of the ships being built with the result that the class was regarded as cancelled when the building programme was drawn up that same month. However, this event did not mark the end of the 1944 Cruiser as, on 31 May 1947, the First Sea Lord, in a paper to the Board, pointed out that the need for these vessels had not lapsed and that it was intended to propose their inclusion 'to such number as may then seem desirable, in a future programme, as soon as the design is

finalised and construction can be commenced'. A ten year expenditure forecast prepared in July 1947 indicated that two ships could be laid down in each of the years 1951, 1952 and 1953. However, a further memorandum prepared for the Board on 28 August 1947, which covered new construction, modernisation and conversion, indicated that new construction in the next five years would be limited to prototypes not larger than frigates. This point probably marked the effective end of the 1944 Cruiser project.

The contract for *Bellerophon* incidentally had remained in place with Vickers Armstrongs (Tyne) until formally cancelled on 28 February 1947. The ship had been progressively an Improved *Fiji, Tiger, Neptune* and finally a *Minotaur* class vessel. Her name had even been earmarked for a 1940 8in gun cruiser!

The 6in Mk26 and the 3in/70 mountings lived on but development was protracted and the guns did not go to sea in an operational warship of the Royal Navy until March 1959 when HMS *Tiger* was finally completed to a drastically altered design.

Table 1: PROPOSED 1943 CRUISERS

August 1942

Standard Displacement (tons)	12,000		Protection
Speed (knots)	31.75/30		Sides 3.5in abreast
			Magazines, 3.25in abreast machinery.
Endurance	6,000 miles at 24kts (six months out of dock home waters)		Deck 2in.
			Main bulkheads 1in bounding machinery spaces.
Armament	9–6in HA/LA 80° elevation three turrets 400 rpg 10 twin Bofors 12 twin Oerlikons 2 Quadruple 21in T.T.		Splinter and other protection – as *Tiger*

25 November 1942

		H	J	K	L
Armament (in)		9–6 3 triple	12–5.25 4 triple	6–5.25 3 twin	9–5.25 3 triple
twin Bofors		12	11	6	8
twin Oerlikons		12	10	6	10
Displacement (tons)	standard	11,500	11,650	6,800	10,500
	deep	14,500	14,700	9,000	13,250
Shp		80,000	80,000	62,000	80,000
Speed (kts)	standard	31.75	31.75	31.25	31.5
	deep	30.5	30.5	29.5	30
Oil fuel (tons)		2,750	2,750	2,000	2,500
Range (miles)	20 kts	6,700	6,700	6,200	6,300
	24 kts	4,500	4,500	4,300	4,300
Protection (as)		*Tiger*	*Tiger*	*Dido*	*Tiger*
Dimensions (ft)		610 × 69 × 33	610 × 69 × 33	615 × 69 × 33	525 × 56 × 30	575 × 68 × 32

(These figures are very approximate.)

Table 2: *PROPOSED 1944 5.25IN CRUISER*

	K4	M1	N1	N2	P1
Length (wl) ft	535	520	550	550	520
Breadth (extreme) ft	56	55	62	64	56
Standard Displacement (tons)	7,600	7,150	8,200	8,650	7,250
Deep Displacement (tons)	9,800	9,050	10,100	–	9,150
Speed (kts) trial conditions	30	28	28	28	28
Shp	–	44,000	44,000	48,000	–
Fuel Capacity (tons)	2,000	1,700	1,700	2,300	1,700
Endurance: deep, six months out of dock, home waters at 18 knots	7,000	6,200	6,000	7,700	6,200
Complement (about) as Flagship	–	600	650	675	–
Armament					
In Twin 5.25in HA/LA 80° elevation	6	6	8	8	6
Bofors in twin mountings	12	12	12	16	12
Oerlikons in twin mountings	16	16	20	24	16
Quadruple Torpedo (no. of tubes)	8	8	8	8	8
Protection – vertical (in)					
Machinery spaces	3	3	3	3	3
Sides – Platform to lower deck at ends	.75	.75	.75	.75	.75
Bulkheads and shellroom ends	1	1	1	1	1
Magazine ends	1	1	1	1.5	1
Turrets	.5	.5	.5	.5	.5
Gun supports	1	1	1	1	1
Protection – horizontal (in)					
Decks	1.25	1.25	2	2	1.25
Magazine Crowns	2	2	2	2	2
Turret roof	.5	.5	.5	.5	.5
Weights (tons) Hull	–	3,925	4,560	4,850	–
Armament	–	745	920	970	–
Equipment	–	490	530	530	–
Machinery	–	1,000	1,010	1,040	–
Armour and Protection	–	830	1,020	1,090	–
	–	6,990	8,040	8,480	–
Board margin	–	140	160	170	–
	–	7,130	8,200	8,650	–

Table 3i: *PROPOSED 1944 6IN CRUISER*

	Q & R.	V.	W.	Y (4.9.44)
Length (wl) ft	630	606	606	655
Breadth (extreme) ft	74	73	73	76
Standard Displacement (tons)	14,200	13,300	13,350	15,350
Speed in standard condition – clean (kts)	32.5	32.5	32.5	32
Speed (kts) trial conditions – six months out of dock tropical waters (kts)	29.5	29.25	29.25	29.5
Fuel Capacity (tons)	2,650	2,650	2,650	2,850
Endurance: deep, six months out of dock, home waters at 20 knots	4,200	4,300	4,300	5,000
Complement	1,050	990	980	1,050
Armament				
6in guns in triple turrets	12	12	12	12
4.5in guns in twin turrets	12	–	8	12
4in guns in twin turrets	–	12	–	–
Bofors in twin mountings	20	18	20	16
Bofors in single mountings	–	–	–	8
Oerlikons in twin mountings	28	28	28	–
Quadruple Torpedo (no. of tubes)	16	16	16	16
Protection – vertical (in)				
Ships sides	4.5	4.5	4.5	4.5
Bulkheads	2.5	2.5	2.5	2.5
Machinery spaces	1	1	1	1
Magazine ends/Shell Room ends	2.5	2.5	2.5	2.5
Turrets – front	4	4	4	4
sides	2	2	2	2
Protection – horizontal (in)				
Decks	2	2	2	2
Magazine Crowns	2	2	2	2
Shell rooms	2	2	2	2
Turret roof	2	2	2	2
Weights (tons) Hull	7,220	–	–	7,850
Armament	1,820	–	–	2,050
Equipment	780	–	–	810
Machinery	1,900	–	–	2,000
Armour and Protection	2,200	–	–	2,340
	13,920	–	–	15,050
Board margin	280	–	–	300
	14,200	–	–	15,350

Table 3ii: *Proposed 1944 6in Cruiser (continued)*

	Y (8.2.46)	With flush forecastle to provide increased amenities maintaining length and sacrificing knot speed	With flush forecastle to provide increased amenities increasing length 10ft & increasing power to maintain original speed
Length (wl) ft	655		
Breadth (extreme) ft	76		
Standard Displacement (tons)	15,560		
Speed in standard condition – clean (kts)	32		
Speed in deep condition six months out of dock tropical waters (kts)	29.5		
Fuel Capacity (tons)	2,850		
Endurance – six months out of dock tropical waters at 20 kts	5,000		
Complement	1,351		
Armament			
6in guns in triple turrets	12		
4.5in guns in twin turrets	12		
Bofors in twin mountings	16		
Bofors in single mountings	8		
Quadruple Torpedo (no. of tubes)	16		
Protection – vertical (in)			
Ships sides	4		
Bulkheads	4 to 2.5		
Machinery spaces	1.5		
Magazine ends/Shell Room ends	1.5		
Turrets – front	4		
sides	2		
Protection – horizontal (in)			
Decks	1.5		
Magazine Crowns	1		
Shell rooms	1.5		
Turret roof	2		

Weights* (tons)		Y (8.2.46)		
* Note – reduction	Hull	7,685	8,060	8,270
in hull weight	Armament	2,190	2,190	2,190
due to welding	Equipment	945	970	970
	Machinery	2,090	2,090	2,240
	Armour and Protection	2,350	2,380	2,410
		15,260	15,690	16,080
	Board margin	300	310	320
		15,560	16,000	16,400

Table 4: *Proposed 1944 6in Cruiser – Gunnery Options*

	A	B	C	Mk XXIV
Rate of fire (p.m.)	8–9	10–12	10–12	5–6
Maximum elevation	60°	60°	80°	60°
Total weight of turret (tons)	195/200	205/220	220/235	162½

Table 5: *Proposed 6in Cruiser (1946 Designs)*

1946 Design – Twin D.P. 6in

	A.	B.	C
Length (wl) (ft)	645	630	(5 turret design as 'A' but with
Breadth (ft)	75	73	revised engine room layout and
			shortened ship.)
Standard Displacement (tons) about	15,000	14,000	
Deep displacement (tons) about	18,400	17,000	
			D
Speed (deep displacement – trial conditions (kts)	31.5	31.5	(5 turret design as A but with revised
Speed (deep condition six months out of			engine room layout keeping same
dock tropical conditions	29.5	29.5	length of ship.)
Shp	100,000	100,000	
Endurance – six months out of dock			
tropical waters at 20kts	5,000	5,000	
Complement (as private ship)	1,090	1,000	
Armament			
6in guns in twin turrets	10	8	
3in guns in twin turrets	16	16	
Quadruple Torpedo (no. of tubes)	16	16	
Protection – vertical (in)			
Ships sides	3.5	3.5	
Machinery spaces	1	1	
Turrets – front	4	4	
sides	2	2	
Protection – horizontal (in)			
Deck	1.5	1.5	
Shell rooms	1.25	1.25	
Turret roof	2	2	

Weights (tons)		A.	B.
	Hull	7,640	7,230
	Armament	2,160	1,910
	Equipment	865	825
	Machinery	1,930	1,900
	Armour and Protection	2,180	1,945
		14,775	13,810
	Board margin	295	278
		15,070	14,088

Table 6: *PROPOSED 6IN CRUISER (1947 DESIGNS)*

1947 Design – Twin D.P. 6in

				Length (ft)	Deep displacement (tons)
P	with torpedoes	8 – 6in	(4 twin)	660	19,250
		24 – 3in	(6 quad)		
	without torpedoes			635	18,500
P1	with torpedoes	8 – 6in	(4 twin)	630	18,250
		12 – 3in	(6 twin)		
	without torpedoes			630	18,000
Q	with torpedoes	6 – 6in	(3 twin)	675	19,730
		32 – 3in	(8 quad)		
	without torpedoes			665	19,250
Q1	with torpedoes	6 – 6in	(3 twin)	610	17,750
		16 – 3in	(8 twin)		
	without torpedoes			600	17,500
R	with torpedoes	10 – 6in	(5 twin)	710	21,000
		32 – 3in	(8 quad)		
	without torpedoes			700	20,500
R1	with torpedoes	10 – 6in	(5 twin)	660	19,500
		16 – 3in	(8 twin)		
	without torpedoes			650	19,250
S	with torpedoes	10 – 6in	(5 twin)	660	19,250
		16 – 3in	(4 quad)		
	without torpedoes			660	19,000
S1	with torpedoes	10 – 6in	(5 twin)	660	18,250
		8 – 3in	(4 twin)		
	without torpedoes			635	18,000

Acknowledgements

My thanks are due to firstly David K Brown, RCNC for providing ideas when this manuscript was being prepared, producing information from his own extensive records, checking the text and for making available his copy of the diary of Sir Stanley Goodall, RCNC, DNC 1936–44.

I would also like to thank J D Brown, Head of the Naval Historical Branch, for assistance in tracing ships names, Guy Robbins and the staff of the National Maritime Museum and the staff of the Public Record Office, Kew for assistance always cheerfully given.

Sources

ADM 1	11344	Construction of new Cruisers including *Fiji* and *Dido* classes 1941.
	11615	1941 Supplementary New Construction Programme.
	14795	New Construction Programme 1943 – War Cabinet Paper.
	17036	New Construction Programme 1944 – War Cabinet Paper.
	20906	1945 New Construction Programme (revised).
	25240	1944–53 5in Medium Calibre dual purpose single weapon.
ADM 116	4601	1940–42 Naval Construction Programme.
	5095	1943/44 New Naval Construction Programme 2/44.
	5150	Future Building Committee.
	5152	
	5342	1945 Naval New Construction Programme.
ADM 138	567 D	*Fiji* Class.
	567 E	*Fiji* Class.
	624	Armoured Cruiser Designs to carry 8in or 9.2in guns.
	729	1944 Cruiser Design.
ADM 167	103	Board Minutes 1939.
	116	Board Minutes 1942.
	118	Board Minutes 1943.
	121	Board Minutes 1944.
	123	Board Minutes 1945.
	127	Board Minutes 1946.
	129	Board Minutes 1947.
ADM 205	21/22	First Sea Lords Records.
	23	First Sea Lords Records.
	32	First Sea Lords Records.
	36	First Sea Lords Records.
ADM 226	49	Admiralty Experiment Works, Haslar.
ADM 229	28	Director of Naval Construction Papers 12/42 – 3/43.
	30	Director of Naval Construction Papers 6/43 – 8/43.
	33	Director of Naval Construction Papers 1 – 3/44.
ADM 265	1	Engineer in Chief – Miscellaneous correspondence and papers 1938–40.
PREM 322	5/6	Prime Minister's files.

Warships Supplement 55 December 1978 World Ship Society.
                                 57 June 1979

Naval New Construction Programmes and their execution
D.M. Mckenna. Unpublished work. Copy at PRO
Record of Naval Orders – Naval Library, Whitehall.
Stephens Archive – University of Glasgow.
The Churchill Papers, Martin Gilbert.
Via David K. Brown. RCNC

THE PEIYANG AND NANYANG CRUISERS OF THE 1880s

The Chinese Empire tried hard to build a credible naval force after the ruinous period of the Opium Wars and Taiping Rebellion. **Richard N J Wright** looks at one aspect of this expansion.

During the 1880s the Empire of China built up one of the largest and most modern squadrons of warships in the Far East, the Peiyang fleet. Starting in 1875 and purchasing mainly from abroad on a limited budget, it bought the gunboats, cruisers and battleships which were at the time considered to be the latest in design and performance. The Peiyang fleet was intended to command the northern waters of China around the coasts of the provinces of Shantung, Chihli and Fengtien; its smaller companion force, the Nanyang fleet, covered the waters south as far as and including the Yangtze river. The story of 'The Chinese Battleships' has already been told; this account covers the cruisers of that era.

The Opium Wars of 1840–42 and 1857–60, which China fought with medieval weapons, had on their conclusion the virtue of opening up China to western technology. An attempt in 1863 to equip China with a ready-made fleet of steam warships acquired in Britain (the Lay-Osborne Flotilla) failed, but the southern province of Kwangtung was one of the first to avail itself of steam warships for use against pirates, by purchases from both Britain and France during the 1860s. The establishment of two modern shipyards, one attached to the Kiangnan Arsenal at Shanghai with western supervisors, the other at Foochow (Fukien Province) under French control, both during the 1860s, then gave China the capability to provide for at least a decade its four regional fleets (Peiyang, Nanyang, Fukien and Kwangtung) with the steamships they required for antipiracy and transport purposes. The Kiangnan shipyard provided most of the warships for the Nanyang fleet; it was said to have made extensive use of imported pine in the construction of its ships, and as such they were inferior to the Foochow-built ones, but notable amongst its output were the steam frigates *Hai An* and *Yu Yuen* (1872/75, 2600 tons). The Foochow shipyard produced a larger number of warships, all built of Burmese or Thai teak, of which the largest was the steam corvette *Yang Wu* (1872, 1600 tons). These ships were either retained for the use of the Fukien fleet, or hired out to or sold to the other regional fleets, and were much in demand as guardships for ports. The Foochow dockyard complex contained in addition most of the training facilities needed for the manning of a rapidly growing steam navy.

In the 1870s international threats to China's borders began to build up; disputes with the French to the south, and disputes with Japan over both Korea to the north and Formosa to the east. In 1874 the French contract for running the Foochow naval yard expired. The yard continued in production under competent Chinese administration, but the one loss to posterity was the lack of precise records from then on. However, the Chinese officials realised that western technology was increasing fast; and that to supply China's fleets with up-to-date vessels to counter the looming threats they would have to purchase from abroad iron frames for the construction of sturdier composite-built vessels, as well as purchasing, again from abroad, the iron- or steel-built ships for which they had as yet no ship-building capacity. In 1875 a Sea Defence Fund was set up, and enquiries began in Britain about suitable types of warships for purchase on a limited budget.

The Alphabetical Gunboats

During the 1870s the western navies had been pondering the problem of ever-increasing sizes of guns versus ever-thickening belts of armour. As a way around the problem Mr Rendel had started producing his series of small and relatively cheap gunboats armed with a monster gun, based on the *Staunch* prototype, which in theory could surround in numbers and destroy a larger armoured adversary with relative impunity. These seemed an eminently suitable solution to China's problem; in the years between 1876 and 1881 she took delivery of eleven of these boats of the most advanced design, so-called Alphabetical gunboats as they were sent out under the red ensign named with letters of the Greek alphabet. A Commander W. M. Lang, RN was in command of the *Gamma*, which sailed from Britain in March 1877 in

Delta, *one of the Alphabetical gunboats, renamed* Che-Tien. *Completed in 1877, she was still in service fifty years later.* (NMM, 58/4763)

company with her sister *Delta*. The small ships were schooner rigged, proving excellent seaboats on passage. The first four boats (in alphabetical order) were delivered to the north, forming the nucleus of the modern Peiyang fleet. The promoted Captain Lang then returned to Britain where he took command of the next four (*Epsilon, Zeta, Eta* and *Theta*), which before sailing from Portsmouth on 24 July 1879 gave a demonstration firing of their assorted armament before a large and appreciative naval audience. The four ships were then delivered to north China, being swapped for the part-worn *Alpha, Beta, Gamma* and *Delta*. These were in turn bestowed on the Nanyang fleet, thus demonstrating the acumen of the Northern Viceroy, Li Hung-chang, who controlled most of the Sea Defence Fund, and who was to be responsible for the building up of the modern Peiyang Fleet. The last three ships were delivered in 1881, the *Iota* and *Kappa* going to Peiyang, the *Lambda* to Kwangtung. All eleven gunboats were, of course, given Chinese names.

Meanwhile, the Foochow naval yard had started the construction of a series of composite sloops in the 1,200–1,300 ton range, barque-rigged but with a 750hp steam plant, which were either ordered by or were sold off to the various regional fleets. These were basically unprotected, but possibly had armoured casemates, and were

distributed as follows: *Wei Yuen*, 1877, to Peiyang; *Chao Wu*, 1878, to Fukien; *K'ang Chi*, 1879, to Peiyang; *Teng Ch'ing*, 1880, to Nanyang; *Heng Hai*, 1885, to Fukien[1]; *Kuang (Kwang) Chia*, 1887, to Kwangtung (an improved version with 1600hp, generally referred to as a cruiser).

'The Fast Gunboats'

The West continued to wrestle with the problem of producing thicker and thicker armour to combat projectiles fired from larger and larger guns. In the cruiser range the British *Comus* class of 1878 introduced a thin flat protective deck for deflecting missiles from the vital areas, while the British firm of Armstrong, extending the Rendel principle, laid down for Chile in 1879 the *Arturo Prat*, a fast craft mounting two 10in guns, with a thin partial protective deck over the machinery spaces and magazines buttressed with coal. Li Hung-chang, who had been looking for ideas for cruiser types, immediately followed up with an order for two such craft for China.

The *Chao Yung* and *Yang Wei* were completed in July 1881. A completely new concept, they received much attention in the press. Steel-built, of 1,350 tons, with a main armament of two 10in guns, one of the most

Either Chao Yung *or* Yang Wei *on completion. Note the schooner rig for passage.* (USN)

powerful weapons then afloat, in fixed turrets with 70°/44°/70° arcs of fire, firing 400lb projectiles capable of piercing 18in of iron plate. With a speed of 16 knots, they were virtually unarmoured apart from the thin steel protective deck: in fact, miniature versions of the battlecruisers of a quarter of a century later. Small, speedy, very manoeuvrable, and thereby difficult targets, they were designed to immobilise a ponderous ironclad swiftly and to escape unharmed. Although schooner-rigged, they had stowage for enough coal to be able to cruise at 8 knots for four weeks; but because of their very low freeboard had to be built up fore and aft for passage.

On this occasion the ships were sailed out with Chinese crews, albeit with European advisers, particularly in the engineering departments. Admiral Ting Ju-ch'ang, a cavalryman recently appointed commander of the rapidly enlarging Peiyang fleet, came to England to take the ships over, with a Captain Clayson RN as his righthand man; and for the first time in British waters the new Chinese naval ensign was flown, a yellow triangular flag with a dragon motif.

The ships arrived in Chinese waters in October 1881, the *Chao Yung* docking in Shanghai the following month. From there they proceeded north to Taku where the Viceroy Li Hung-chang was embarked to a salute from the six Alphabetical gunboats, after which the two cruisers knifed across the waters of the Gulf of Pechihli at 15 knots for a quick tour of inspection of the site of the proposed naval base at Port Li (normally known as Port Arthur). By 1882 the Peiyang fleet was made up of the two cruisers, the six gunboats and the sloops *Wei Yuen* and *K'ang Chi*, all under the command of Admiral Ting, and from April with Captain W. M. Lang appointed as his deputy.

Armstrongs continued the development of what was to prove an immensely successful type, the protected cruiser, with in the early years China and Japan in competition as keen buyers. The completion of the *Arturo Prat* was a leisurely affair, as she was not handed over to Chile until 1883, but in 1885 she was bought by Japan. From her Armstrongs developed the *Esmeralda*, launched for Chile in June 1883 (2,920 tons, two 10in), with a full 1in vaulted protective deck, the first cruiser actually designed for cruising without sails; and she too was sold on to Japan in 1894. Next to come were the Japanese *Naniwa* and *Takachiho*, launched 1885 (3,650 tons, two 10in), with a 3–2in protective deck. Smaller cruisers for China followed. The *Chih Yuen* and *Ching Yuen*, launched 1886/7 (2,300 tons, three 8.2in) were described as the most powerful cruisers for their size. Unfortunately China ran out of money for shipbuilding at this critical stage; critical because the medium calibre quick-firing gun was introduced at the end of the 1880s, and although Japan went to France for her next class of cruisers fitted with a 'battleship-killing' single 12.6in gun, they were also fitted with a full secondary armament of Armstrong 4.7in quick-firers. And when in 1892 Armstrongs offered the last word in protected cruisers (4,150 tons, four 6in QF, eight 4.7in QF), she too *(Yoshino)* went to Japan.

The First German-built Ships

In the meanwhile China, in an attempt to achieve full naval supremacy in the China Seas, had been in the market for battleships. This was a major departure, liable to tip the balance of power in the Far East, and one not to be considered lightly by the western powers. Britain was probably too worried about relations with Russia to countenance a

The Japanese cruiser Tsukushi, *ex Chilean* Arturo Prat,
and sister-ship to the Chinese Chao Yung/Yang Wei.
(Drawn by John Roberts.)

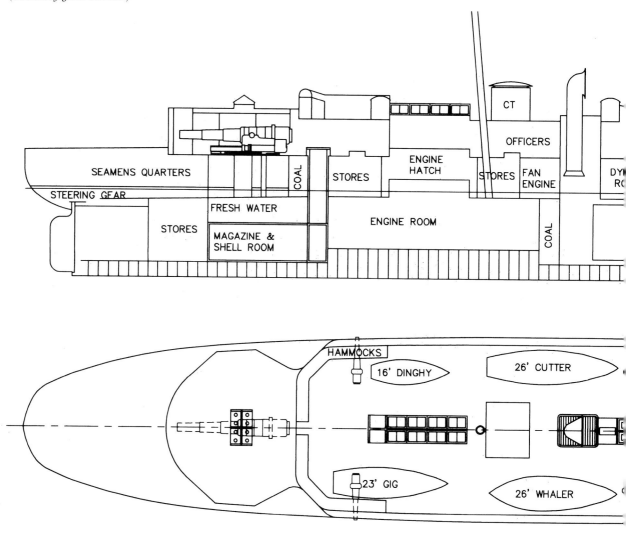

sale; in any event the order went to Germany where the
Saschen class of battleships had attracted Chinese attention. China's battleships (7,400 tons, four 12in) have been
fully described, but the manner of their going might with
benefit be supplemented by some contemporary comments from *The Times* newspaper.

The *Ting Yuen* was ordered early in 1881 from Vulcan,
Stettin, laid down 31 March 1881, and launched 28
December 1881. Her sister ship, *Chen Yuen*, was laid down
in March 1882, being launched the following November.
Money was proving to be a problem at this stage, with the
result that instead of the intended three battleships, the third
ship was a smaller vessel, the 'turtle-deck' cruiser *Tsi Yuen*
(alternatively romanized as *Tche Yuen* or *Chi Yuen*), ordered
in January 1883 and launched 1 Dec 1883. The three ships
were probably built in succession on the same slip.

Ting Yuen was fitted out, and after carrying out trials in
May 1883 was due to sail for China: 'A fine ironclad
corvette . . . she will soon proceed to the East . . . all the
sooner, perhaps, that a French fleet threatens to make its
appearance in Chinese waters'. However, the delays
started. Six weeks later:

> It was agreed [the *Ting Yuen*] should be navigated out to
> Chinese waters by a German crew, who were to take the
> opportunity of relieving an equal naval force on the
> Eastern stations. The captain and crew had been selected
> and the corvette was about to start on its voyage when
> suddenly orders reached Stettin from the German
> Admiralty, cancelling the whole arrangement . . .'

The Chinese Minister to Berlin, Li Feng-pao, was quoted

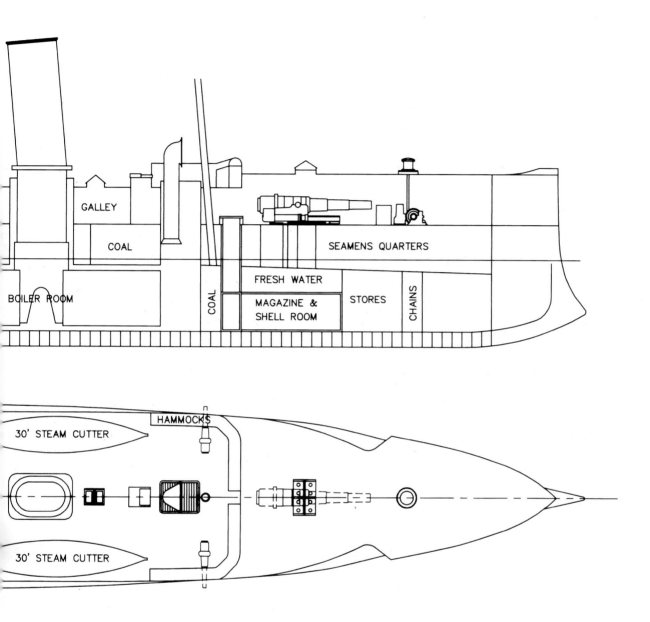

as trying to enlist a merchant marine crew to take the battleship out to China, but by that time the Chinese and French were at loggerheads over the Annam (now Vietnam) border dispute; and the restraining hand of the German Chancellor became evident. Instead, as a programme filler the *Ting Yuen* was taken into the Baltic with a scratch crew from the Imperial German Navy for a full-calibre firing of her 12in armament. The guns had already stood a test firing at Essen with an extra charge of powder; what happened on the day was simply the result of firing all four guns together: a split funnel was the worst damage, splintered furniture the least. Although spectacular to the observers it was not all that surprising. Eleven years later in the opening salvo of the Yalu battle, the same guns, incautiously fired, caused further havoc.

The *Ting Yuen* returned to Stettin for repairs and

adjustments, but failed to sail for China that year. Nine months later her sister ship *Chen Yuen* had a successful firing of her main armament, probably singly or on safer bearings. Nevertheless, on 4 July 1884, '. . . at the last moment and for about the tenth time, the departure of the Chinese corvettes . . . from Stettin to Kiel with German crews, has again been delayed, this time no doubt for reasons connected with the present hitch in relations between France and China . . .' A month later war was declared between China and France. Thus, when the cruiser *Tsi Yuen* completed her trials in August 1884, she too joined the battleships in harbour at Stettin, officially interned until the cessation of hostilities.

Tsi Yuen, (the name was translated as 'Help in Need'), launched some six months after Armstrong's *Esmeralda*, was smaller and with weaker armament (2,355 tons, two

8.2in), yet had the advantage of a 3in protective deck, as well as a 10in barbette for her twin 8.2in guns.[2] Although reportedly fitted with extra masts and sails for the passage out to China, once there, with her one military mast, twin screws, armour and protective deck, she looked the latest thing in modern cruisers.

On the other hand the two cruisers of similar tonnage concurrently building for the Nanyang squadrom at the Howaldt shipyard at Kiel were barquentine-rigged, unprotected, single screw and already outdated. *Nan Shui* (variously romanised over the years as *Nan Shin*, *Nan Juin*, *Nan Jui*) and *Nan Ch'en (Nan Thin, Nan Ting* or *Nan Tin)* (the names were translated as 'Blessing of the South' and 'Ornament of the South' respectively) were to all appearances only larger, faster versions in steel of the Foochow Yard's *Wei Yuen* class of composite-built sloops. Probably ordered early in 1883 at the same time as *Tsi Yuen*, they were also launched at about the same time, but being of simpler design were completed earlier in March 1884. Apart from their design they differed from the Stettin-built ships in one vital particular: their planned armament of two 8in and eight 4.7in was for Armstrong, not Krupp, guns. Therefore there was no apparent difficulty about their sailing from Kiel, with German mercantile crews and under the German flag, during the prevailing Sino-French confrontation, as they were then unarmed. The problem came to *Nan Ch'en (Thin)*, the first away, when she arrived on the Tyne to have her guns fitted. She was promptly interned for a week under the neutrality laws while the British Foreign Office agonised over whether to upset the Germans, the French, or the Chinese by either allowing or not allowing the guns to be embarked. In the event both ships left the Tyne with their armaments embarked, but not tested. The main problem arose when they arrived at Nanking in July 1884, conveniently in time to reinforce the Nanyang fleet against the French, as at that late hour it was discovered that it was dangerous structurally to fire the main armament at full charge. They had to be strengthened at Shanghai at some expense, and 'at an awkward moment, as Admiral Courbet was expected to raid Nanking'

The Foochow-built fast cruisers

References abound of *Nan Shui* copies being built by the Chinese, mainly at the Foochow dockyard, and the ships were even named. *Yung Pao, Ye Sing, Fu Ch'ing, Foo Sing* and *Hi Ying*, 'super-cruisers' of 2,500 tons with an armament of three 8in, all featured prominently in Brassey's *Naval Annual* at various times for a decade or two. In fact, the main favourite, *Fu Ch'ing*, was positively identified by HBM consul at Foochow as being a torpedo-gunboat of the *Kuang Ping* type, and the others seem to have been misidentifications of other ships. Nevertheless, they remained a potent 'phantom fleet' hovering about in the background, causing endless confusion for writers.

What actually seems to have happened was completely the opposite. The Nanyang Viceroy required five large fast cruisers for the Nanyang squadron to replace units built during the 1870s, and the first of these, the composite *K'ai Chi* (2,110 tons, 2,400hp, two 8.2in), a larger and faster version of the *Wei Yuen* class of composite sloop was laid down at Foochow at the end of 1881, launched late 1883, and completed early in 1884 at the Kiangnan Arsenal where her armament was fitted. Meanwhile, in order to bring forward delivery, and possibly because they were cheaper, the Nanyang Viceroy ordered two all-steel versions of the *K'ai Chi* from Germany, the *Nan Shui* and *Nan Ch'en*. Then, after the *K'ai Chi* had been launched at Foochow the last two composite fast cruisers were laid down at that yard, in January 1884. These were recorded as 'Fast cruisers No. 2 and No. 3' with ribs and ironwork purchased in Germany by Li Feng-pao and shipped out. The other ship being constructed in the arsenal at the time was quoted as No. 5 and 'half completed', and was presumably *Heng Hai*, the fifth of the *Wei Yuen* series. In Feb 1884 another source stated that two new 'gunboats' were building at Foochow, and that on completion two more of the same type to be laid down. Here the intention may have been for Foochow to build a further two fast cruisers of the *K'ai Chi/Nan Shui* type, thereby fostering the rumours of *Nan Shui* copies: but things did not work out that way.

The Sino-French War

During 1884 Sino-French relations deteriorated fast. In June 1884 the Northern Viceroy Li Hung-chang embarked in the sloop *K'ang Chi* and escorted by the *Chao Yung, Yang Wei, Wei Yuen* and the Fukien steam corvette *Yang Wu*, met the French Admiral Lespès with the French fleet at Chefoo for discussions. The occasion was notable for a full and frank display of muscle flexing by French. Two months later French warships infiltrated into the Foochow anchorage, so that when the Chinese failed to respond to ultimata over the border dispute they were ready in position to destroy the Fukien fleet. The obsolete and mostly wooden ships from the 1870s were suddenly attacked by the French on 23 August. The arsenal and dockyard were then shelled, after which the French ships fought their way out, destroying the Chinese forts as they went.

Of the many eye-witness accounts of the two-day action that found their way into the newspapers, one source stated unambiguously about the French bombardment of the Foochow dockyard, '. . . only one of three ships on the stocks was far enough advanced to be severely injured and she has been hit several times. Her copper is in some places torn off, and the timbers wounded. She will not be launched for some months yet'. From this report it seems likely that the *Heng Hai* was the one hit, while the two fast cruisers escaped unscathed, although damage to the arsenal would have delayed their building.

After the Foochow attack there was panic in the Yangtze, with expectations of a further French attack at any minute. Woosung, commanding the river entrance to Shanghai, was protected with mines, torpedoes and the four Nanyang Alphabetical gunboats, while stone-filled junks were sunk as blockships. The rest of the Nanyang fleet took up a defensive position at Kiangyin, where the Yangtze river narrows, guarding the approaches to Nanking. However, the French fleet turned its attention on Formosa, taking and occupying the port of Keelung in October 1884, and instituting a blockade of Formosa's west coast.

Much discussion followed as to the action that could be taken by China's modern naval forces. In the north Captain Lang had resigned as a matter of principle at the outbreak of hostilities; the Peiyang cruisers *Chao Yung* and *Yang Wei* were in fact put on standby and then sent to Shanghai to assist, only to be recalled over problems arising with Korea. In the event it was the Nanyang fleet alone which started offensive operations, but not until December and having been staffed with western 'advisers'. The fast cruisers *K'ai Chi, Nan Shui, Nan Thin,* together with the sloop *Teng Ch'ing* and the steam frigate *Yu Yuen* (described as useless), cruised the coast rather aimlessly south of the Yangtse for a month or so, until the two slower ships were left behind at the small port of Shipu, cornered by the French, and sunk. The three fast cruisers then put into Chenhai (the seaport of Ningpo), were joined by reinforcements in the form of the Fukien sloop *Chao Wu* and another, and all five were promptly blockaded in by the French. The cessation of hostilities in April 1885 ended this unhappy period for the emerging Chinese Navy: one where the presence of one of the modern but unfortunately Stettin-bound warships could have had a very salutary effect on the outcome – had of course she been properly manned.

The signing of the peace treaty released the German-built battleships and cruiser. Rigged with masts and sails, and manned by the German mercantile marine, they left in convoy on 3 July 1885, arriving at long last in Chinese waters in October 1885. Their arrival coincided with the recall and disgrace of the Chinese Minister Li Feng-pao. Although there were at the time some (largely unsubstantiated) criticisms about the German-built ships, the Minister's inability to extract at least one of the battleships from German hands may have had a little to do with his disgrace; and undoubtedly influenced the later decision to split the next warship order between Germany and Britain.

The Peiyang fleet now comprised the battleships *Ting Yuen* and *Chen Yuen,* the protected cruiser *Tsi Yuen,* the smaller cruisers *Chao Yung* and *Yang Wei,* and two sloops, as well as the six Alphabetical gunboats and some torpedo boats, all under the command of Admiral Ting and his re-appointed deputy, Captain Lang.

Table 1:

Ship Data	K'ai Chi	a. Nan Shui b. Nan Ch'en	a. Ching Ch'ing b. Huan T'ai
Displacement (tons)	2,100	2,200 (metric)	2,100
Length (ft)		275.5 oa	
	250	252.5	250
Breadth (ft)	36	37.5	36
Draft (ft)	20	18	20
Machinery	1 shaft	1 shaft	1 shaft
hp	2,400	2,400/2,800*	2,400
Speed (kts)	15	14.5–15	15–17
Coal (tons)	360	600	360
Hull	Composite	Steel	Composite
Armour	Unprotected, but probably with armoured casemates		
Armament (in)	2–8.2 Krupp	2–8 Armstrong	3–7
	6–4.7 Krupp	8–4.7 Armstrong	7–40 pdr
	Nordenfelts	Mitrailleuse	Gatlings
Torpedo tubes	–	1 TB carried	2
Complement	183*	217–250	200–300
Built at	Foochow	Howaldt, Kiel	Foochow
Laid down	Late 1881	1883?	a. 4 Jan 1884 b. 12 Jan 1884
Launched	Late 1883	a. 12 Dec 1883 b. 8 Jan 1884	a. 17 Jan 1886 b. Nov 1886
Completed	Early 1884	a. Mar 1884 b. Mar 1884	a. Aug 1886 b. 30 Aug 1887*
Arrived China	–	July 1884	–
Data based on	Rawlinson/Brassey	Times/Brassey	Brassey/PG
Notes	* from PG	* from PG	* ex armament

PG – *Peking Gazette*

The Nanyang Cruisers

The next fleet to be reinforced was the Nanyang, with the small Chinese-built cruiser *Pao Min*. The Kiangnan Arsenal shipyard had to some extent given up shipbuilding after the completion of the two steam frigates in the 1870s, but in 1881 it had launched a further ship, a 400 ton gunboat for the Salt Commissioner. This was followed by yet another project in 1883 when a 'fine war vessel' (unnamed) was laid down, designed 'by Mr William Denman, late of the Royal Dockyards at Woolwich and Deptford'. Described as built entirely of steel, she had a displacement of 1477 tons, length 213ft 6in, six cylindrical boilers and two horizontal engines producing 1,200hp, giving an estimated speed of 15 knots. In appearance she had a spoon bow and a light schooner rig with no bowsprit. Her projected armament was to be two 200 pdr mounted at the bow and stern, with six 80pdr BL on the broadside. From the description the ship was undoubtedly the *Pao Min*.

Unfortunately the details conflict somewhat with *Pao Min*'s further description of 'magnificent' and 'swift'. 200- and 80pdrs, possibly arsenal-built, could equate with 8.2in and 5.9in Krupps of the period, which would have been a monstrously large armament for a ship of her size. When she eventually appeared in reference books her armament had been reduced to a more reasonable two 5.9in and six 5in. Moreover, 15 knots looks over-optimistic for her tonnage and the stated 1,200 horse-power. The latter may have been a misprint; Rawlinson, from other sources, quotes 1,900hp giving 16kts which sounds more realistic. 'Hoped to be launched in another 3 months' [July 1884], *Pao Min* probably joined Nanyang cruiser squadron in the Spring 1885, as she was obviously not available in time for the Nanyang operations in Jan/Feb 1885, when she could have been a useful substitute for the obsolete *Yu Yuen*.

Next to come was the Foochow-built 'Fast cruiser No. 2', running trials on 11 August 1886, making about 17 kts and positively identified as the *Ching Ch'ing (King Ch'ing)*. The *Huan T'ai*, running trials a year later, made 15.5kts in windy weather and was almost certainly 'Fast cruiser No. 3'. Although data for both ships varied wildly in contemporary naval annuals, it is worth noting that all three of these Foochow-built ships – the *K'ai Chi* being the first – ended up in the Nanyang fleet, and all three cost the same, 366,000–386,000 taels as against the 200,000–220,000 taels of the *Wei Yuen* sloops. The arrival of the *Huan T'ai* in 1887 brought the numbers of the Nanyang squadron up to six[3], at which level it remained unchanged for the ensuing fifteen years.

The later British- and German-built Cruisers

More foreign-built ships were to come. In November 1885 orders were placed for two different batches of cruisers. From Germany came two larger armour-belted versions of the cruiser *Tsi Yuen*, while from Armstrongs came two smaller protected cruisers for comparison. Although all

China's torpedo boats had previously come from Germany, the opportunity was taken to order one for comparison purposes from England. All four cruisers were launched at the end of 1886 and early 1887, and in August 1887 foregathered in the Solent, off Portsmouth, England; *Chih Yuen* and *Ching Yuen* (2,300 tons, three 8.2in) from Armstrongs, *Lai Yuen* and *King Yuen* (also confusingly written as *Ching Yuen* on occasions) (2,900 tons, two 8.2in) from Vulcans, together with the 'Yarrow' torpedo boat[4]. The development of warship machinery during the 1880s had been so rapid that sails were now no longer a necessity for long ocean voyages.

In the Solent the cruiser squadron was inspected, and under the command of the omnipresent (and now Admiral) Lang, were to sail in company for the Far East. The crews this time were Chinese, reinforced for passage by European instructors. The ships were due to sail at the end of August, with the torpedo boat in tow of one of the Armstrong cruisers, but adverse weather delayed their departure for a further fortnight.

The four new cruisers arrived in Chinese waters in November 1887, subsequently putting in to Amoy for inspection and to spend the winter. In the spring they were taken north to join the Peiyang fleet, where Li Hung-chang himself inspected them, following which he went on a cruise of inspection of the proposed naval base at Port Arthur (still much delayed in its construction), as well as the fleet anchorage at Wei-Hai-Wei.

Like the earlier *Tsi Yuen*, the new German- and Armstrong-built ships were notable for having a twin 8.2in Krupp mounting forward, fitted in an armoured barbette in the case of the armoured cruisers, and on a shielded turntable mounting in the Armstrong cruisers, which also carried a further single 8.2in 12 ton gun aft. All four cruisers had a protective deck covering the engines, boilers and magazines, while the German-built ships had the addition of thick armour belts. Accounts of these vary slightly, but they were evidently in the form of three horizontal strakes, 2–2.5ft deep, the upper 9.5in in thickness, the lower two 5.25in in thickness (also quoted as 8in and 6in) and thus giving rise to doubts about their liability to being 'easily broken across by moderately heavy projectiles'. Another problem with the armour belts was that at full load the top of the armour belt was quoted as being flush with the waterline, thus undermining its efficiency.

Worth noting is the fact that the Armstrong cruisers had a good battery of eight 6pdrs, but that these were the largest quick-firing weapons in the whole fleet. In the same context, only six months after the cruiser squadron had sailed from England another minor batch of vessels had been completed for China, the three Armstrong-built customs or revenue cruisers reported as sailing from Britain in the spring of 1888, the *Likin* and *Kaipan* (500 tons), and *Chen Tiao* (700 tons). These were reported in Plymouth Sound, three small white-painted cruisers, mounting the first of the new '4in' quick-firers.[5]

The arrival of the new cruiser squadron for the Peiyang fleet completed, of necessity, the buying programme for foreign-built battleships and cruisers.[6] The money had run out: much, it is said, had been diverted by the Empress Dowager for the rebuilding of the Summer Palace. Only

Lai Yuen *before delivery to China. Note the grey paint scheme* (IWM, Q22237)

The protected cruiser Chih Yuen *in the Solent. Note the triangular ensign with the dragon motif, and the dragon on the bow.* (IWM, Q22233)

Table 2:

Ship Data	Tsi Yuen	Ping Yuen	Pao Min
Displacement (tons)	2,355	2,150	1,477
Length (ft)	236 wl	230 wl	227.75 oa
		197 pp	213.5 pp
Breadth (ft)	34.5	40	36
Draft (ft)	15.75	13.5–18.5	14
Machinery	2 shaft HCE	2 shaft	? 2 shaft HCE
	? boilers	? boilers	6 boilers
hp	2,800	2,400	1,900 ?★
Speed (kts)	15 est	10.5	16 ?★
Coal (tons)	250 max	350	250/360
Hull	Steel	Steel	Steel ?
Armour (in)	Deck 3	Deck 2	Prob. nil
	Barbette 10	Barbette 5	
	Belt –	Belt 8	
	CT ?	CT 5	
Armament (in)	2–8.2 Krupp	1–10.2 Krupp	2–6★
	1–5.9 Krupp	2–5.9 Krupp	6–5
	6 Hotchkiss	8–3pdr QF	
Torpedo tubes (in)	4–15 AW	4	2 in bow +
Complement	180	200	200
Built at	Vulcan, Stettin	Foochow	Shanghai
Laid down	16 Jan 1883★	Late 1886	Late 1883
Launched	1 Dec 1883	Mid 1889	Mid 1884
Completed	Aug 1884	End 1889	1885
Arrived China	Oct 1885	–	–
Data based on	*Times*	*F.T. Jane*	*NCH*
	F.T. Jane	*PG & NCH*	

Notes	★ Ordered		★ See text
			+ In 1914

PG – Peking Gazette   NCH – North China Herald

one other cruiser was to join the Peiyang fleet, the Chinese-built ironclad *Ping Yuen*, ex *Lung Wei*, the first all-steel warship to be produced by the Foochow shipyard.

The Chinese-built Ironclad

It may have been the intention of the Foochow yard to carry on building a further two 2,400hp 'fast cruisers' of the *K'ai Chi* type after launching the *Ching Ch'ing* and *Huan T'ai*, but this plan was clearly overtaken by events. Out of the blue it received a large order for ten ships from the Kwangtung provincial government, which apart from including the composite cruiser/sloop *Kuang Chia* (laid down in December 1885) and sundry shallow draft gunboats, involved new technology in the shape of three French-designed 2,400hp all-steel torpedo-gunboats of the *Kuang (Kwang) Ping* class. Furthermore, the arrival in Chinese waters of the two modern battleships and the cruiser *Tsi Yuen* at the end of 1885 had offered the shipyard a further challenge. After inspection of the three German-built ships and the British-built *Chao Yung/Yang Wei* the dockyard officials considered they too could build

a modern ironclad warship, at a lower cost; and at the end of 1886 the keel was laid of the *Lung Wei*. When the *Huan T'ai* ran trials in August 1887 the Foochow arsenal was reported as 'now extremely busy, having a steel-clad vessel in course of construction, as well as . . . vessels for Canton'.

Data on the *Lung Wei* is sparse, with many dates at variance. She was reported launched in the summer of 1889, but on 18 September, on her second trial trip, struck a rock and had to return to the yard for repairs. Completed in the winter of 1889, she was taken up to Shanghai, there to be inspected by Admiral Lang. Promptly returned to the Foochow shipyard for some one hundred 'Alterations & Additions', she was on 16 May 1890 finally turned over to the Peiyang fleet, her name being changed to *Ping Yuen* to bring her 'in harmony' with the remainder of the fleet.

It was and is commonly said of the *Lung Wei/Ping Yuen* that she was begun as a copy of the *King Yuen*, but was cut down in length for financial reasons during the course of construction. Nevertheless, there appears to be no contemporary confirmation of this story, and the story could well be apocryphal. For example, *Lung Wei* had been quietly built in the seclusion of the Foochow shipyard, and then suddenly arrived out of the blue at Shanghai to be inspected by Admiral Lang, probably during the visit of a Peiyang squadron to that port in December 1889 (see below). The squadron included the cruisers *King Yuen* and *Lai Yuen*. With her beam-mounted 6in BL guns the *Lung Wei* might well have looked to cynical observers on the Shanghai bund to be but a Chinese-built cut-down copy of those fine German-built cruisers: and the first impression became legend. Actually, the *King Yuen* (2,900 tons, 270ft × 40ft, 3,400hp) was still on the stocks in a German shipyard when the *Lung Wei* was laid down, and the German-built cruiser the Foochow officials would have inspected in 1886 was the smaller *Tsi Yuen* (2,300 tons, 236ft × 34ft, 2,800hp). Hence the design of the *Lung Wei* (2,150 tons, 200 ft × 40ft, 2,400hp) may well have been based loosely on the more similar-looking *Tsi Yuen*, with an armour belt added and a standard Foochow 2,400hp machinery package. The idea for the single large 10.2in gun could have come either from the *Chao Yung/Yang Wei*, or even from one of the Alphabetical gunboats. Nonetheless, with a maximum speed of only 10.5 knots

she was more of a coast defence ship than a cruiser, and was the first and last attempt by the Foochow yard to build an armoured ship.

The Peiyang and Nanyang Fleets

By 1890 the Peiyang fleet was at its maximum strength, with two battleships, eight cruisers, two training ships (*K'ang Chi* and *Wei Yuen*)[7] and six Alphabetical gunboats as well as a number of torpedo boats. In addition the Kwangtung government had had to cancel half its shipbuilding programme at Foochow owing to money problems, and seemed only too keen to offer the seagoing element (*Kuang Chia*, and the torpedo gunboats *Kuang Yi* [*Kuang I*] and *Kuang Ping* from 1892) to the Peiyang fleet for training: where one suspects the Peiyang administration paid for their upkeep. Peiyang and Nanyang annual joint exercises had been instituted from 1886, and so the six-ship Nanyang cruiser squadron was a frequent visitor to Northern waters during the summer months. A joint

Table 3:

Ship Data	a. *Chao Yung* b. *Yang Wei*	a. *Chi Yuen* b. *Ching Yuen*	a. *King Yuen* b. *Lai Yuen*
Displacement (tons)	1,350	2,300	2,900
Length (ft)	220 oa 210 pp	268 oa 250 pp	270 oa
Breadth (ft)	32	38	39–40
Draft (ft)	15.66	14 F & 16 A	16.66
Machinery	2 shaft HCE 4 boilers	2 shaft HTE 4 boilers	2 shaft HTE 4 boilers
hp	2,600	5,500/6,500 forced	3,400/5,000 forced
Speed (kts)	16	18.5 forced	15.5 forced
Coal (tons)	300	450	320
Radius	5000 miles @ 8kts	–	–
Hull	Steel	Steel	Steel
Armour (in)		Deck 4–2 CT 3	Deck 3–1.5 CT 6 Barbette 8 Belt 9.5–5.25★
Armament (in)	2–10 Armstrong 4–4.7 Armstrong 2–9 pdr 2 Nordenfelt 4 Gatling	3–8.2 Krupp 2–6 Armstrong 8–6 pdr QF 8–1 pdr Hotchkiss 6 Gatling	2–8.2 Krupp 2–5.9 Krupp 2–47mm Hotchkiss 5–37mm revolving
Torpedo tubes	2 cutters with spar torpedoes	4 AW	1 bow, 3 AW
Complement	130–150	200	270
Built at	Mitchell, Tyne	Elswick	Vulcan, Stettin
Laid down	Jan 1880	Oct 1885	Late 1885
Launched	a. 4 Nov 1880 b. 29 Jan 1881	a. 29 Sept 1886 b. 14 Dec 1886	a. 3 Jan 1887 b. 25 March 1887
Completed	July 1881	July 1887	July 1887
Arrived China	Oct 1881	Nov 1887	Nov 1887
Date based on	*Times*	*Chinese Times*	*CT/Reed*
Notes			★ See text

livery was adopted, similar if not identical to the 'Victorian' colour scheme (black hull, white upperworks and buff funnels/masts), the gold scrollwork on the bows forming the imperial dragon.[8]

Docking had always been a problem for the major units of the Peiyang fleet for the first five years on station, with the ships requring but not necessarily getting two dockings a year, as the nearest docks were at Shanghai, and for the battleships at Hong Kong and Yokohama. This had resulted in part with squadron cruises combined with dockings, generally with a Peiyang squadron coming south for the winter. The first visit to Japan, to Nagasaki in 1886, had ended in recrimination following a clash between the Japanese police and Chinese libertymen; but with Admiral Lang in charge of training, discipline and efficiency in general were steadily improving, although leadership was weak in places. With its large fleet of foreign-built warships and the recently completed Port Arthur dockyard available for its use from 1890, China was already beginning to be regarded by some international circles as the new naval power in the Far East.

In December 1889, under the command of Admiral Ting and Admiral Lang, six of the largest ships of the Peiyang fleet visited Shanghai, continuing south to Hong Kong for docking and overhauling. In March the squadron set off on a major cruise of the South China Seas, to Saigon, Singapore and Manila, returning north via Hong Kong. The cruise went off well, yet unknowingly the squadron had reached its zenith in terms of efficiency. Subsequently one newspaper wrote '. . . of fears that after the success of the cruise the Chinese will want to manage their ships themselves': a prescient remark, for in June 1890 as the result of a (probably continuing) clash with the Chinese commodore over precedence, Admiral Lang resigned. This event was greeted with gloom by all those who had reason to wish the Peiyang fleet well.

In the following summer of 1891 the Peiyang and Nanyang squadrons continued their annual manoeuvres, being reviewed by the Viceroys of both Chihli and Shantung at Wei-Hai-Wei. Following on from an exercise period five ships of the Peiyang Squadron visited Japan once again. It was during this stay that a Captain Togo commented unfavourably about their appearance and efficiency. The Nanyang fleet had never been notable for its efficiency, and by 1893 it was being said that some of the commanding officers were entirely unfitted for their posts. Things were no longer progressing satisfactorily.

The Japanese had viewed the formation of the Peiyang Fleet with alarm, particularly in view of the continuing friction with China over Korea. Whereas the Chinese had ceased ship buying and building in 1889/90 for financial reasons, the Japanese had started up again at this point, building and purchasing no less than six modern cruisers. Three of these were custom-built with one 12.6in Canet gun apiece specifically for use against the Chinese battle-ships, and five were in excess of 3,000 tons displacement, as indeed were the older 10in-armed *Naniwa* and *Takachiho*. Moreover, it was particularly unfortunate for the Chinese that the Japanese cruiser building programme coincided with the general introduction of the medium calibre 4.7in and 6in quick-firing guns, with which all six

modern ships were generously fitted, and which had a rate of fire some 3 to 6 times faster than the earlier weapons. The Chinese cruisers, on the other hand, were smaller, slower, and received neither reinforcements nor updating of their equipment; as is demonstrated by this extract from a carefully worded memorial of early 1894 concerning a proposed enhancement of the Nanyang fleet:

> . . . owing to the scarcity of funds, it was determined to effect some economies in the Nanyang naval service by a system of reducing the number of the crew in each vessel, and the result of the economy thus effected to be used for gradually buying new ships of war of the newest types procurable, and increasing the Nanyang Fleet. Owing to the enormous sums requisite for the purchase of armour clad cruisers, which the present finances of the Nanyang administration could not admit of buying, if was deter-mined . . . to buy torpedo-boat catchers, which would be a powerful arm in both attack and defence for the Nanyang. The money economised as above, being sufficient for the purchase and complete arming of four of these new torpedo-boat catchers . . .

War with Japan

Three more years passed by, until in July 1894 affairs in Korea came to a head. In an initial clash of warships the cruiser *Tsi Yuen* and the torpedo-gunboat *Kuang Yi* fell in

The Kwangtung torpedo gunboat Kuang Yi *in service with the Peiyang fleet in 1894. Note the colour scheme. She was the first warship sunk during the 1894–5 war.* (MPL)

with some Japanese cruisers, a chance and misinterpreted encounter which ended in bloodshed. The *Kuang Yi* was sunk, while the Chinese cruiser was chased off, but not before putting a shell into the bridge of the brand-new Japanese *Yoshino*. *Tsi Yuen* fled back to Port Arthur with awe-inspiring above-water damage, yet was actually untouched below her protective deck. The Japanese ships went on to sink the transport *Kowshing*, the action that precipitated the war.

With war in the offing the Peiyang fleet had embarked

some hurriedly recruited western 'advisers', none unfortunately of the stature of Captain Lang, RN. It was being discovered too late that the shell supplied to the ships over the preceding years was largely unsatisfactory, being partially cement filled, or possibly just ordinary armour piercing shell, or even plain practice shell, when what was needed was plenty of fused H.E. Corruption and incompetence at the arsenal were blamed; unhappily this does not explain why the problem had not been pinpointed in the ships before. Quick-firing guns had been asked for, but only twenty Gruson 4pdrs had arrived. Lack of proper maintenance over past years meant that the speeds of all the ships was much reduced.

The Japanese and Chinese fleets escorted troop convoys until, inevitably, they met up at last at the Battle of the Yalu, some fifteen miles south of the Yalu estuary on 17 September 1894. The Chinese fought in line abreast, the battleships in the centre, the weakest and slowest ships on the flanks. In particular the *Chao Yung* and *Yang Wei* were the first 'battlecruisers' in modern naval warfare to be included in a battleline. Totally unarmoured and now with worn-out boilers, they formed the right wing. The

Japanese adopted line ahead, with a flying column of four fast cruisers. The battleship *Ting Yuen* fired the first salvo of the action with her 12in guns trained on an incautious bearing at maximum elevation, and blew Admiral Ting and his immediate staff off the flying bridge on to the deck below.[9]

Over the ensuing four hours the Chinese warships operated virtually independently, but in pairs. The Japanese encircled the Chinese battleline, reducing the *Chao Yung* and *Yang Wei* to blazing wrecks, due in part to past overuse of paint and varnish, while on the left flank the unprotected composite *Kuang Chia* broke away under a hail of shells and fled, later to be destroyed. More importantly she was followed by the protected cruiser *Tsi Yuen*, an action for which her Captain was subsequently executed. Next to be disabled were the armour-belted *King Yuen* and the protected cruiser *Chih Yuen*, trained gun-crews decimated by the relentless barrage of shells, large and small. Both ships were eventually sunk, the *Chih Yuen* receiving her *coup de grâce* from a well-aimed 10in, or a hit on a broadside torpedo tube, or both. The *Lai Yuen* and *Ching Yuen* were set on fire, the former ending

Officers of the Chih Yuen, *probably taken in 1894. The commanding officer will be Teng Shih-chang (Captain Tang), and the European the engineer officer, Mr Purvis. He was one of the longest serving western instructors in the Chinese fleet. Both were killed at the Battle of the Yalu.* (The Graphic, 1894)

up nearly burnt out amidships. The four 1887-built Chinese cruisers were sound, well-manned ships, but they paid the penalty of suddenly out-dated armaments and bad shell.

The Japanese battleline then closed in on the pair of Chinese battleships. Nevertheless, their 4.7in and 6in guns (and even, apparently, their 10in guns) were virtually powerless against the 14in armoured citadels, which were well pitted but never pierced. Here the one significant failure of modern technology was highlighted; the abysmal performance of the Japanese 12.6in Canet guns. Due to repeated malfunctions, only thirteen shells were actually fired by the three *Matsushima* class cruisers, giving an average rate of fire of one round per hour: and all the shells missed their targets. Conversely, one of the few 12in rounds fired by the Chinese battleships which actually exploded scored a direct hit on the Japanese flagship *Matsushima*, and disabled her. The battle as a result slowly ground to halt, partially due to this, partially due to the fact that ammunition was practically exhausted, and partially due to the continuing presence of Chinese torpedo boats (*Kuang Ping*, *Fu Lung* and *Choi Ti*) which, together with the cruiser *Ping Yuen*, were hovering on the outskirts of the action.

The two fleets steamed slowly off into the gathering dusk, the Chinese fleet much depleted, the Japanese more intact, albeit damaged. During the night the Chinese doubled back to Port Arthur, from whence in due course the training ship *Wei Yuen* had the grisly task of towing over to Chefoo the barge containing the Chinese dead.

After essential repairs the Peiyang fleet moved back to operate from the fleet anchorage at Wei-Hai-Wei, where on 7 November there was a major disaster when the *Chen Yuen* hit an obstruction on entering harbour. As the Japanese took Port Arthur with its drydock shortly afterwards, the battleship had to be patched up by divers over a period of two months, and was never again fully seagoing for the Chinese. With its remaining offensive ability halved at a stroke, the morale of the Peiyang fleet slumped. For example, when the captain of the *Chen Yuen* committed suicide, no-one could be found to take over the command other than a western 'adviser'. Of the cruisers the *Lai Yuen* was virtually burnt out, and the *Tsi Yuen*, *Ching Yuen* and *Ping Yuen* damaged in varying degrees. All the other ships of the fleet were present at Wei-Hai-Wei, the two training ships, the six Alphabetical gunboats, about eleven torpedo boats and the Kwangtung *Kuang Ping*. And there they stayed.

In January a Japanese army landed on the mainland and infiltrated Wei-Hai-Wei, while at sea the Japanese fleet blockaded the port, monitored the while by an interested half circle of the world's warships. Torpedo boat warfare took place; while at first unsuccessful, the Japanese boats at last succeeded in breaking through the harbour booms, torpedoing and sinking the flagship *Ting Yuen*, the *Wei Yuen*, and the *Lai Yuen*, the latter turning turtle in shallow water and entombing some of her crew. The Chinese torpedo boats broke out[10], possibly in two sorties, only to be hunted down by the Japanese cruisers and sunk, captured or beached. The Japanese took over the encircling forts,

The China coast in the 1880s.

with the result that the *Ching Yuen* later succumbed to a 8.2in or 9.4in shell fired from one of Wei-Hai-Wei's guns. On 12 February 1895 Admiral Ting surrendered, and committed suicide.

The Japanese released the old training ship *K'ang Chi* to carry the body of Admiral Ting to Chefoo. The remaining ships were taken over to be incorporated in the Imperial Japanese Navy, including the battleship *Chen Yuen* (which the victors were able to refit at Port Arthur in the drydock built for her by their opponents), the cruisers *Tsi Yuen* and *Ping Yuen*, the *Kuang Ping* and the six Alphabetical gunboats. Of these the *Kuang Ping* (Ko-hei) was wrecked on the Pescadores at the end of the year, while the *Ping Yuen* *(Hei-en)* and *Tsi Yuen (Sai-en)* were both mined and sunk in 1904 when blockading Port Arthur during the subsequent Russo-Japanese war.

The Aftermath

The Peace Treaty was signed in April 1895, but the great powers were not happy with the idea of the new naval base at Port Arthur remaining in Japanese hands. Japan was leaned on, and reluctantly agreed to return Port Arthur to China. However, a Chinese naval force was required to take over the port at the time of the retrocession, and the Peiyang fleet had literally one ship left intact, the *K'ang Chi*. Here the Nanyang Squadron came to the fore as the only Chinese fleet in being: it was hired out to the Peiyang authorities for a year. In September 1895 the Fukien Foochow-built torpedo gunboat *Fu Ch'ing* was sent north to Nanking to reinforce the cruisers which were to compose the relieving force; the *K'ai Chi, Nan Jui (Nan Shui), Huan T'ai* and *Ching Ch'ing*. (*Pao Min* was being used as a headquarters ship for the postwar mine clearance of the Yangtze). These five ships formed an impromptu Peiyang squadron in the Gulf of Pechihli until the summer of 1896 when it was relieved by the new skeleton Peiyang squadron, to which the *Fu Ch'ing* was then transferred.

In 1898 the distinguished British naval officer and author Lord Charles Beresford made a lightning tour of China. During his time on the Yangtze, the *Nan Shin (Nan Shui)* was placed at his disposal. In his ensuing book on the subject the admiral recorded of the Chinese fleet that it was on the whole undermanned, and of the Nanyang squadron that it still comprised six cruisers, the four Alphabetical gunboats, and the 'four torpedo-boats, built in Germany, modern and in excellent order'[11] which were the only updating that the squadron ever received.

The Nanyang cruisers kept well clear of Shanghai and westerners during the events of the Boxer Rebellion in 1900, but in 1902 the *K'ai Chi* blew up off Nanking, and in 1903 the *Huan T'ai* was lost by collision. In any case the Nanyang Viceroy had decreed in 1902 that obsolete warships were to be sold off as an economy measure, and so only the *Ching Ch'ing* and possibly the *Nan Chen* survived for much longer, the former being listed as a training cruiser in the 1920s.

One Conclusion

Much was made of the provincial nature of the Chinese fleets, and the way that the Peiyang fleet had to face the Japanese alone. In 1894 one China Coast newspaper had published an apparently authoritative list, based on local knowledge, of the ships in China's fleets: but on closer examination this was nothing more than a list taken from Brassey's *Naval Annual* of 1893, and thus caused confusion to naval historians as there appeared to be more 8in-gunned modern 'super-cruisers' in the background: the 'phantom fleet'. In point of fact, as has been shown in this article, the weak and anyway antiquated Fukien fleet had been destroyed by the French in 1884; the Kwangtung fleet had provided the only three modern ships it had; and the Nanyang fleet's six totally out-dated and unprotected cruisers would have had no effect upon the Japanese battlefleet whatsoever. (The Japanese had carefully deployed their elderly and composite-built ships in support of their army). The Nanyang squadron was undoubtedly best employed where it was, a longstop, watching over the minefields of the lower Yangtze; and in any case was able to save considerable 'face' for the Empire by being immediately available after the war as a substitute for the Peiyang fleet at the retrocession of Port Arthur and the Liaotung peninsular.

Notes

[1] See *Peking Gazette*, 28 May and 19 July 1886, where it was reported that the *Heng Hai* grounded on the Pescadores in thick fog in March 1886, and was broken up by a subsequent gale. Rawlinson, op cit, p.252, implies she grounded but was repaired.

The *Peking Gazette (PG)* was an official government organ used for the promulgation of memorials. These were translated for inclusion in the English language *North China Herald*, and the translations were later conveniently reprinted in book form.

[2] The thickness of the barbette was given by some authorities as 14in or 15in, but is unlikely to have been thicker than the 12in of the battleships' barbettes.

[3] She probably relieved the *Hai An*, which may then have been hulked. See *PG*, 22 September 1889.

[4] The Chinese 'lettered and numbered' their torpedo boats with a reference character followed by a number. This was the *Tso One* of 69 tons. She was later named *Choi Ti*, presumably to bring her into line with the larger contemporary German-built torpedo boat which had already been named *Fu Lung*. These two were the only torpedo boats present at the Battle of the Yalu.

[5] W. F. Tyler, *Pulling Strings in China*, Constable, (London, 1929), p.21. Actually 20pdrs, and probably Armstrong 3.5in quick-firers. Tyler was an RNR officer working for the Chinese Imperial Maritime Customs. He volunteered as an adviser to the Peiyang fleet, being present at both the Battle of the Yalu and the siege of Wei-Hai-Wei.

[6] The *Fee Cheu (Foo Chow)*, cable-layer, sometimes quoted as a steel cruiser, was a merchant ship.

[7] *K'ang Chi* was reboilered at Foochow in 1890, and fitted out as a torpedo training ship. *Celestial Empire (CE)* (Shanghai), 23 May 1890.

[8] Most photographs of that period show Chinese warships as they were painted either prior to delivery or while in Japanese hands. A sketch by an eyewitness shows the ships at Port Arthur after the battle of Yalu with black hulls and white upperworks. The black-hulled livery was abandoned about 1903, probably following the example of the Royal Navy.

[9] They all survived, albeit temporarily deafened and with injuries.

[10] It is sometimes suggested that they were ordered to escape. However, the memorial in *PG*, 10 May 1895, states that they ran away, and that the commanding officers should be 'instantly cashiered and when captured be summarily decapitated'.

[11] Lord Charles Beresford, *The Break-Up of China*, (Harper & Bros, London & New York, 1899), p.285.

General Bibliography

David Pong, *Shen Pao-chen and China's Modernization in the Nineteenth Century*, Cambridge University Press, 1994.

John L. Rawlinson, *China's Struggle for Naval Development 1839–1895*, Harvard University Press, Massachusetts, USA, 1967.

J. W. King, *Navies of the World, 1880*, (Reprinted CMP, London, 1982).

H. W. Wilson, *Ironclads in Action*, Vol II, Sampson Low Marston & Co, London, 1896.

H. W. Wilson, *Battleships in Action*, Vol I, Sampson Low Marston & Co, London, 1926.

Sir Edward Reed, *Modern Ships of War*, Harper & Bros, New York, 1888.

W. Hovgaard, *Modern History of Warships*, 1920, (Reprinted CMP, London, 1978).

Fred T. Jane, *The Imperial Japanese Navy*, 1904, (Reprinted CMP, London, 1984.)

Hansgeorg Jentschura, Dieter Jung, Peter Mickel, *Warships of the Imperial Japanese Navy, 1869–1945*, Arms & Armour Press, London, 1977.

Dr Oscar Parkes, *British Battleships*, Seeley Service & Co, London, 1956.

Brassey's *Naval Annual*, various, J. Griffin & Co, Portsmouth, UK.

Jane's Fighting Ships, various editions, Sampson Low, London.

Conway's All the World's Fighting Ships, 1860–1905, CMP, London.

Sir W. Laird Clowes, *The Naval Pocket Book*, W. Thacker & Co, London, 1905 & 1914.

China Coast Newspapers

Picture Sources

The Graphic, 1894

Imperial War Museum (IWM)

Maritime Photographic Library (MPL)

National Maritime Museum (NMM)

US Naval Historical Center (USN)

THE LOSS OF HMS *QUEEN MARY* AT JUTLAND

The catastrophic loss of three battlecruisers at the Battle of Jutland is firmly fixed in most readers' minds. **M W Williams** reconstructs the tragic loss of HMS *Queen Mary* from eyewitness accounts.

On Wednesday 31 May 1916, the bulk of the British Grand Fleet was at sea, converging for a rendezvous off the entrance to the Skagerrak. What was to transpire is a very well documented story, and this is not just another version of the epic clash of the dreadnoughts at the Battle of Jutland. Instead this narrative will concentrate upon the experiences of just one vessel, from the hundreds congregating in those waters, and will describe the fate which befell *HMS Queen Mary*.

On board her were 1,286 men, including four who were to provide a unique insight into the final experiences of this ship, midshipmen, Jocelyn L. Storey serving in 'Q' turret amidships, and John Hugh Lhoyd-Owen, Peregrine R. Deardon, along with Petty Officer Ernest Benjamin Francis, all from 'X' turret aft.

Immediately before the opening phase of the action, just after 2pm. Admiral Beatty had deployed his Battle Cruiser Fleet, prior to heading north to join up with Admiral Jellicoe, then advancing southwards with the bulk of The Grand Fleet.

The afternoon was seemingly shaping up to be yet another fruitless sweep of the North Sea. But a chance of fate now intervened, with the spotting of a Danish tramp steamer by a light cruiser on the extreme eastern edge of the Beatty's screen. Shortly after she reported enemy light units, an opening exchange of fire at 2.28pm prompted action.

Alter course leading ships together the rest in succession to SSE. *(Beatty, 2.32pm)*

Hands are to be stationed at Action Stations. *(Beatty, 2.38pm)*

. . . heard in the distance a bugle sound of 'Action'. I was so surprised that I could hardly believe my ears, but the rush of feet by the door forced it upon me. I called Harrison and Petty Officer Clarke and told them they had sounded off 'Action'. I took the first hatchway up and raced for 'X' turret. When I got inside everyone was there.

I yelled out, 'Turret's crew, number'. They were correct from top to bottom, and I reported to the Lieutenant of the Turret. He said, 'Test loading gear, but for goodness sake do not let them be too rash. I would not miss one round in this smash for worlds.' *(Francis)*

At 2.45pm, while gunroom tea was in progress, the bugle call 'Action Stations' was sounded, and we went to our action stations little dreaming even then, that we were about to meet our hitherto shy friends, the enemy. On reaching my action station in the gunhouse, where I was responsible for the loading of the two 13.5in guns, I tested the loading gear and firing circuits, and having reported them correct awaited further instructions. *(Lhoyd-Owen)*

At about 2.50pm we sounded off 'Action' and we all went to our turrets and tested through everything. 'Q' turret was my turret, the one amidships in the waist between the funnels. *(Storey)*

The *Queen Mary's* Gunnery Officer, Commander Llewelyn, would be controlling the ship's fire, with all four main gunhouses conforming to his directions. The crew, upon the bugler sounding off 'Action Stations', followed by the 'Double', had reacted quickly to the often practised procedure.

Now all the decks and ships boats would be hosed down, splinter mats, leak-stopping gear, shoring-up spars, fire hoses, boxes of sand, stretchers, medical facilities, spare electrical, hydraulic, and engineers' gear would be got ready, all within the span of a couple of minutes as everything would have been kept ready for action whilst she was at sea.

She would now have presented an impressive spectacle, with her trailing plumes of funnel smoke, hoisting her large Battle Ensigns to complement those flags and signals already streaming aloft. The image of a mighty battlecruiser in pursuit of its prey and ready to pounce. After an hour's chase, the action was about to commence.

Queen Mary *underway for the first time on the 17 May 1913, with the assistance of the screw tug* Great Emperor *and paddle tug* Gauntlet *at the bows. Not visible in this view, but secured to her stern lay the screw tug* Plover *and paddle tug* Washington, *for her passage down the Tyne, now heading bows down stream after being turned. Note the passing river traffic which some reports mention as being stopped during her passage, but this was obviously not the case. (Newcastle Central Library)*

At 3.25pm 'Action' was sounded and we all went to our stations and at 3.40pm the order was given 'Load all Guns'. We all realised that the real thing had come at last. *(Storey)*

It was not until about ten minutes to four that they came through. The order I then received was to load both guns with Lyddite shell. I passed it on to the guns' crews, and as soon as the breech-blocks of each gun had swung open, the two great gunloading cages came crashing up from below. A few moments sufficed to ram the projectiles and charges into their respective guns, and the two cages disappeared below to receive a fresh supply of ammunition. As the cages dropped out of sight the two great breech-blocks, on the movement of a lever, swung forward into place. I then reported to the small control cabinet in the rear of the turret that both guns were loaded. As we did not as a rule load our guns, I inquired from Deardon, the midshipman in the control cabinet, if there was any news. He informed me that the enemy were in sight and that we were to be prepared to engage them at any moment. I conveyed this unexpected though welcome information to my men, who received it with great enthusiasm. This, at last, was the chance we had awaited so long and for which we had scarcely dared to hope. We had the greatest confidence in our leaders, our ship, and ourselves, and when one of the gunhouse crew remarked, 'So much the worse for the bloody Uns', I felt that he had put into words the feelings of us all. *(Lhoyd-Owen)*

On board the *Derfflinger* in Hipper's line, a battlecruiser soon to play a telling part in the final phase of this story, there was a similar mood prevailing. As was noted by her experienced Gunnery Commander:

Enemy battle cruisers have been reported, I passed this message on to the guns crews. It was now clear that within a short time a life-and-death struggle would develop. For a moment there was a marked hush in the fore-control. But this only lasted a minute or so, then humour broke out again, and everything went on in perfect order and calm. Suddenly my periscope revealed some big ships. Black monsters; six tall, broad-beamed giants steaming in two columns. They were still a long way off, but they showed up clearly on the horizon, and even at this great distance they looked powerful, massive. The six ships, which had at first been proceeding in two columns, formed line ahead. Like a herd of prehistoric monsters they closed on one another with slow movements, spectre-like, irresistible. *(Von Hase)*

The range eventually closed for the antagonists to manoeuvre into their respective deployments for the action to commence. Beatty's six battlecruisers against Hipper's five. At 3.45pm the *Lion* hoisted a stream of instructions. The first formed his force into a staggered line *en echelon*, to minimise the effects of the banks of obscuring funnel smoke now being emitted, on a line bearing north-west from the *Lion*. The second sequence gave the Admiral's intended gunnery distribution, for his first two ships to concentrate upon the leading one, with the others pairing off abaft this. This signal was, however, to be fatally corrupted in transmission down the line.

In Hipper's line, as a suitable counter to these leviathans, armour-piercing shells were specified in the *Derfflinger*, as *'Take targets from the left'* was ordered from the *Lutzow*. This meant that each German ship was to train on its corresponding British number in the line. Reckoning from the van this designated the *Seydlitz* to engage the *Queen Mary*.

3.48pm, 15,000 metres, as my last order rang out there was a dull roar. I looked ahead. The *Lutzow* is firing her first salvo and immediately the signal 'Open fire' is hoisted. In the same second I shout 'Salvoes-fire', and like thunder our first salvo crashes out. The ships astern follow suit at once and we see all round the enemy jets of fire and rolling clouds of smoke – the battle has begun. *(Von Hase)*

At 3.53pm we opened fire at eight-and-three-quarter miles range at the third ship in the enemy's line. *(Storey)*

Lion opened fire, and a minute or two later our own foremost turrets followed suit. As soon as my turret would bear on the enemy I was told to bring the right gun to the 'Ready', and we began, firing each gun alternately. The general noise of the battle now became deafening and it was quite impossible to obtain any idea of what was happening outside the turret. *(Lhoyd-Owen)*

The first salvo was fired, and we had started on the great game. Getting a turret started is an anxious rushing time for a Captain of a gun, once started it is easy to keep going. *(Francis)*

However in the British line there was some confusion, as the *Lion* and *Princess Royal* correctly engaged the *Lutzow*, *Derfflinger* was left unmolested as the *Queen Mary* opened up upon the *Seydlitz*, the *Tiger* upon the *Moltke*, soon to be joined by the *New Zealand*, leaving the trailing *Indefatigable* to engage the *Von der Tann*. It is obvious that on board Beatty's four trailing ships, there was doubt as to the distribution of fire.

Where this vital communications breakdown had occurred is now impossible to determine. But this left the *Derfflinger* to carry out an undisturbed shoot against

Now free of her supporting tugs, she leaves the Tyne to commence her passage to Portsmouth for trials. Her distinctive sternwalk is well illustrated, as is her prominent ship's name board bearing her Royal title in large brass letters upon its polished teak base. The large rectangular structure, located in the recess of the boat well of the after superstructure is a water filled ballast tank, employed on such trials, to compensate for fittings not yet installed. (South Tyneside Libraries)

Dominating this September 1913 scene is 'X' main mounting with its pair of 13.5in guns and their highly polished muzzles, capped by scrolled and decorative tampions carrying the ship's crest. On the crown of the gunhouse are the sighting ports, all sealed by covers, while to the rear can be seen the rangefinder position. This was the mounting under the command of Lieutenant Ewart at Jutland, from which Petty Officer Francis, along with midshipmen Lhoyd-Owen and Deardon managed to escape. Just forward lies the after 4in battery, showing four of its eight pieces from this angle. Also present is the aft torpedo control tower, the mainmast seemingly framed by its web of attendant standing rigging, and after funnel, towering above the hidden boat well. (IWM. A39893)

the *Princess Royal* during the opening phase of the battle, a fact soon noted with grim satisfaction.

> What astonished me was that so far we had apparently not been hit once. Only quite rarely did a shot stray near us. I observed the gun-turrets of our target more closely and established that this ship was not firing at us. She too was firing at our Flagship. I observed the third enemy ship for a moment, by some mistake we were being left out. *(Von Hase)*

Communications were not the only problem. Sometimes even the smoothly working machine of war that was the *Queen Mary* could stumble in its stride, but quickly recover.

> The gun's crew were absolutely perfect, inclined to be a little swift in loading, but I gave them a yell and pointed out to them that I wanted a steady stride, and after that everything went like clockwork, until suddenly both rammers gave out, my gun going first. This was caused through

No.3 opening the breech before the gun had run out after firing, the carrier arm part of the breech must have hit the rammer head and slightly metal-bound it. I dropped the elevating wheel, got hold of a steel pinch bar, forced the end in behind the rammer head, at the same time putting the rammer lever over to 'Run out', out went the rammer, and I rushed it back again, and then out again, and it went all gay once more. Then the lever was passed over to the right gun, and both rammers were once more in working order. I was pleased to get them going again, as it would have been such a damper on the crew if we had had to go into hand loading. *(Francis)*

Despite this hiccup, the *Queen Mary* had clearly displayed her superb gunnery, by hitting and inflicting telling damage upon the *Seydlitz*. But once having cut the range accurately, she was now required to re-direct her fire at 3.58pm, as the mistake in fire-distribution became glaringly apparent. During this phase, Hipper's ships were replying to Beatty's with effect.

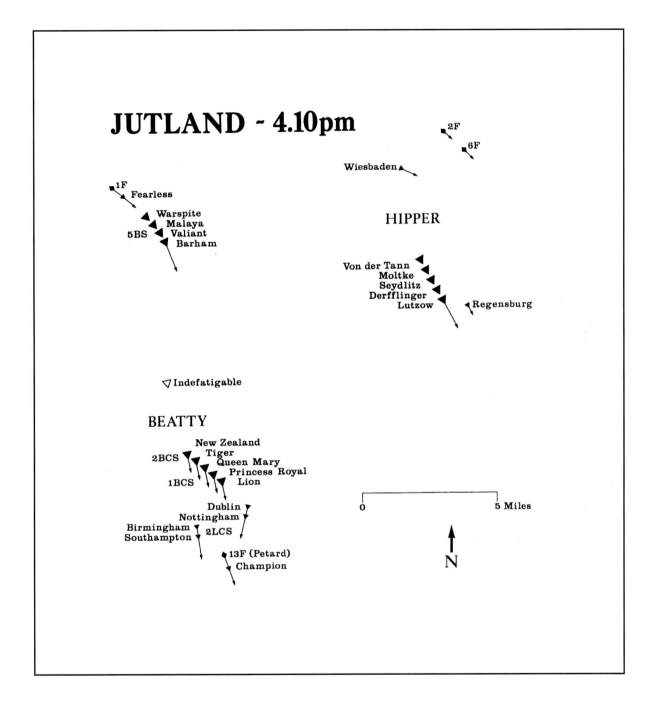

Jutland – 4.10pm: *Beatty and Hipper's final deployment during the 'Run to the South'. In this critical phase of the Battle of Jutland, the respective lines heavily engaged each other at 3.48pm. The* Indefatigable *had just been sunk, and Evan-Thomas with his four battleships close, fell upon the tail of the German line. Each squadron had its attendant screening light cruisers and flotillas (F), destroyers for the British, torpedoboats for the Germans.*

Some 40 miles to the south, Sheer was advancing upon the scene with the bulk of the High Seas Fleet, while 50 miles to the north Jellicoe was endeavouring to close with his Grand Fleet. Just out of the immediate arena other units were manoeuvring: around 20 miles to the north-west of the Queen Mary, *the seaplane carrier* Engadine *was retiring from the gunnery duel; and 20 miles to the north the 1/3LCS's was steaming eastwards towards the rear of the German force, the 2SG, which was trailing 5 miles astern of the 2F.*

At 4.26pm the Queen Mary *sank. Fourteen minutes after this Beatty sighted Sheer's massed dreadnoughts advancing. He swung his depleted force around and commenced the 'Run to the North', leading the HSF northwards towards Jellicoe, and the conclusion of the Battle of Jutland.*

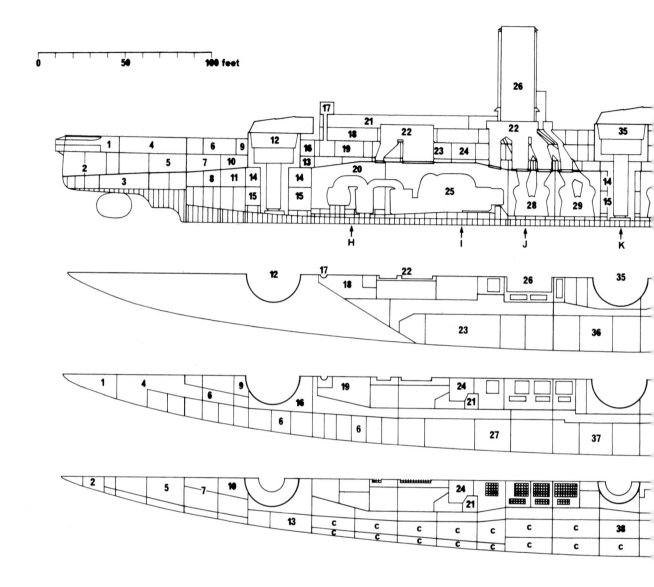

Schematic set of views of the Queen Mary's *internal structure. The overall side elevation illustrates her arrangement of main 13in ordnance, extensive commitment towards her propulsion plant's five boiler rooms, and turbine/condenser plant.*

The three half deck plans, from top to bottom illustrate her upper, main and lower deck general arrangements. The numerous openings for her vents and trunks, provided for her machinery installation are quite apparent, with those on the lower deck protected by armoured grates. The indicated cross sections, labelled 'H' to 'O' are covered in the subsequent figures.

1. *Admiral's day cabin, with the sternwalk aft*
2. *Watertight compartments, fore and aft*
3. *Steering machinery*
4. *Admiral's dining cabin*
5. *Admiral's store*
6. *Senior officer's cabins, and offices*
7. *Air space*
8. *Spare capstan gear*
9. *Distributing station*
10. *CO$_2$ compartment*
11. *Canteen stores*
12. *'X' 13.5in mounting*
13. *Engineering workshop*
14. *13.5in magazine and handling room*
15. *13.5in shell and handling room*

16. *Accommodation space for officer's stewards and cooks*
17. *Aft conning tower, with auxiliary conning position below*
18. *Captain's day cabin*
19. *Engineering stores*
20. *Main and secondary condensers, double bottom below*
21. *Aft 4in battery location, ready use magazine on lower deck*
22. *Ventilator trunks*
23. *Wardroom*
24. *Boat hoist machinery compartment*
25. *Engine room*
26. *Funnel casing and boiler uptakes*
27. *Meat room, insulated*
28. *'G' boiler room*

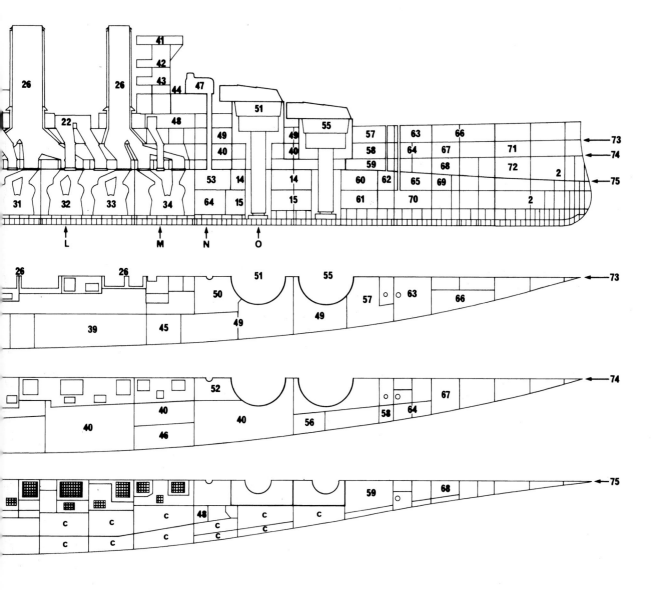

29. 'F' boiler room
30. 'E' boiler room
31. 'D' boiler room
32. 'C' boiler room
33. 'B' boiler room
34. 'A' boiler room
35. 'Q' 13.5in mounting
36. Officer's stores, WC and offices
37. Proprietary enamel compartment
38. Auxiliary spare gear
39. Engine room Artificer's mess
40. Stoker's mess
41. Compass platform
42. Chart house platform
43. Sea cabin platform
44. Conning tower platform
45. Dry canteen, civilian manned
46. Signal station

47. Conning and gunnery control tower
48. Forward 4in battery, ready use magazine on lower deck
49. Seamen's mess
50. Cook's kitchen
51. 'B' 13.5in mounting
52. Medical Distribution station
53. Lower conning tower, and adjacent transmitting station
54. 4in, 3 pounder, and small arms magazine
55. 'A' 13.5in mounting
56. Royal Marine Band instrument room
57. Petty Officer's quarters
58. Secondary torpedo director station
59. Stowage for torpedo bodies

60. Submerged torpedo room, two tubes, one on each beam
61. Torpedo head magazine
62. Capstan machinery compartment
63. Hammock stowage compartment
64. Prison cells
65. Flour store
66. Ratings heads
67. Coaling equipment, shovels, trolleys and bags
68. Canvas room, awnings
69. Royal Marine stores
70. Cable locker
71. Paint store
72. Inflammable liquid store
73. Upper deck
74. Main deck
75. Lower deck

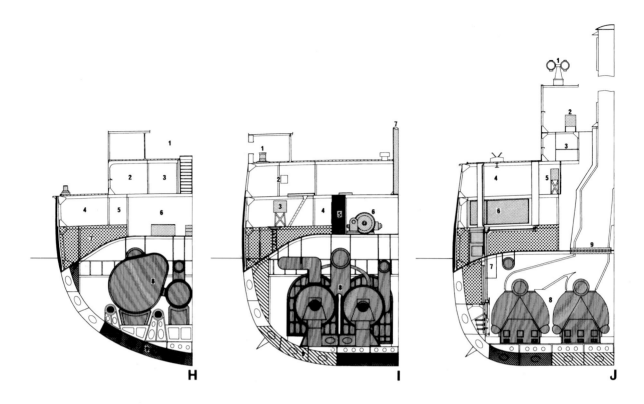

H   I   J

(Sections A to G forward and P to S aft not shown)

H. Section through frame 242.

1. The well on the forecastle deck, formed by the aft superstructure rising to shelter deck level. Here the larger boats were stowed, and handled by the derrick mounted on the mainmast just forward.
2. Captain's day cabin.
3. Lobby.
4. Senior Engineer's cabin.
5. Passage.
6. Engineer's store, with a representation of its series of bins and drawers.
7. Coal bunker. This particular feature will be very prominent in the following sections, with their location principally in the area of the propulsion plant. From this section it should be noticed that this material's location on the armoured lower deck enhanced and strengthened the ship's protection system. Note also the reserve coal running passage out board, necessary for the transference and supply of coal to the boilers.
8. The general location of the main and secondary condensers abaft the turbines. Note their position above the supported propeller shafts running through the compartment.
9. Fuel oil compartments located in the double bottom. These would have been served by a series of fuel lines and pumps.

I. Section through frame 212.

1. Location of a forecastle deck 4in gun mounting in the aft superstructure.

2. Wardroom. Its steward's serving hatch can be seen.
3. Heater located on the Main deck, a steam supplied unit.
4. Passage.
5. An aft 4in secondary ready use ammunition magazine located above the armoured lower deck, lightly protected and rather exposed.
6. Boat hoist compartment, and its attendant machinery, located below the mainmast.
7. Mainmast, rising from the upper deck, to which the main derrick was mounted.
8. Engine room, where the outer high pressure and the inner low pressure turbines were mounted. An arrangement duplicated on the other side of the ship.
9. Reserve feed water compartments in the double bottom, linked up to provide the boilers forward with their basic requirements. Those compartments towards the keel contain fuel oil.

J. Section through frame 194.

1. Searchlight group number 3.
2. Daily supply tank located on the shelter deck.
3. Admiral's galley.
4. Wardroom, note the forecastle deck skylight, and the coal shute running through the compartment, down to the passage and bunkers on the lower deck below.
5. Passage, with a heater.
6. Meat room, suitably insulated and sealed to keep its contents as fresh as possible.
7. Trunk for electrical leads. This feature will be seen in the

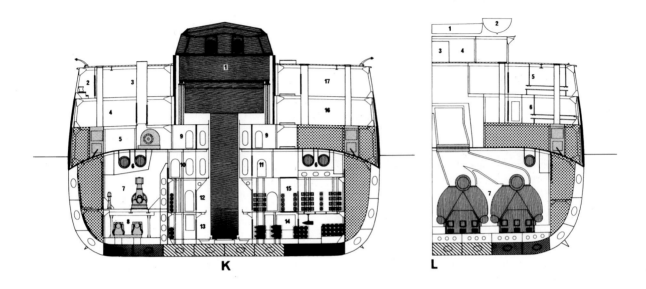

K   L

following sections involving the propulsion plant. With
these vital power and communication links running
through this sealed channel, under and behind the
principal armour.

8. 'G' boiler room. The nature of the bevelled cog and linking
rod arrangement to the left indicates a coal feed
arrangement between the boilers and bunkers, through the
hatch at the side. Not illustrated here, but necessary, was
the device for expelling the ash and debris from the boiler
fires. In this a pressurised water nozzle sent this material
up a pipe, to the level of the upper deck, there to be
discharged.

9. An indication of the armoured grate placed over the
openings in the armoured lower deck, in the area of boiler
uptakes, funnel casings and vents.

K. Section through frame 169.

1. 'Q' 13.5in mounting.
2. Officer's WC.
3. Compartment for the stowage of officers oilskins.
4. Compartment for the stowage of proprietary enamel.
5. Auxiliary spare gear store.
6. Running inboard from the passage for electrical leads,
the tunnel for the main steam lines was located. These
carried the heavily lagged steam pipes from the forward
boiler rooms to the turbines aft.
7. Dynamo room.
8. Hydraulic engine room.
9. Gunners stores running around 'Q' mountings barbette.

10. Space for the gyro compass motor.
11. CO_2 compartment.
12. Magazine handling room.
13. Shell handling room.
14. 13. 5in shell room, with its contents in bins, served by a
series of overhead rail mounted grabs.
15. 'Q' magazine, with its racks of cased cordite.
16. Spare armature compartment.
17. Engineer's office.

L. Section through frame 131.

1. Position of 30ft gig on its shelter deck crutch.
2. 34ft cutter location.
3. Beef screen.
4. Potato locker, on the forecastle deck.
5. Engine room artificers mess on the upper deck. Shown
here, along with all other mess spaces, with its tables and
benches down.
6. Stoker's mess on the main deck.
7. 'C' boiler room. With its supply of coal from the large
bunker on the lower deck above feed through the outboard
coal passage, to a hatch in the side bulkhead, from there to
be transported by trolleys to reserve banks besides the
furnaces. Below, in the double bottom, compartments for
feed water and fuel oil were located.

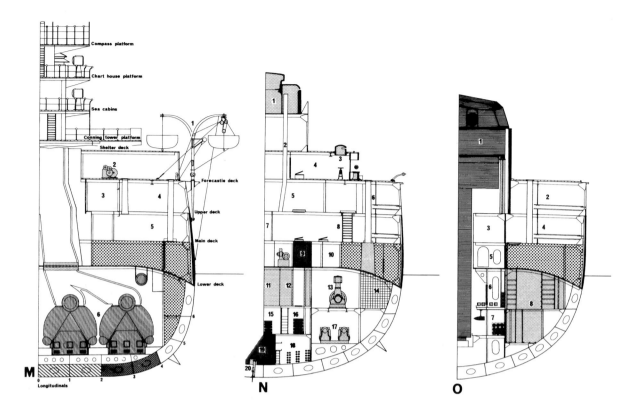

M. Section through frame 115.

1. *34ft cutter, illustrating it swung out on its davit, or its position inboard.*
2. *Coaling winch. Note yet another coal shute to the right at the deck edge, descending down to the coal passage and bunkers below.*
3. *Passage.*
4. *Dry canteen. Run by six civilian personnel.*
5. *Signal station. To the upper left of the compartment is a portable signal tube.*
6. *'C' boiler room.*

N. Section through frame 88.

1. *Conning tower and gun control tower, with its connecting armoured tube below*
2. *Aerial trunk for short wireless, located abaft the conning tower.*
3. *The 4in batteries armoured sighting hood, along with its controlling officers portable platform below.*
4. *The location of the 4in forward battery, note the 3in armour plate out board, none was granted to the after battery.*
5. *Cook's kitchen, where prepared food from the various messes was finally cooked.*
6. *Seamen's mess.*
7. *Silent cabinet.*
8. *Stoker's mess.*

9. *4in ready use magazine, and as with the aft position, it was located on the lower deck, above armour.*
10. *Fan room machinery compartment.*
11. *Lower conning tower.*
12. *Transmitting station, note the 4in ammunition supply trunk passing up through the compartment.*
13. *Dynamo room.*
14. *Provisions.*
15. *Magazine for the 6 pounder (later 3 pounder) and small arms.*
16. *forward 4in magazine.*
17. *Hydraulic engine room.*
18. *Forward 4in shell room.*
19. *Mine room. There is no evidence to suggest that these were ever carried, it is likely that this compartment was used instead for the stowage of 3 pounder and light munitions.*
20. *Compartment*

O. Section through frame 76.

1. *'B' 13.5in mounting.*
2. *Seamen's mess.*
3. *Medical distributing station.*
4. *Stoker's mess.*
5. *Gunner's stores.*
6. *13.5in magazine and its handling space.*
7. *13.5in shell room and handling space.*
8. *Flour store on two levels, the platform deck and hold.*

Another view of the forecastle in 1913 looking aft, captioned by an unknown hand as 'England's teeth'. A fair collection of ratings are posed here, with the two astride 'A' turret's gun barrels, giving a very good scale impression of their impressive proportions. (NMM. C9865)

Midshipman Storey's amidships 'Q' turret trained off the starboard quarter, with a Marine private under its dominating barrels. This view looking forward from the starboard side of the after superstructure illustrates the centre turret, its surrounding structural features and deck fittings. A consignment of sealed cordite containers is ranged on deck, with the working party in the back-ground. They are in the act of striking them down to the magazine, through the embarkation hatch on deck. (NMM C9864)

I had now found the target *(Princess Royal)*, and that meant that midshipman Stachow in the transmitting station was to give the order 'Salvoes-fire', to the heavy guns once every 20 seconds. And the word 'Wirkung' meant that after each salvo of the heavy guns the secondary arma-ment was to fire two salvoes in quick succession and thenceforward fire in conjunction with the heavy guns. Then began an ear-splitting, stupefying din. And now the battle continued. Our shots raised water spouts from 80 to 100 metres high, twice as high as the enemy's masts. Our joy at being immune from fire was short lived. The other side *(Queen Mary)* had noticed the mistake, and now we were often straddled by salvoes. I again fixed the enemy gun-turrets with my periscope and watched them care-fully. I now saw that they were directly trained on us. *(Von Hase)*

Clouds of billowing funnel smoke from the coal burners, and continual salvoes increased the growing background haze. This deteriorating visibility was now to affect German gunnery as the head of the British line was obscured by columns of water from their near misses and an impenetrable shroud of gun and funnel smoke, which caused some distraction on board the *Derfflinger* as to what ship she was to engage.

At 4.17pm I again engaged the second battle cruiser from the left. I was under the impression that it was the same ship that I had engaged before, the *Princess Royal*. Actually, however, it was the *Queen Mary*, the third ship of the enemy line. This was due to the fact that, just as I was finding my target, Admiral Beatty's flagship the *Lion*, was obliged to fall out of the enemy line for a time, and owing to the heavy smoke covering the enemy line, could not be seen by us. *(Von Hase)*

This significant redistribution of enemy fire effectively sealed the fate of the *Queen Mary*. Von Hase, mistaking the *Princess Royal* as the British Flagship at the head of the

line, now moved his fire onto what he thought was the second ship in the line, his designated target. But which was in actual fact the third ship in line the *Queen Mary*, already heavily engaged by the *Seydlitz*.

From 4.17pm, therefore, I was engaging the *Queen Mary*. Certain difficulties in the fire-control now occurred, as a result of the dense smoke from the guns and funnels, which continually blurred the lenses of the periscopes over the deck of the fore-control, making it almost impossible to see anything. When this occurred I was entirely dependent on the observations of the spotting officer in the fore-top, Lieutenant-Commander von Stosch. This excellent officer observed and reported the fall of shot with astonishing coolness, and by his admirable observation, on the correctness of which I had to rely absolutely, he con-tributed very considerably to the success of our gunfire. At this stage of the battle, when the enemy had got our range better, it frequently occurred that these waterspouts broke over the ship, swamping everything, but at the same time putting out any fires. The *Queen Mary* was firing less rapidly than we, but usually full salvoes. As she had an armament of eight 13.5in guns this meant that she was mostly firing eight of these powerful 'coffers', as the Russians called the heaviest guns during the Russo-Japanese war, against us at the same time. I could see the shells coming and I had to admit that the enemy were shooting superbly. As a rule all eight shots fell together. But they were almost always over or short, only twice did the *Derfflinger* come under this infernal hail, and each time only one heavy shell hit her. *(Von Hase)*

In reply, the first of the rapid enemy four-gun salvoes were now straddling and hitting the *Queen Mary*. The effects of this were perceived in the aft gunhouse in a very personal manner:

Up until now I had not noticed any noise, such as being struck by a shell, but soon afterwards there was a heavy blow struck, I should imagine, in the after 4 inch battery, and a lot of dust and pieces were flying around on top of 'X' turret. My attention was called by the turret trainer, Able Seaman Long, who reported the front glass of his periscope blocked up. This was not very important, because we were in director training, but someone in rear heard him report his glass foul, and without orders dashed on top and cleared it. He must have been smashed as he did it, for he fell in front of the periscope, groaning, and then apparently fell off the turret. I wish I knew his name, poor chap, but it's no use guessing. *(Francis)*

Around 4.20pm, the *Queen Mary* received a hit amidships. Although not penetrating, it inflicted serious internal damage through its impact.

Everything went beautifully till 4.21pm when 'Q' turret was hit by a big shell and the right gun put out of action. *(Storey)*

Despite this, it was obvious to Francis that the gunnery exchange was a two-sided affair. Through overheard messages, and his own observations from his post, he notes the earlier success against the *Seydlitz*, the shift of target, and apparent damage to the enemy line.

Another shock was felt shortly after this, but it did not affect the turret, so no notice was taken. The Transmitting Station reported that the third ship was dropping out. First blood to the *Queen Mary*. The shout they gave was good to hear. I could not resist taking a quick look at her at their request, and I saw the third ship of their line was going down by the bows. I felt the turret training a bit faster that she had been, and surmised we must have shifted, being in director firing no orders were required for training. I looked again, and the third ship of the line was gone. I turned to the spare gunlayer, Petty Officer Killick, who was recording the number of rounds fired, and asked him how many rounds the left gun had fired, and he said thirty something. A few more rounds were fired, and I took another look through my periscope, and there was quite a fair distance between the second ship, and what I believe was the fourth ship, due I think, to the third ship going under. Flames were belching up from what I believe to be the fourth ship of the line. *(Francis)*

Unfortunately for the *Queen Mary*, the *Derfflinger* and *Seydlitz* were still very much in action, straddling her in tall columns of tormented exploding water.

I was trying to get in two salvoes to the enemy's one. Several times I was unable to attain this, as for full salvoes

The 'Raison d'être' of the Queen Mary, *her 13.5in ordnance in action. In this telling picture shot from her bridge, looking over her forecastle, 'A' and 'B' turrets have just fired a salvo off her starboard bow. Note the dark grey paint finish to the crowns of the gunhouses, as well as the stowed anti-torpedo net to starboard and lowered stanchions. The conspicuous crowns sighting port and central periscope hoods, are well seen in this unique view of her guns firing. Although she undertook a number of practice shoots in her career, this is the only known photograph. (Royal Marine Museum 7/17/4/24)*

Lying off Rosyth in mid 1915, with a parade (?) on her quarter deck. Clearly visible is her camouflage pattern, a distinctive dark grey waterline band amidships. Notice early wartime changes: the removal of the sternwalk's cover aft, the result of storm damage incurred during a North Sea sweep in late 1914, the tarpaulin covering the 3in anti-aircraft piece just aft of the mainmast derrick, and the director tower and supporting legs to the foremast. (IWM. SP2775)

the enemy was firing with fabulous rapidity. All the guns fired and the shots fell absolutely simultaneously. *(Von Hase)*

Queen Mary's experienced team was obviously performing magnificently under this trial, which they had so long desired and practised for. It is estimated that the *Queen Mary* expended some 150 main rounds, hitting the *Seydlitz* and *Derfflinger*. In return she had certainly received three direct hits, compounded by numerous near misses. Two struck home in the area of the after 4in battery, wrecking this lightly armoured area. The third hit amidships, with possibly a fourth in this area as well.

The hits to the after superstructure were observed from the *Seydlitz* to have raised a serious fire. Fed presumably from the splintered craft, decking and surrounding flammable material, and from detonating 4in ammunition, it was clearly discernible. Although this conflagration does not attain importance in any official account, it was noted onboard.

A salvo of German shells hit the quarter deck, setting the whole of that part on fire. *(Deardon)*

During the last four minutes of the *Queen Mary's* life, German salvoes began to deluge the ship. As the range reduced from 14,000 metres to 13,000 metres, no less than ten four-gun salvoes were fired by the *Derfflinger* alone.

And so the *Queen Mary* and the *Derfflinger* fought out a regular gunnery duel. But the poor *Queen Mary* was having a bad time. In addition to the *Derfflinger* she was being engaged by the *Seydlitz*, and the gunnery officer of the

Seydlitz, Lieutenant-Commander Foerster, was our crack gunnery expert, tried in all the previous engagements in which the ship had taken part, cool-headed and of quick decision. *(Von Hase)*

Explicit accounts of this onslaught, along with an indication of the scene and dreadful sounds imparted under this intense bombardment were registered.

The *Queen Mary* was next ahead of us, and I remember watching her for a little and I saw one salvo straddle her. Three shells out of four hit, and the impression one got of seeing the splinters fly and the dull red burst was as if no damage was being done, but that the armour was keeping the shell out. *(Conning Tower, Tiger)*

The German squadron again came ahead, their guns being concentrated on the *Queen Mary*. They had been poking about for the range for some minutes without effect, when suddenly a most remarkable thing happened. Every shell that the Germans threw seemed suddenly to strike the battle cruiser at once. It was as if a whirlwind was smashing a forest down, and reminded me very much of the rending that is heard when a big vessel is launched and the stays are being smashed. *(Gun-layer, Tiger)*

In the *Derfflinger's* gunnery log, a number of salvoes were noted for their success. With that at 4hr 22min 40sec pm / 13,900 metres straddling with two observed shells splashes short and the other pair over. That from 4.23.45pm / 13,700 metres similar, while the 4.24.20pm / 13,500 metres salvo, earned the noted remark *'Good, Rapid'* in the log, which caused von Hase to dispatch a salvo every

20 seconds, until the final telling one at 4.25.50pm / 13,000 metres.

Suddenly at around 4.26pm, the *Queen Mary* was straddled and hit by two shells. The first of these struck her hull in the region of 'A' and 'B' mountings, penetrating and detonating inside the ship's structure, with a vented external presence of its burst. The second shell was observed to have struck amidships, on or near the already damaged 'Q' turret. However it was the hit forward which was to prove immediately decisive, with the second one amidships giving the *Coup de Grace*.

The magazines housing the propellant were located above the shell rooms. These compartments were provided with safety devices and checks in the way of automatic flash proof doors, hatches and ports in the supply chain. There was also a definite break in supply to the gunhouse at the sealed and supposedly flash-proof working chamber below it. Further to these checks, vent paths had been established within the structure surrounding the magazines, to dissipate the effects of an internal flash or ignition of propellant to the air, in the event of a charge detonating in the gunhouse, trunk, or handling room. This series of flash-proof feature and safety devices are not often commented upon, but the danger inherent in this explosive substance had been recognised, and had certainly been given some consideration in British designs of this period.

Required for one full charge was a total of 297 lbs of cordite, made up in the form of four quarter-charges contained in pure silk bags, with a black powder igniter pad located at the base of each individual charge. This silk containing medium was employed simply because it was easily consumed in the combustion of a discharge, leaving minimal residue in the chamber. While in the magazines the component cordite charges were stowed in secure metal cases, these were sealed containers with specially weakened lids to enable the contents to vent if one accidentally detonated. But as was to be demonstrated on a number of occasions, British propellant did not lend itself to controlled venting, it exploded violently if ignited and did not flare-up as did its German equivalent.

One vital factor in the disasters which where to overtake a number of British ships at Jutland, not often commented upon, was the handling of propellant within this supposedly protected chain of supply from the magazines to gunhouses. Despite the fact that British mounting were provided with these anti-flash fittings and checks, in the heat of battle these mechanisms were actually by-passed by crews, striving to achieve a high rate of fire, leaving various openings ajar for the rapid movement of personnel and charges.

It also appears that during the early years of the war, in action it was the practice to remove the lids of propellant cases in the magazines before they were passed through the flash-proofed hatches into the handling room. Compounding this, stacks of charges could pile up in these rooms in the lower trunk, with their powder igniters uncovered. All of these effectively nullified a mounting's in-built anti-flash safety devices.

This distinctly 'Open' approach seems to have been common practice, with crews eager and 'gingered-up' to a very high degree, being expected to perform at top efficiency, especially in the area of rapid gunnery. One should clearly bear the points above in mind when reading further into the reasons behind the loss of the battlecruisers at Jutland.

As a graphic indication of this aspect of the *Queen Mary's* story the account of AB Seaman Gunner G.F. Bowen RNVR, on board her near sister the *Princess Royal* at the Heligoland Bight action, contains a passage worth quoting.

> I arrived down in 'A' magazine within a few seconds of the 'Action' bugle, and we loaded the hopper and got about five rounds in the handling room. Then there was a lull, during which we stripped off our flannels, opened up plenty of cases and waited.

It is very likely that such a custom was adopted by the eager magazine handling parties of the *Queen Mary*, opening up a number of sealed propellant cases and stacking their contents in potentially exposed positions, with, as was to transpire, fatal results for her.

> All seemed to be going well with us, when suddenly I saw a salvo hit the *Queen Mary* on her port side. A small cloud of what looked like coal dust came out from were she was hit, but nothing more until several moments later, when a terrific yellow flame with a heavy and very dense mass of black smoke showed ahead, and the *Queen Mary* herself was no longer visible. *(New Zealand)*

> About 4.26pm was the historic moment when the *Queen Mary*, the proudest ship of the English fleet, met her doom. Since 4.24pm every one of our salvoes had straddled the enemy. When the salvo fired at 4.26pm fell, heavy explosions had already began in the *Queen Mary*. *(Von Hase)*

> The foretop was knocked right off and fell into the sea at some distance. *(Chaplain Bradley, New Zealand)*

Following this tremendous blow forward, there was now a frozen moment in time for those in 'Q' mounting amidship and 'X' turret right aft sufficient for their crews to perceive distinct sensations of the cataclysmic events overtaking them.

> A most awful explosion took place which broke the ship in half by the foremast, it was I believe a torpedo into one of the fore-turret magazines. When the explosion took place our left gun broke off outside the turret, and the rear end fell into the working chamber. The right gun also slid down. *(Storey)*

> There was a terrific explosion close by. I thought that the turret had received a direct hit, as it gave a sudden lurch and actually seemed to have been knocked off its roller-path, anyhow, I could feel the lurch was not due to any natural movement of the ship herself. All our machinery had at once been put out of action, as the hydraulic pressure had immediately and completely failed. To make

matters worse, the electric light had gone out and we were in almost complete darkness. *(Lhoyd-Owen)*

Then came the big explosion, which shook us a bit, and on looking at the pressure gauge I saw the pressure had failed. *(Francis)*

After this shattering event forward, in 'Q' turret amidship the dire position of the ship soon became obvious to all, and each man's survival thereafter was a matter of fate.

The Officer of the Turret told me that the ship was sinking rapidly and I was to get the turret crew out as quickly as possible, which I did. I left the turret through the hatch on the top and found the ship was lying on her side. She was broken, the stern sticking out of the water at an acute angle. I sat on the turret for a few moments, and while there I thought I saw several men fall into the water. The stern was on fire and red hot. Then an explosion blew the whole bow right out of the water, causing the after part of the ship to give a tremendous lurch, and throwing me off the turret into the water. *(Storey: Published 'I Was There' account)*

The turret was filled with flying metal, and several men were killed. A lot of cordite caught fire below me and blazed up, and several people were gassed. The men left and myself got to the ladder leading out of the turret and climbed quickly out. There was no panic or shouting at all, the men were splendid heroes. Just as I got out the turret and climbed over the funnels and masts which were lying beside the turret, and had got off my coat and one shoe, another awful explosion occurred, blowing me into the water. *(Storey: Private account)*

Another version of this very fortunate individual's escape is included within *More Sea Fights of the Great War*, indicating how he was violently blown clear of the ship.

A midshipman in an after-turret stated that he felt the tremendous shock, and both the enormous 50 ton guns appeared to stand on end and sink breech first into the ship. How he got out of the turret seems doubtful, but he found himself standing on the after funnel, now lying flat upon the deck. Realising that it was a case for swimming, he took off his coat, and was stooping down to unlace his boots when there came a second explosion. He does not remember going up, but only the sensation of falling, falling, falling that is known so well in dreams. It ended in a splash as he arrived in the embrace of the North Sea.

To those in 'X' gunhouse, this second explosion amidships was brutal. But order and discipline still reigned within Lieutenant Ewart's wrecked command. He was by then, very possibly, the most senior surviving officer on board.

A few minutes afterwards, a terrific explosion occurred in the second magazine. Both our guns were then right back on their slides and out of action. The general opinion was that the whole turret had been unseated by the German salvo. *(Deardon)*

After that came what I term the big smash, and I was dangling in the air on a bowline, which saved me from being thrown down on to the floor of the turret. The men who had them on were not injured in the big smash. Nos.2 and 3 of the left gun slipped down under the gun, and the gun appeared to me to have fallen through its trunnions and smashed up these two numbers. Everything in the ship went quiet as a church, the floor of the turret was bulged up, and the guns were absolutely useless. I must mention here that there was not a sign of excitement. One man turned to me and said, 'What do you think has happened?'. I said 'Steady everyone, I will speak to Mr. Ewart'. I went back to the cabinet and said , 'What do you think has happened sir?'. He said, 'God only knows'. 'Well sir', I said, 'Its no use keeping them all down here, why not send them up round the 4in guns, and give them a chance to fight it out. He said, 'Yes, good idea. Just see whether the 4in guns aft are still standing' I put my head up through the hole in the roof of the turret, and I nearly fell back through again. The after battery was smashed right out of all recognition, and then I noticed the ship had an awful list to port. I dropped back inside the turret and told Lieutenant Ewart the state of affairs. *(Francis)*

It now seemed as if Ewart required confirmation of this utter devastation, by dispatching two others to appraise the grim spectacle. From this was to come the inevitable conclusion that the ship was now indeed irretrievably lost, and those that could be saved must vacate the turret immediately.

Lieutenant Ewart told me to find out if possible what had happened and then to report to him. I accordingly climbed halfway through the hatch in the roof of the turret. An appalling scene greeted my eyes. I could see neither funnels nor masts. A huge column of black and yellow smoke shot with flame hung like a funeral pall over the forepart of the ship, casting a lurid glow over the scene. The masts and funnels had fallen inwards, but fortunately the ship had remained on an even keel. A rapid glance showed me that the *Queen Mary* had been heavily hit, and I climbed down into the turret and told Lieutenant Ewart that she was on fire. He ordered me to clear the gunhouse as quickly as possible, and I sent all the men I could see up on deck. The Petty Officer in the working-chamber below the gunhouse asked me through the voice pipe what had happened and I ordered him to send his men up on deck as quickly as possible. This order could never have been carried out, for soon after it had been given the ship began to heel slowly over to port, and the men below, with no chance of escaping, must have been drowned. *(Lhoyd-Owen)*

I was sent out on the top of our turret to see what was happening, and had to put on a lung respirator owing to clouds of smoke and fire. I could see nothing for a minute and then all cleared away as the foremost part of the ship went under water. I then told the Officer of the Turret that the ship was sinking rapidly and so as many as possible were got out of the turret. *(Deardon)*

The evacuation of the mounting was now a matter of

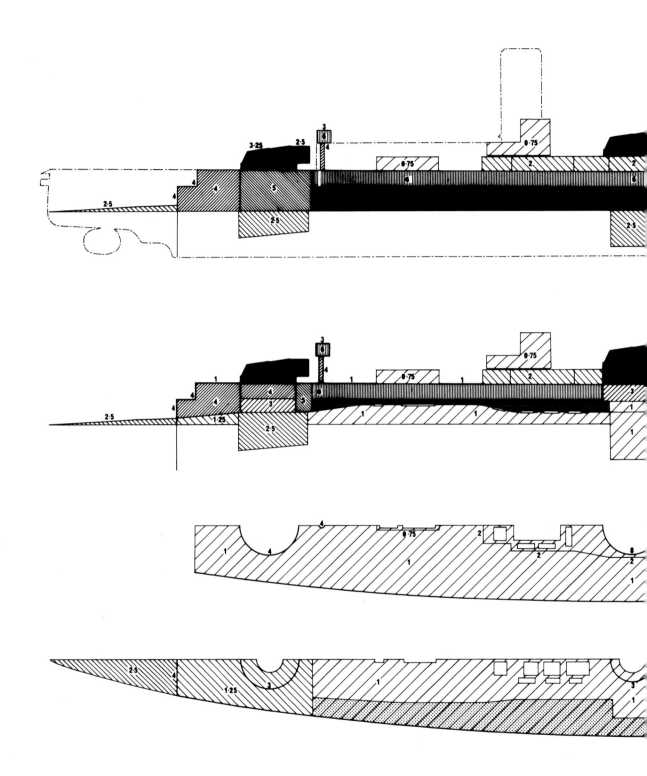

The general distribution and scale of armour, with all measurements in inches. Four views, from top to bottom.

1. *A broadside elevation, in which the external armour presented in this design is fully indicated. Here the darker the section shown, the heavier the plate of armour.*

2. *A centreline section through the ship, showing what lay behind the external armour. Especially noteworthy has to be the undulating trace of the lower deck, with the downward slope at the stem and stern, and the 'hump' over her engines, quite marked. For a good indication of the curve of the lower decks outboard edge, to the bottom edge of the external*

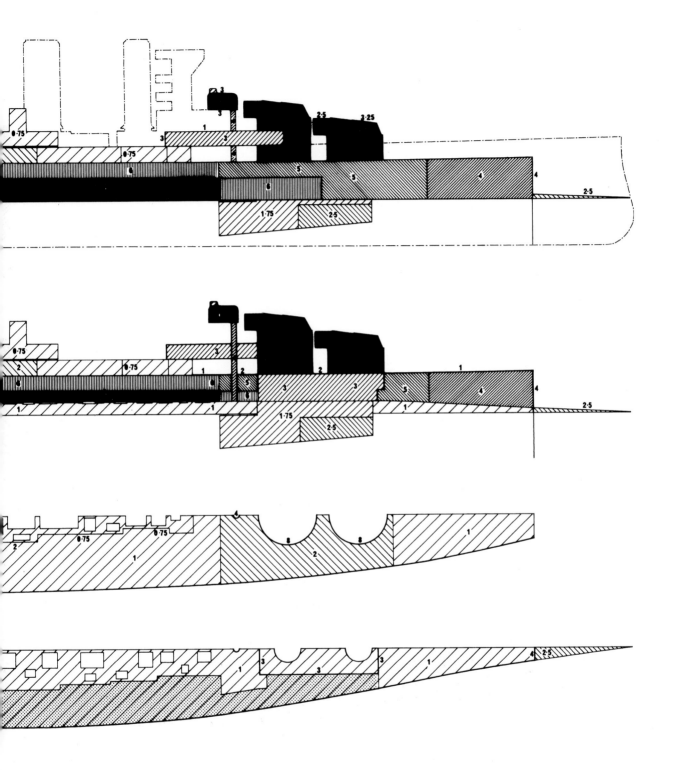

armour, reference to the cross sections is
suggested.

3. The upper deck, basically of 1in thick construction,
formed of two layers of 20 pound (half-inch) plate. Here
the lightly armoured bulkheads screening the propulsion
installations openings are quite marked.

4. The lower deck, of again predominantly 1in (2×20

pound) construction, but with its exposed extremities of
2.5in weight armour beyond the main citadel. Armoured
grates over all openings. Note in the bottom view, the
'toned' indication of the extensive coal bunkers present on
the lower deck, a factor contributing to the strength of the
protection system.

urgency, with the growing list to port, and a bows-down attitude of the ship. As she settled, her stern rose majestically with her four propellers still slowly revolving. Given her 700 foot length, her stem must have hit the 150 foot deep bottom in this plunge, and she began to pivot on her imbedded prow. Her capsize continued irredeemably to port. It was now obviously time to leave.

I went through the cabinet and out through the top and Lieutenant Ewart was following me, suddenly he stopped and went back into the turret, I believe he went back because he thought there was someone left inside. I cannot say enough for Lieutenant Ewart, nothing I can say would do him justice. He was grand, and I would like to publish this account to the world. It makes me feel sore hearted when I think of Lieutenant Ewart and that fine crowd who were with me in the turret. I was half-way down the ladder at the back of the turret when Lieutenant Ewart went back, the ship had an awful list to port by this time, so much so that men getting off the ladder went sliding down to port. I got on to the bottom rung of the ladder, but could not by my own efforts reach the stanchions lying on the deck from the starboard side. I knew if I let go that I should go sliding down to port like some of the others must have done, and probably get smashed up sliding down. Two of my turret's crew, seeing my difficulty, came to my assistance, they were Able Seamen Long and Lane. Lane held Long at full stretch from the ship's side, and I dropped from the ladder, caught Long's legs, and so gained the starboard side. These two men had no thought for their own safety, they saw I wanted

assistance, and that was good enough for them. They were both worth a VC twice over. When I got to the ship's side there seemed to be quite a fair crowd, and they did not appear to be very anxious to take to the water. I called out to them, 'Come on, you chaps, who's coming for a swim'. Someone answered, 'She will float for a long time yet'. But something, I don't pretend to understand what it was, seemed to be urging me to get away, so I clambered up over the slimy bilge keel and fell off into the water, followed, I should think, by about five other men. *(Francis)*

I was about half-way out of the turret when the ship suddenly rolled right over on her port side, her stern high in the air. I then climbed on to the back of the turret, which in the ordinary way would have been vertical, but now had become horizontal, and saw several of my men slide down the deck and fall into the sea. Some of them struck the port rail and were probably killed before they even reached the water. As I stood on the back of the turret, the stricken ship plunged deeper into the sea. To prevent myself from being sucked down with her I jumped into the water, intending to swim clear of the vortex. *(Lhoyd-Owen)*

The whole foc'sle was almost blown off and I immediately took off all my gear except my shirt and vest. As soon as in the water I swam clear and astern of the ship about thirty yards. *(Deardon)*

An edited second-hand account, of the experiences of Stoker Arthur Bower Clark, renders another vivid insight

Usually credited as being the last photograph of the Queen Mary, *this was probably taken just prior to* Jutland. *Note the then standard overall Grand Fleet light grey, against which her stowed anti-torpedo net defence and its attendant booms are easily seen. Also just discernible is her recently added lattice framework on the after superstructure, carrying a searchlight platform. The battlecruisers have adopted a staggered line formation as in the opening moves at* Jutland. *(IWM. SP1605)*

The oft-reproduced and remarkable only known photograph of the demise of the Queen Mary, *at 4.26pm on the afternoon of 31 May 1916. The billowing column of smoke and steam is roughly the full 700 foot length of the ship at its base, and extends to a height of some 2,000 feet. (IWM. SP1708)*

into personal survival against staggering odds from escape below decks.

> He was one of the fire party on the starboard side. Many of the stokers were on the mess deck. The doors on the flats were open starboard side, that being away from the enemy. A shell came through the port side and burst on or near the mess deck. Water poured in and the ship began to list. They saw the water rushing in. Many of the men rushed forward and tried to get up the hatchway onto the cabin deck. But the hatch was battened down and they tried to force it with their heads. Clark and a carpenter hand made off to the starboard side. The ship after listing to port righted herself. They went right off to the quarter deck hatchway. This was still open with the awning over it. The carpenter went up first but a second later his head came rolling down severed from his body. Clark ran up and stepped over the dead body, ran to the side and jumped overboard.

Onboard her passing consorts, various witnesses saw the entire sequence of events overtaking this rapidly floundering battlecruiser's death throes. The *Tiger* was steaming right into the thick pall of smoke then blanketing the area, with falling fragments of debris raining upon her decks in the darkness. Captain Pelly stated that initially this smoke column had stood up like a solid wall before his ship. And as he entered the bank of smoke it seemed to drift northwards, exposing the stern of *Queen Mary* standing high out of the sea, the propellers still turning, with the water around her boiling fiercely. To him the between decks appeared to be a mass of flames. He also relates how a skylight had been blown open aft, and up the hatch a great wind from below was whirling a column of papers high into the air.

> The *Tiger* was steaming at 24 knots only 500 yards astern of the *Queen Mary*, and hauled sharply out of the line to port and disappeared in this dense mass of smoke. We hauled out to starboard, and *Tiger* and ourselves passed one on each side of the *Queen Mary*. We passed her about 50 yards on our port beam, by which time the smoke had blown fairly clear, revealing the stern from the after funnel aft afloat, and the propellers still revolving, but the for'ard part had already gone under. *(New Zealand)*

> Men were crawling out of the top of the after turret and up the hatchway. When we were abreast and only about 150 yards away from her, this after portion rolled over and, as

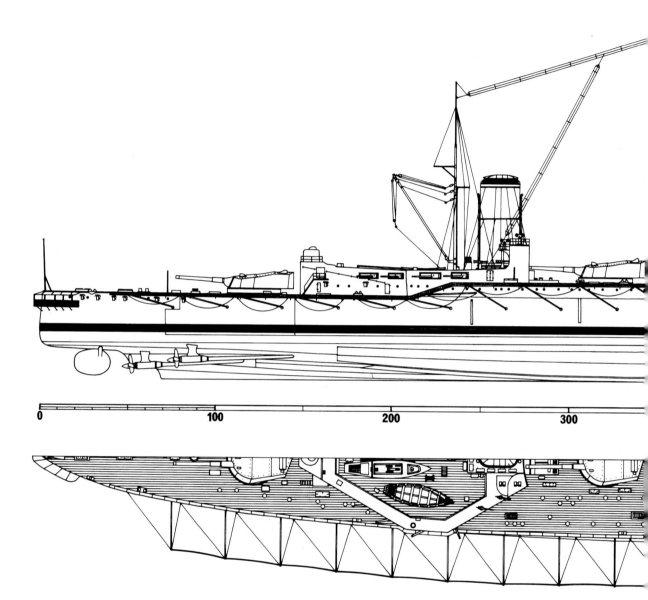

0   100   200   300

it did so, blew up. Great masses of iron were thrown into the air, and things were falling into the sea round us. There was still up in the air, I suppose at least 100 or 200 feet high, a boat which may have been a dinghy or a pinnace, still intact but upside down as I could see the thwarts. Before we had quite passed, *Queen Mary* completely disappeared. *(Navigating Officer, New Zealand)*

The *Queen Mary* seemed to roll slowly to port, her masts and funnels gone, and with a huge hole in her side. She listed again, the hole disappeared beneath the water, which rushed into her and turned her completely over. A minute and a half, and all that could be seen of the *Queen Mary*

was her keel, and then that disappeared. *(unnamed gun-layer, Tiger)*

The stern part exploded when abreast of the *New Zealand* and the stern broke in two pieces longways. *(Chaplain Bradley, New Zealand)*

For those who had just managed to escape from the foundering vessel, this final detonation was obviously shattering, given its close proximity.

As I struck the sea I heard a heavy explosion above my head and felt myself being sucked down, when I came to

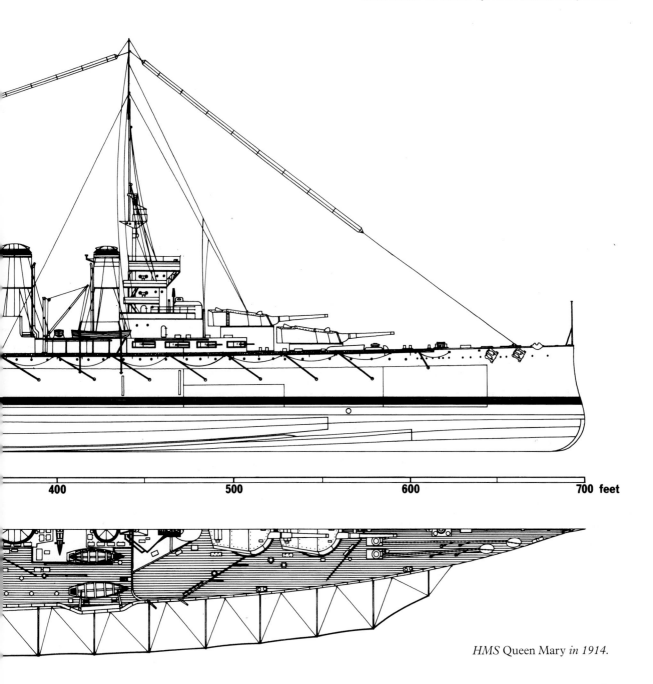

HMS Queen Mary *in 1914.*

the surface again, except for some small pieces of wreckage and a great quantity of oil, all trace of the gallant *Queen Mary* had disappeared. Another great battlecruiser, the *New Zealand*, was passing close by me. *(Lhoyd-Owen)*

She suddenly blew up completely. I was luckily sucked under water and so all the wreckage chucked about did not come with its full weight on my head. I held my breath for a long time and at last came to the surface and started looking round for something to support me as much as possible. *(Deardon)*

I heard another terrific explosion above my head, as

apparently the after magazine exploded. When I came to the surface of the water, nothing of the *Queen Mary* was to be seen, except a lot of wreckage, spars, and that sort of thing. The *Tiger* was steaming behind us during the action, and probably passed right over the spot where the *Queen Mary* had gone down. The *Queen Mary* took only a minute to sink. *(Storey)*

I struck away from the ship as hard as I could, and must have covered nearly 50 yards, when there was a big smash, and stopping and looking round the air seemed to be full of fragments and flying pieces. A large piece seemed to be right above my head, and acting on an impulse I dipped under to avoid being struck, and stayed under as long as I could, and then came to the top again, when coming behind me I heard a rush of water, which looked very much like a surf breaking on a beach, and I realised it was the suction or back-wash from the ship which had just gone. I hardly had time to fill my lungs with air when it was on me, I felt it was no use struggling against it, so I let myself go for a moment or two, then I struck out, and something bumped against me. I grasped it, and afterwards found it was a large hammock, it undoubtedly pulled me to the top, more dead than alive, and I rested on it, but I felt I was getting very weak. *(Francis)*

A gigantic cloud of smoke rose, the masts collapsed inwards, the smoke-cloud hid everything, and rose higher and higher. Finally nothing but a thick. black cloud of smoke remained where the ship had been. At its base the smoke column only covered a small area, but it widened towards the summit and looked like a monstrous black pine. I estimate the height of the smoke column at from 300 to 400 metres. *(Von Hase)*

However the battle was obviously far from over. For the victorious *Derfflinger* the obscuring banks of spray and smoke, which had earlier hidden the head of the British line and lead directly to this concentration upon the *Queen Mary*, now suddenly cleared.

Scarcely had the *Queen Mary* disappeared in the cloud of smoke when I began to find a new target with my periscope. I veered the periscope to the left and saw to my astonishment that there were still two battlecruisers there. It was not until this moment that I realised that hitherto I had been engaging the third ship in the line. The *Lion*, then, had meanwhile taken station again at the head of the enemy line. Our target was once more the *Princess Royal. (Von Hase)*

Beatty's four remaining battlecruisers, and four super-Dreadnoughts, continued to engage Hipper's five capital ships. The ebb and flow of battle would again sweep over the grave of the *Queen Mary*, as Beatty lured the High Seas Fleet north, onto the massed might of Jellicoe's Grand Fleet in 'The Run to the North' phase of the battle.

For the fortunate small band of survivors now cast adrift on the cold inhospitable waters of the North Sea, these greater issues of the battle were now secondary. Their survival rested with the screening destroyers *Laurel* and *Petard*, which saved just 18 men, while two others were subsequently picked up by the Germans and made POWs. The gallant *Queen Mary* had gone to the bottom, taking 1,266 officers and men with her. But by now presenting the evocative accounts of some participants in her demise, it is hoped her name is not forgotten.

Epilogue

In 1991, on the 75th Anniversary of the battle, the survey ship *Cable Protector* carried a joint services diving team to the location of the *Queen Mary*'s wreck. Here it was discovered that she had indeed completed her capsize to port, and is now resting completely upside down. The shattered remains of her once dominating and mighty upper works and superstructure have driven into the yielding sea bottom, leaving only the wide expanse of her rusted, growth-encrusted hull and keel accessible for investigation.

By exploring the remains of the *Queen Mary*, the full extent of her cataclysmic end was revealed. The up-turned hull revealed that she was still in one piece, her back had not broken. However the devastation wrought by the explosion of her magazines was quite evident – especially in the region of 'Q' mounting, which had been rent asunder. Surrounding her lay a debris field with a number of recognisable fixtures and fittings.

Working along her structure form its distinctive ram prow, the dive team came across such instantly recognisable features as her bilge keels, grilled inlets, and, abaft the devastated central portion, her propellers, brackets and shafts along with her twin rudders now pointing towards the surface. The time granted to the team on site was however limited, so with a documented record of her present state, complemented by a series of photographs and video footage, the 1991 dive on the *Queen Mary*'s mortal remains drew to a close, and she was left in peace once again.

Principal Sources

H. Fawcett, *The Fighting at Jutland*, 1921
J. Hammerton, *I Was There*, 1938
S. King-Hall, *A North Sea Diary 1914–18*, 1936
R. Burt, *British Battleships of WW1*, 1986
G. Von Hase, *Kiel and Jutland*, 1922

The private accounts and narratives of:
    Midshipman John Hugh Lhoyd-Owen
    Midshipman Peregrine R. Deardon
    Midshipman Jocelyn L. Storey
    Petty Officer Ernest Benjamin Francis

National Maritime Museum
Imperial War Museum

[The damage caused by heavy shells fired by the gun crews of the *Queen Mary* and other dreadnoughts on the *Seydlitz* and *Derfflinger* were graphically recorded after the battle by photographers and artists, some of whose work is reproduced in David Howarth, *The Dreadnoughts*, Time-Life Books, 1979 – Eds.]

GERMAN TYPE 35, 40 AND 43 MINESWEEPERS AT WAR

The role of minesweepers in all navies is unglamorous but essential. The German *Kriegsmarine*'s minesweepers fought a hard war and often made up for the lack of escorts. **Pierre Hervieux** documents their varied service in 1939–45.

When the Second World War began on 1 September 1939, there were 13 Type 35 minesweepers commissioned or nearing completion by the Kriegsmarine, *M–1* to *M–13*. Six of them, *M–1*, *M–3*, *M–4*, *M–5*, *M–7* and *M–8*, with two old First World War 'M' type minesweepers, were sent to the Baltic to operate against Polish forces. They formed the 1st Minesweeper Flotilla under the command of Korvettenkapitän Wenier in *M–8*. They were used for blockading, submarine-chasing and coastal shelling, and were kept busy. Polish submarines were detected several times, and even sighted and attacked, but despite several claims, none was sunk. *Rys*, *Orzel* and *Wilk* were damaged by depth charges from the First Minesweeper Flotilla, between 4 and 6 September.

On 11 September *M–8* destroyed a 75mm Polish coastal gun after she came into Grossendorf, at the foot of the Hela Peninsula. Half the modern minesweepers were then sent to the West, for hunting submarines, leaving only three in the Baltic. On 19 September, under the command of Kapitän zur See Ruge, Officer Commanding Minesweepers, *M–3*, *M–4*, with seven old minesweepers and one tender, and supported by the old battleship *Schleswig-Holstein*, shelled Polish positions near Oxhöft, Ostrowogrund and Hexengrund, particularly the Hela 150mm coastal battery. On 1 October *M–4* with two old minesweepers and a tender shelled the Hela Peninsula in co-operation with army batteries and a naval railway battery, in preparation for the infantry attack. The garrison of Hela (Rear Admiral Unrug) capitulated on the next day, and so the last resistance on the coast was broken. The Kriegsmarine action in the Baltic was over and, after 7 October, warships sailed back to the North Sea, but the minesweepers were left behind to sweep Polish minefields, which was done with no loss. One old minesweeper, *M–85*, was lost on a mine on 1 October, before the end of the fighting.

On 13 December, after the German light cruisers *Leipzig* and *Nürnberg* were torpedoed and damaged in the Heligoland Bight by the submarine HMS *Salmon*, one of the escorting destroyers collided with *M–2*, which was heavily damaged.

On 7 January 1940, in submarine-hunting operations in the Heligoland Bight, Type 35 minesweepers attacked a submarine, HMS *Seahorse*, and sank her with depth charges. Two days later *M–7* detected a submerged submarine, and dropped depth charges. Probably damaged, she was lying on the seabed. After dark *M–7* dropped two lighted buoys over the position of the unknown submarine and waited. The 'prey' began to move and, later in the night, surfaced exactly between the two buoys. As she seemed to be sinking, *M–7* recovered the crew, and HMS *Starfish* sank. She had indeed been damaged by *M–7*'s depth charges and could not escape. Following these losses, and that of the submarine HMS *Undine*, also sunk on 7 January by German auxiliary minesweepers, the British submarine operations in the Inner Heligoland Bight were halted. During the Norwegian Campaign *M–1*, *M–2*, *M–9* and *M–13* formed Group 6, destined to occupy the harbour of Egersund under the command of Korvetten-kapitän Thoma, leader of the 2nd Minesweeper Flotilla. Group 10, which was assigned to take the harbours of Esbjerg and Nordby on Fanö, included *M–4* and *M–20*, together with two old minesweepers, the command vessel *Königin Luise* (F–6) with Commodore Rüge (Officer Commanding Minesweepers West) on board, eight auxiliary minesweepers and eight motor minesweepers. Group 6 and Group 10 did not have any serious problem. *M–1* developed engine trouble, and was unable to return to Germany with the rest of the flotilla but, before that, under the command of Kapitänleutnant Bartels, she is claimed to have captured a Norwegian destroyer, and an entire torpedo-boat flotilla. Later, *M–1* is claimed to have captured a convoy of several ships and took them into a German-held port, although no confirmation exists. But it is a fact that *M–1* captured the Norwegian torpedo boat *Skarv* at Egersund on 9 April. It

A Type 35 minesweeper in Norway in 1940. In the background two heavy units can be seen.

is possible that the already-stricken Norwegian torpedo boats *Hval* and *Delfin* were also captured on this occasion, and perhaps also the patrol craft *Blink*, *Lyn* and *Kvik*, all former torpedo boats. As for the captured destroyer, it could have been the *Troll*, but she was abandoned at Florö on 4 May, and taken over by the Germans on 18 May, together with the torpedo boat *Snögg*, so this is unconfirmed. On 14 April *M–6* dropped depth charges on a submarine off Southern Norway. It was claimed to be HMS *Tarpon*, but she had already been sunk on 10 April 1940 by the German Q-ship *Schiff 40*; so on 14 April the unidentified submarine escaped.

When the submarine HMS *Seal* was captured by German patrol boats and an *Arado Ar196* floatplane on 5 May, charts of her minefields were seized by the Kriegsmarine, and it was discovered that there was one south-west of the Norwegian coast. Type 35 boats swept 49 mines but, in doing so, *M–11* was lost on 6 June, off Feisten. During the rest of the year they escorted many coastal convoys, providing protection against enemy surface ships, submarines and aircraft. They also swept and destroyed many mines from Norway to the Bay of Biscay, with only one other loss, the *M–5*.

On the night of 10 February 1941, the *M–2*, *M–13* and *M–25* were conducting an anti-submarine sweep south-west of Ushant. At 0239, in position 47°52N/05°47W, the group was attacked by a submarine which fired three or more torpedoes. The submarine was sighted, but an attempt by the minesweepers to ram failed, although the gear of one of the sweepers caught the submarine and was carried away. The minesweeper force, belonging to the 2nd Flotilla, then carried out depth-charge attacks. A total of 56 depth charges was released but no surface evidence emerged to indicate whether or not the submarine had been sunk or damaged, though it was felt that the submarine had not escaped unharmed. A strong sonar contact had been tracked, but this had suddenly faded and then ceased. British Flag Officer Submarines estimated HMS *Snapper*'s likely position for 0800 on 11 February as 48°40N/05°50W, placing her in the area of the incident at about the right time, and no other submarines were in the area. There is no concrete evidence as to how the *Snapper* met her end, though there is a strong possibility that she was mortally damaged by the three minesweepers.

On 19 May, the battleship *Bismarck* and the heavy cruiser *Prinz Eugen*, escorted by the destroyers *Z–23*, *Friedrich Eckoldt* and two *Sperrbrechers*, were joined off the Belt by the destroyer *Hans Lody* and the 5th Minesweeper Flotilla.

After the German invasion of the Soviet Union on 22 June 1941, seven Soviet destroyers laid about 500 mines in the western half of the Irben Strait in the Baltic, during the nights of 24/27 June. *M–201* and *M–23* were badly damaged in these barrages, together with two motor minesweepers, and three were slightly damaged. However, the Soviet Navy had been preceded by the *Kriegsmarine*, which on the nights of 18–21 June, with six minesweepers of the 6th Flotilla and the minelayers *Preussen*, *Grille*, *Skagerrak* and *Versailles*, laid three mine barrages comprising 1150 moored mines and 1800 explosive floats between Memel and Öland.

As the German Army suffered from lack of supplies, the *Kriegsmarine* was asked to escort ships with army supplies to Ust-Dwinsk. It was to be assumed that the Soviets had mined the approaches to that port and also the Irben Strait, the entrance to the Gulf of Riga. Therefore, *Minenräumschiff 11 (MRS–11)* (minesweeper depot ship) received orders to proceed to Ust-Dwinsk. She was the former German merchant ship *Osnabrück* (5094 tons), armed with three 105-mm guns, and carrying 12 motor pinnaces for sweeping shallow mines. Escorted by *M–23* and *M–31*, she arrived off the Irben Strait on the morning of 6 July. During her approach, she was unsuccessfully attacked by Soviet planes. At 1026, the Commanding Officer of *MRS–11* received a radio message ordering him to wait at the entrance of Irben Strait for a convoy of four motor barges with army supplies destined for Riga. It was escorted by trawlers of the 31st Minesweeping Flotilla. As more air attacks were to be expected, the Commanding Officer decided to leave only *M–23* with the convoy, and to proceed at once with *MRS–11* astern of *M–31*, minesweeping gear out. At 1045, the two ships were attacked by three planes which dropped eight bombs near them, but suffered no hits. At 1200 four vessels were sighted almost due north. When they approached they were made out to be two large and two small destroyers. The course of *MRS–11* was east-north-east. Three destroyers steered east, one south-west, probably to cut off the retreat. At a distance of about 18,000 metres the three destroyers opened fire. Their first salvoes straddled *MRS–11* but, when the fire was returned at a distance of 15,000 metres, the Soviet fire soon became less accurate. *M–31* received orders to lay a smoke screen, and to do so she took up a position on the port bow of *MRS–11*. The apparatus for making artificial smoke did not work, but the Soviet destroyers turned away, possibly because they took the manoeuvres of *M–31* as an attempt to attack with torpedoes! The fourth destroyer now turned onto a parallel course, while the other destroyers reopened fire without hitting the German ships; *MRS–11* observed at least one hit. They laid a smoke screen, and there was then an interval in the engagement from 1255 to 1330, in which *MRS–11* rounded Kolka Lighthouse, entered the Gulf of Riga, and changed course to the south. At 1330, five planes attacked with 14 bombs, scoring no hits, and losing one plane. At 1335, the two larger destroyers approached from the starboard quarter and attempted to fire at the two German ships across Cape Kolka. The distance was about 25,000 metres, and the first salvoes fell very short, but as the enemy closed at high speed, the salvoes came nearer. The fire was returned although the distance was still too great. At 1415 the destroyers broke off the fight and disappeared to the north-west.

At 1430 there was another attack by three planes, with six bombs dropped but no hits; and at 1900, the ship anchored off Ust-Dwinsk, protected by patrolling S-Boats.

It seems that the Soviets had no clear picture of the type of ship they were facing. Probably they were deceived by the quick succession of the German salvoes. The Germans also identified the enemy incorrectly, for there were only two destroyers, *Serdity* and *Silny*, which were laying mines when they encountered the two German

The after 4.1in gun of an M–*class minesweeper in Norway in 1940. There are German soldiers on board and, in the foreground, depth-charges can be seen.*

ships. They hurriedly dropped the remaining mines and then attacked, the *Silny* being lightly hit during the engagement. The two Soviet warships identified as 'two smaller destroyers' were perhaps *Taifun* class torpedo boats, or *Tral* class minesweepers. In any case, the convoy escorted by *M–23* reached Ust-Dwinsk (Dünamünde) unmolested. On 9 July the first German convoy, with six coasters and four drifters, escorted by five minesweepers, left Libau for Riga. On 1 August, the 1st Minesweeper Flotilla, near Cape Domesnös, beat off an attack by six Soviet motor torpedo boats, covered at some distance by two destroyers. *TKA–122* was sunk. On 11 August, boats of the 5th Minesweeper Flotilla laid flanking mine barrages, with 47 moored mines, off Cape Domesnös.

On 2 September, in the Irben Strait, *M–3* and *M–20* were attacked by four Soviet motor torpedo boats, and *M–3* sank one of them (unidentified). On 12–13 October, seven boats of the 1st and 2nd Minesweeper Flotillas were involved in the feint operation 'Westfalen' with the light cruiser *Köln* and four Type 35 torpedo boats, near Cape Ristna.

Before the start of Operation 'Cerberus', the famous Channel Dash, on 12 February 1942, for several weeks boats of the 1st, 2nd 4th and 5th Minesweeper Flotillas swept mines, with auxiliary minesweepers and motor

minesweepers, in the Channel and in the southern North Sea, representing 460 nautical miles (770 Km) between Brest and the Scheldt Estuary. On 13–14 March, eight minesweepers from the 1st and 2nd Flotillas escorted, with nine motor minesweepers [Not nine M-boats, as stated in *Warship 26 – April 1983* (p. 74).] and five torpedo boats, the successful breakthrough of the auxiliary cruiser *Michel* to the Atlantic. In the Arctic, on 19 April, *M–154* and *M–251* prevented an attack by the Soviet submarine *Shch–401* on a convoy off Tanafjord. In the Baltic, on 25 April, began the transfer of German forces to the Gulf of Finland for the summer of 1942.

When she broke through the Dover Strait on 13 May, the auxiliary cruiser *Stier*'s escort comprised ten M-boats, six of the 2nd Flotilla, four of the 8th with, in addition, six R-boats and four torpedo boats. Two of the latter were sunk by British MTBs, which lost one of their own. (See *Warship 26*), but the *Stier* reached Royan safely on 19 May.

In the Baltic, between 20 and 24 May, the 3rd Minesweeper Flotilla, the minelayers *Kaiser*, *Roland* and the 27th Landing Flotilla, laid the mine barrages *Seeigel 1–8*, south-east of Suursaari, with 2522 mines. In the North Sea, during the night of 6/7 July, *M–82*, *M–102* and minelayers *Roland* and *Ulm* laid the *Thusnelda* mine barrage in the *Westwall* area. They were escorted first by one *Sperrbrecher* and one anti-aircraft whaler, and then by *M–301*, *M–321*, *M–322* and *M–382*. On the night of 7–8 July, Soviet motor torpedo boats and patrol boats attacked the island of Someri, in the inner Gulf of Finland. They were able to land men, and later brought reinforcements. But the Finnish defenders held out until Finnish gunboats, patrol boats and minelayers came up, together with a few German warships, including *M–18* and *M–37*, who supported, with their 105mm guns, the counter-attack of a newly-arrived Finnish company. Shortly after noon on 9 July the Soviets surrendered, after a last Soviet attempt to land more men was beaten off in the early morning. However, until the evening of 11 July, Soviet vessels repeatedly tried to approach, evidently under the impression that the fighting was not yet ended. In numerous engagements, the Soviets did not put a single ship out of action. The Soviet gunboat *Kama* was sunk by a Finnish aircraft, and seven Soviet MTBs (TKA) and eight patrol boats (MO) were sunk by Finnish coastal guns and planes.

In the Strait of Dover, on the night of 6–7 August, the British *MTB–44*, *MTB–45*, *MTB–48* and *MGB–324*, *MGB–330* and *MGB–331* attacked a German convoy comprising the following 25 vessels, proceeding from Boulogne to Dunkirk: the catapult ship *Schwabenland* under escort of:

minesweepers *M–24*, *M–27*, *M–28*, *M–152*, *M–254*;
patrol boats *VP–1501*, *VP–1505*, *VP–1506*, *VP–1802*, *VP–1806*, *VP–1809*, *VP–1812*;
R-boat tenders *Brommy*, *Von der Gröben*;
R-boats *R–34*, *R–39*, *R–40*, *R–75*, *R–82*, *R–87*, *R–175*, *R–177*, *R–194*, *R–195*.

An M–boat in a Norwegian fjord in 1940, transporting German troops. In the foreground, showing his back, is General Dietl in command of German mountain troops in Narvik.

MTB–44 was soon disabled in the attack and, being close to the enemy coast, the crew had to abandon ship, destroying their vessel by fire. As the Germans claimed no fewer than five MTBs and MGBs sunk with certainty, it is impossible to decide which escort or escorts disabled *MTB–44*. It is likely that most of the starboard-side escorts contributed, particularly the *Brommy*, which claimed one hit with a 105mm and several more with flak guns on one of the MTBs, presumably *MTB–44*.

In the North Sea, between 21 and 25 August, *M–20*, *M–82*, *M–102*, minelayers *Roland*, *Kaiser* and *Skagerrak*, laid two mine barrages in the *Westwall* area.

In the North Sea too, on the night of 5–6 October, at 0042, the British *MTB–29* collided with the British *MTB–30*, and returned to harbour. Whilst doing so she ran across the enemy, boats of the 2nd R-boat Flotilla and 2nd Minesweeper Flotilla. *M–21* (Oberleutnant zur See Retzmann) of the latter heard the MTB approaching, and illuminated with starshell. On seeing the MTB, the minesweeper manoeuvred to ram her and, after having set the MTB on fire with gunfire, *M–21* struck her abreast of the bridge. The MTB drifted astern of the minesweeper, caught up in her gear, which was slipped owing to the danger of explosion. *M–21* then reopened fire, and continued firing until *MTB–29* blew up and sank by the bows in a blazing sea.

Units of the German Commander Naval Defence Forces West (Vice-Admiral Rüge, but with Kapitän zur See Hagen acting in his absence) had protected the U-boats, in the Bay of Biscay, against mines with minimal losses to themselves from the second half of 1940, with the 2nd, 6th, 8th, 10th, 24th, 26th and 28th Minesweeping Flotillas, equipped with Type 35 and Type 40 minesweepers. By 1 January 1943, there were 31 minesweepers (21 Type 35 and 10 Type 40) in the West, from Holland to the Bay of Biscay.

In the North Sea, the British *MTB–617*, *MTB–622* and *MTB–624* of the 21st Flotilla left Great Yarmouth on the afternoon of 9 March, to carry out an offensive sweep in an area off Terschelling. Earlier that day, a reconnaissance aircraft had reported a west-bound convoy of 11 ships 15 miles north of Wangeroog. Just after 2300 the unit obtained contact with what they identified as M-class minesweepers or armed trawlers. Assuming these vessels to be the screen for the convoy, the unit altered course to avoid them, but the German boats saw the MTBs, challenged and opened fire. The MTBs had not, in fact, fallen in with the convoy escort, but with a patrol comprising V–1247 and V–1248 of 'B' Group of the 12th Flotilla. A lively action ensued, which lasted until 2320. Whilst disengaging, *MTB–617* became separated from the other two MTBs, and failed to rejoin subsequently. The remaining two boats, with the aid of cooperating aircraft, did eventually succeed in establishing contact with the German convoy, which was sighted at 0116. This convoy, No. 410, proceeding from the Elbe to the Hook of Holland, was made up of eight ships:

Its minefield escort was provided by *M–3*, *M–4*, M14 and *M–37* of the 1st Flotilla, and its close escort by *V–803*, *V–805*, *V–807* and *V–1300* of the 8th and 13th Flotillas, and also patrol boat *HS–DB4*.

The MTBs attacked from the convoy's port side, both firing their torpedoes at what they identified as a tanker of 6500 tons, before disengaging under heavy fire from the port-side escorts (*M–3* and *M–4*, *V–805* and *V–807*), one of which at 0150 obtained a hit on *MTB–622*. The MTB immediately made smoke, but it was obvious to *MTB–624* that she was in difficulties. The latter reduced speed in an attempt to assist, but was forced to withdraw as what appeared to be a destroyer was closing rapidly. *MTB–622* was abandoned on fire, and sank, the survivors being rescued by *V–1300*.

In Norway, on 14 March, Norwegian *MTB–619* and *MTB–631* attacked a small German convoy of three merchant ships and sank one of 1249 tons, off Florö. Soon after, *MTB–631* (1942, 102 tons) grounded and was abandoned by her crew, after an attempt to sink her was made by *MTB–619*. Discovered by the Germans, *MTB–631* was towed to Bergen by the *M–1* on 18 March and put on a slipway. She was commissioned in the *Kriegsmarine* on 12 December 1943 as *S–631*.

In the Arctic, on 18 April, minelayers *Brummer* and *Skagerrak*, escorted by *M–31*, *M–154*, *M–202*, *M–251*, eight motor minesweepers and three submarine-chasers, laid the *Sagitta* mine barrage east of the Varanger peninsula. Attacks by Soviet MTBs and shelling from coastal batteries were unsuccessful.

In the Arctic, M-boats were also protecting convoys against Soviet submarines. On 19 April, west of Syltefjord, *Shch–422* missed a convoy escorted by *M–361*. The same submarine was damaged on 31 May by depth charges from *M–343* and a submarine-chaser.

In the southern part of the North Sea, west of the Hook of Holland, the German mine barrage *SW.12* (Operation "Stemmbogen") was laid out by the 1st and 7th Minesweeper Flotillas and a motor minesweeper flotilla during the night of 13–14 May. On their return, the British *MTB–232*, *MTB–234*, *MTB–241* and *MTB–244* attacked the German force, which they estimated to be *T–1* class torpedo boats and R-boats. They were expecting a convoy, and were surprised. The Germans sent a reconnaissance signal, to which the British answered with an indeterminate letter. There were a few moments of confusion. *MTB–234* and *MTB–244* fired mistakenly at the same target which was hit, causing a double and violent reddish explosion. This was probably *M–8*, which was sunk in the engagement by two torpedo hits at 0340, 52°04N/03°55E. *MTB–232* and *MTB–241* also launched their torpedoes, and there was an explosion – possibly a minesweeper which was only damaged. On their way back home, the British MTBs were attacked and strafed by Focke-Wulf FW190 fighters. Three of the British boats were slightly damaged.

In Norway, on 4 June, the Norwegian *MTB–620* and *MTB–626* torpedoed and sank the German freighter *Altenfels* (8132 tons), which was sailing in the company of *M–468* in Korsfjord.

In the North Sea, between 21 and 28 June, minelayers *Ostmark*, *Elsass*, *Brummer*, with destroyers *Z–27* and *Z–30*, laid three mine barrages to lengthen the *Westwall* barrage to the North. Off Norway, they were escorted by *M–1*, *M–2* and gunboat *K–2*. In Brittany, during the night of

M–boat in Brittany, in about 1943, with reinforced armament: a quadruple 20mm between the rear 4.1in gun and the rear mast and a single 20mm in each bridge wing, all with shields.

9–10 July, a German convoy was sailing near Ushant, screened by the 2nd Minesweeper Flotilla (Korvettenkapitän Heydel) comprising *M–9*, *M–10*, *M–12*, *M–84* and *M–153*. Distant cover was provided by the torpedo boats *T–24* and *T–25*. The convoy was attacked by the escort destroyers HMS *Melbreak*, HMS *Wensleydale* and the Norwegian escort destroyer KNN *Glaisdale*, which disabled *M–153* with their gunfire. HMS *Melbreak* was badly damaged by the German torpedo boats, which then came up. Taken in tow, *M–153* was so heavily damaged that she sank, at 0250, 48°50N/04°05W.

In the Arctic, between 15 and 17 July, *M–272*, *M–346* and *M–364*, with two motor minesweepers, escorted the minelayer *Ostmark* who laid a flanking mine barrage. On 17 July, off Gamvik (Tanafjord), *M–346*, was torpedoed and sunk, 71°07N/28°19E, by the Soviet submarine *S–56*.

In the Baltic, the Soviets were also sending their MTBs to attack the German minesweepers, together with planes to divert the German gunners' attention. On 14 September, *M–22* sank one of them. In the meantime, in the North Sea, between 8–10 October, the German minelayers *Ostmark* and *Roland*, escorted by *M–426* and *M–445*, laid three mine barrages off the Skagerrak.

On 1 November, in the Narva Bay, nine Soviet MTBs and gunboats attacked the 3rd Minesweeper Flotilla's

boats, followed by an attack from Soviet minesweepers. In all, three Soviet boats were claimed sunk by the Germans – two MTBs and one minesweeper. On 30 November, the same flotilla was attacked by eleven MTBs, two being claimed sunk. All these losses are unidentified and unconfirmed to date.

In the Arctic, on 28 January 1944, *M–273* was in the escort of the convoy which was attacked by the Soviet submarine *S–56* (see Warship 40). On 31 January, in the Baltic, *M–451* was grounded and wrecked, off Helsinki, in a storm.

In the Channel, off the North Brittany coast, on 5 February, the torpedo boat *T–29*, together with *M–156* and *M–206*, was sailing to Brest. They were attacked by night by the escort destroyers HMS *Brissenden*, HMS *Talybont*, HMS *Tanatside* and HMS *Wensleydale*. *M–156* received eight direct hits (4-in). With three compartments leaking, she was towed to l'Aber-Wrac'h and, there, was restored to an upright position. She was attacked and bombed the next morning, at 1045, by British Typhoon fighter-bombers, and capsized in shallow water. When the author went to l'Aber-Wrac'h in August 1948 the wreck was still there, and appeared to be in quite good condition.

In the North Sea, between 4 and 6 March, *M–301*, *M–406*, *M–426*, *M–462*, minelayers *Brummer*, *Linz* and

Roland, laid the *Grossgörschen* mine barrage in the western Skagerrak.

In the Channel, 3 miles off Dunkirk, on 14 March at 2145, *M–10* was torpedoed and sunk by the British *MTB–353* in an attack on a convoy. In the Channel again, on 21 March, the 10th Minesweeper Flotilla (Korvettenkapitän Josephi), in escorting a convoy north-east of Lezardrieux, beat off attacks by British MTBs. In Norway, on 24 March, the German tanker *Wörth* was damaged by aerial torpedoes, off Listerfjord, and was towed to Akers by *M–2*.

In the North Sea, two divisions of British MTBs, the first comprising *MTB–224*, *MTB–241* and *MTB–244*, the second *MTB–223* and *MTB–350*, were ordered to be off Egmond at 2300 on 30 March, to sweep south for a northbound convoy. The convoy, which was No. 1237 on passage from the Hook of Holland to the Elbe, was located five miles off Ijmuiden at 2337. It consisted of six German steamers: *Weichselland*, *Poseidon*, *Espagne*, *Preussische Holland*, *Bernlef* and *Hedwigshütte*, and was heavily escorted. Sweeping ahead as additional anti-MTB screen were eight motor minesweepers of the 9th Flotilla. Astern of the R-boats came the minesweeper escort of four minesweepers of the 27th Flotilla. Close escort was pro-vided by six patrol boats of the 8th and 11th Flotillas. The MTBs planned an attack by divisions from either bow of the convoy, the first division inshore but, at 2346, as the

MTBs were lying in wait ahead of the convoy, they were seen in the lee of the moon by the R-boats, which opened fire. The MTBs then increased speed for the attack which was, however, frustrated by heavy gunfire from the escorts. Whilst the first division was disengaging to the north-west across the bow of the convoy, *MTB–241* sus-tained an underwater hit in the engine room, by what was calculated to have been a 4-inch shell. If so, it could have been a 105-mm from one of the M-class minesweepers, but it may also have been an 88-mm from one of the V-boats. The MTBs then made to attack from seaward because of the large amount of starshell from the escorts, who were firing in all directions, and who were now also being backed up by harbour defence vessels from the Hook, which meant the gunfire was intense. Meanwhile, *MTB–241*'s main engine gear-boxes had become awash, and she was taken in two by *MTB–224* and *MTB–244*. After the Senior Officer had transferred from *MTB–241* to *MTB–224*, *MTB–241* was left in tow of *MTB–244*, who towed her stern first until 0655, when the tow parted. *MTB–241* then had a heavy list to starboard, and her stern was awash. The tow was repassed by 0720, but parted twice after that. Shortly after 0800, on 31 March, *MTB–241* (1942, 39 tons) rolled over and sank in position 52°22N/03°12E.

In the Baltic, on the night of 13–14 April, *M–14*, *M–22*, minelayers *Brummer*, *Roland*, *Linz*, with three destroyers

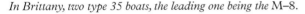

In Brittany, two type 35 boats, the leading one being the M–8.

and a torpedo boat, laid the *Seeigel 6b* mine barrage south of Suur Tytärsaari. On 21–22 April, a new operation was cancelled, with four minesweepers, after *Roland* hit a mine, probably from a barrage laid earlier, and sank. On 23–24 April and 25–26 April, *M–20*, *M–37* and *M–204*, took part in two other minelaying operations, together with the three destroyers, the torpedo boat and five motor minesweepers. All those April operations took place for strengthening the German *Seeigel* mine barrage in the inner Gulf of Finland. During Soviet minesweeping operations, from 10 May to 20 October, 13 minesweepers were lost, five Soviet MTBs being also lost on mines in June.

On 29 April, off St Brieuc, torpedo boat *T–27* had to be beached after an engagement with the destroyer HMCS *Haida*. 24th Flotilla's minesweepers made an attempt at salvaging her but, being unsuccessful, only the crew were rescued.

In the Channel, on 24 May, the 6th Minesweeper Flotilla sailed from Cherbourg to Le Havre with five torpedo boats. On the way one of them, the *Greif*, was torpedoed by a British Albacore aircraft, then collided with another torpedo boat and sank (See Warship 26). *M–39*, north-west of Ouistreham in the Seine Bay, was torpedoed and sunk by British *MTB–354* and *MTB–361*. *M–84* and one torpedo boat reached Le Havre badly damaged by ground mines.

In the Baltic, on 30 May, in the Gulf of Finland, six minesweepers of the 3rd Flotilla, were attacked by five Soviet motor torpedo boats, and claimed one of them

sunk. In Narva Bay, on 4 June, *M–37* was first attacked by four Soviet MTBs, and sank one of them. Then eight MTBs attacked *M–37* and another minesweeper, one again being sunk and eight survivors rescued by the Germans. During this second attack, *M–37* was torpedoed by Soviet MTB *TKA–101*, at 0010, and sank. On 8 June, 3rd Flotilla's boats were attacked by five Soviet MTBs sinking two of them. On 19 June another Soviet MTB was sunk by minesweepers belonging also to the 3rd Flotilla. By the middle of June, that flotilla, following a call from the Finns, was employed in Viborg Bay and in Koivisto Sound to support them with their 105-mm guns. Off Halli, on 30 June, eight Soviet MTBs attacked four 3rd Flotilla's M-boats and four Finnish MTBs; one Soviet MTB was hit by German gunfire, burned and sank, four men being rescued. Soviet MTB losses from the end of May to the end of June 1944 are difficult to identify or to confirm, but *TKA–43*, *TKA–63* and *TKA–161* were all sunk in Narva Bay at that time.

In Spring and Summer 1944, in the Gulf of Finland, the number of minesweepers was:

1st Flotilla	–	Seven type 35.
3rd Flotilla	–	Eight type 35.
25th Flotilla	–	Eight type 40.

In the meantime, the D-Day landings took place in Normandy on 6 June and, at that time, there were 56 type 35 and type 40 minesweepers between Holland and the Bay of Biscay, 38 of them being based in French waters.

The 6th Minesweeper Flotilla, after coming to Le Havre

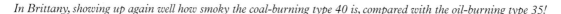

In Brittany, showing up again well how smoky the coal-burning type 40 is, compared with the oil-burning type 35!

A close-up of a type 40's bridge in Brittany. In front of the bridge a 37mm and a 20mm AA guns with protective shields can be seen.

from Brest via Cherbourg, had just time to lay mines off the Norman coast in the last days of May, before D-Day. On 14 June, in the early morning, the destroyer HMS *Ashanti* and the Polish destroyer ORP *Piorun* sank *M–83*, at 0140, off Cap de la Hague, 24 men being rescued. Later on, between St. Malo and Jersey, a running battle took place between the same two destroyers and a group of six minesweepers. At 0230 *M–343* was also sunk and all the others were more or less damaged, *M–412* severely, but were able to make port. The *Piorun* was damaged, with four of her crew wounded.

In the Channel, on the night of 16–17 June, the Canadian *MTB–726*, *MTB–727*, *MTB–745* and *MTB–748*, attacked a German convoy, west of the Cotentin Peninsula. *MTB–748* torpedoed and heavily damaged *M–133*, which was towed to St. Helier, and later on to St. Malo where she was considered a constructive total loss. In the night of 27–28 June, a German-Finnish commando operation, 'Steinhäger' was launched against the island of Narvi, occupied by the Soviets on 22 June with light craft. With the support of three torpedo boats, the 3rd Minesweeper Flotilla (Korvettenkapitän Kieffer), with five 'M' type and four motor minesweepers, Finnish units were to be landed by ten Finnish patrol boats and nine Finnish MTBs. The operation failed because of the strong Soviet defence and inadequate co-ordination between Germans and Finns. German minesweepers were stubbornly guarding the obstructions, made of minefields and protective floats to blockade the Soviet surface ships and submarines in the Gulf of Finland. Only the small Soviet motor torpedo boats and patrol boats (TKAs and MOs) could get through them, thanks to their small draught. The German minesweepers were each normally at sea for four days and four nights (!) near the barrages, then they were allowed to withdraw, and were relieved by other minesweepers. So the ammunition problem was of the first importance, and the minesweepers used to take on board at least twice the usual amount, mainly because of Soviet air attacks. The minesweepers guarding the mine and net barrages were persistently attacked when near the barrages, but hardly molested when they retired close to the coast. The attacks in the vicinity of the barrages were usually carried out by groups of three to ten planes, following each other at short intervals. This forced the patrols to expend their ammunition, but the Soviet planes did not follow the German ships when they retreated a few miles. Armoured shields for the anti-aircraft guns, developed for the German minesweepers in France, proved valuable here too. Nevertheless, in the course of time, the great number of the air attacks caused considerable losses of personnel. Many boats were damaged by fragments, although direct bomb hits were rare. Just to give a couple of examples, the 3rd Flotilla was surveying the obstructions on 30 July. Three attacks were endured, each time with 30–40 Il-2 planes, protected by fighters. Six Soviet planes were shot down. German losses were one crew member killed and twenty-six wounded. On the next day, a bigger attack took place, with about 70 planes comprising Il-2, Pe-2, Bostons and fighters. Two planes were shot down, seven men killed and 30 wounded – mainly aboard *M–15*, which was hit and heavily damaged. The Soviet planes had con-

centrated their attacks on her, but she stayed afloat and was repaired and ready for action in September.

Returning to the Channel Islands, on 2 August the commanding officer of the 24th Minesweeper Flotilla (Fregattenkapitän Breithaupt) received the order to position his six boats in the river Rance, to support German ground forces defending the southern approaches of St. Malo. Anchored in the Rance, off Saint-Sulliac, the minesweepers demonstrated the effectiveness of their 105mm gunfire, in pinning to the ground the Task Force 'Earnest's' American troops advancing along the National Road 137 (Rennes–St. Malo). They were, however, quickly located by reconnaissance aircraft and, on the evening of 3 August, were attacked by fighter-bombers. *M–424* was damaged beyond repair first, and two others were heavily damaged. Next day, the planes came back and, this time *M–422* was sunk. The four remaining minesweepers were obliged to sail away, and reached St. Malo safely. On 6 August, in St. Malo, *M–133* and *M–206* were scuttled. On the same day, the four surviving minesweepers (*M–412*, *M–432*, *M–442*, *M–452*), after sailing from St. Malo for the Channel Islands, were attacked off Jersey by a mixed force of two French MTBs, six American PT-boats and two destroyers. As a result two of the German minesweepers were damaged, but they reached safety.

In the meantime, in the North Sea, two German minelaying operations took place, in the Skagerrak, during the nights of 3–4 and 5–6 August, with *M–406*, *M–425*, *M–470*, the minelayers *Ostmark*, *Kaiser*, three destroyers and one *Sperrbrecher*.

By the beginning of August, British task forces frequently made sorties into the Bay of Biscay. On 6 August, the light cruiser HMS *Bellona*, the destroyers HMS *Tartar*, HMS *Ashanti*, HMCS *Haida* and HMCS *Iroquois* attacked a German convoy north of the Ile D'Yeu, near St. Nazaire. *M–263* and *M–486* (at 0040), a patrol boat and a motor launch, were sunk by gunfire, and the *Haida* was slightly damaged. On 11 August, after being damaged on 24 May, and unfit for sea, *M–84* was scuttled in dock in Le Havre, shortly before the evacuation by the *Kriegsmarine*, and the damaged *M–384*, was scuttled in Nantes as there was no tug available to tow her away.

In the night of 11–12 August, boats of the 24th Minesweeper Flotilla were attacked by the American MTBs *PT–500* and *PT–502* under the command of the American destroyer escort *Borum*, off the south-west coast of Jersey. Even though torpedoes were fired, no results were achieved by either side. In the night of 13–14 August, the Flotilla had another skirmish off the Channel Islands, with the destroyers HMS *Onslaught*, HMS *Saumarez*, the American destroyer escort *Borum*, three American MTBs and two British MTBs. In another engagement near Guernsey, in which *M–432* was heavily damaged during the night of 18/19 August, she was taken in tow under the protection of German coastal batteries. In the meantime, in the night of 14–15 August, north of Les Sables d'Olonne, at about 0300, *M–385* was heavily damaged by gunfire from the light cruiser HMS *Mauritius*, and from the destroyers HMS *Ursa* and HMCS *Iroquois*, being beached as a total loss. *M–275* was badly damaged but

A type 35, off St Nazaire, on 12 October 1941. Note that the two 4.1in (105mm) guns are not protected by shields.

reached La Pallice. On 25 August, in Bordeaux, *M–262*, *M–304*, *M–363* and *M–463* were scuttled, to avoid capture, as was *M–344* in Rochefort on 28 August.

In the Arctic, August was quite eventful for the M-boats, and there were several Soviet combined operations against German convoys on the Polar coast, involving submarines, MTBs and aircraft. A convoy of six steamers, which was attacked by Soviet MTBs and submarines on 18/19 August, off Persfjord, was escorted by 18 escort vessels, among them *M–31*, *M–35*, *M–154*, *M–202*, *M–251* and *M–252*. One steamer and one patrol boat were sunk by Soviet MTBs, and another patrol boat by a Soviet submarine. *M–31* and *M–202* each sank an MTB with their gunfire, one of which was TKA–203 (ex-U.S. PT266, 1942, 46 tons). The German records acknowledged the skillful tactics of these attacks. On 23 August a west-bound convoy of five ships was located by Soviet aircraft. It was escorted by fifteen escort vessels; among them were the six minesweepers of the former convoy. Two Soviet submarines attacked, and one of them damaged a steamer.

In the Baltic, on 14 September, the Germans tried to occupy the Finnish island of Suursaari, but the operation did not succeed. The landing was covered by the 3rd and 25th Minesweeper Flotillas, and landing craft, gun carriers, motor minesweepers and S-boats.

In Norway, on 20 September, off Egersund, the submarine HMS *Sceptre* (Lieutenant-Commander McIntosh) torpedoed and sank *M–132* and one merchant ship of 1184 tons. On 26 September, on the Polar Coast, the Soviet submarine *S–56* unsuccessfully attacked *M–31* and *M–251*, and was damaged by depth charges.

On the night of 7/8 October, *M–17* was escorting the S-boats' depot ship, *Hermann Von Wissmann*, and the German transport *RO–24* (ex-Dutch *Zonnewijk*) from Windau to Libau. The latter had about 500 soldiers on board, some on leave and some slightly wounded, with their nurses. After sailing for a few miles, at 2330, *RO–24* (4499 tons) was torpedoed and sunk by the Soviet submarine *Shch.310* (Captain 3rd Class Bogorad). *M–17* depth-charged the submarine, which escaped, and then recovered 471 survivors out of 501 people who were on board. Others were saved by S-boats.

In the Arctic, in October, the evacuation of the German troops fighting on the Murmansk front took place. Soviet motor torpedo boats, planes and submarines attacked German convoys. In two attacks, by a total of ten Soviet MTBs, only two minesweepers were lost, not the ten vessels claimed! First, on 11 October, off Kiborg, an east-bound German convoy, escorted by four minesweepers and five motor minesweepers, was attacked and the leading *M–303* was torpedoed and sunk by Soviet MTB *TKA–205* (or *TKA–219*) who both attacked her. Then, on 21 October, a German westbound convoy, comprising one steamer, two tugs and nine escorts, was attacked off Havningsberg by more Soviet MTBs. *TKA–215* succeeded in torpedoing and sinking *M–31*. On these two occasions, three Soviet MTBs were sunk; among them

The lucky M–155 with a sister-ship behind. Of the 38 omnipresent M–class minesweepers based in Western France on 6 June 1944, only M–155 returned to Germany through the Dover Strait. All the others were sunk, scuttled or paid off, the last-mentioned being repaired and used by the French Navy after the war. M–155 survived the war and became Soviet in 1945.

were probably *TKA–202* (ex-US *PT–89*, 1941, 46 tons) and *TKA–222* (ex-US *PT–54*, 1942, 43 tons).

In Norway, in the night of 12/13 November, a British naval force, consisting of the heavy cruiser HMS *Kent*, the light cruiser HMS *Bellona*, the destroyers HMS *Myngs*, HMS *Verulam*, HMS *Zambesi* and HMCS *Algonquin*, attacked the German convoy *KS–357* off Listerfjord, south-east of Egersund. Of the four freighters of the convoy, *Greif* and *Cornouailles* were sunk and, of the six escort vessels, three submarine-chasers were sunk, as well as *M–416* which was sunk by destroyers. It seems that *M–427* was only heavily damaged by destroyers, and was bombed and sunk on the next day, in Rekkefjord, by British aircraft.

In the Baltic, during the Soviet offensive against the Sworbe Peninsula, on 18 November, German minesweepers engaged Soviet ships on the eastern side of Sworbe. On 20–21 November, *M–328*, *M–423* and two patrol boats had also engagements with Soviet *Tral* class minesweepers, armoured motor gunboats and motor torpedo boats. *M–328*'s gunfire was particularly successful for, on 18 November, she sank a Soviet MTB and, three days later, she sank the Soviet minesweeper *T–207 Shpil*, and one Soviet armoured motor gunboat was damaged and beached. *M–328* had been converted into a gunboat, carrying a reinforced armament that could explain her successes. In the meantime, in the same area, *M–460*

claimed to have sunk a Soviet MTB on 19 November, and *M–203* claimed to have sunk another one on 22 November out of a group of twelve.

During the nights of 24/25 November, 29/30 November and 4/5 December, to block the exit of the Irben Strait, *M–17*, *M–155*, *M–203*, together with minelayers *Linz* and *Brummer*, laid three mine barrages. On 12 December, *M–203* collided with the German submarine *U–416* who sank at the entrance to Pillau.

In Norway, the Norwegian *MTB–712* and *MTB–722* attacked a German force in Bömlofjord on the evening of 23 December, and *M–489* was torpedoed and sunk. From the beginning of January 1945 to the beginning of March 1945, at first from the Gulf of Danzig, and later from the Western Baltic, regular German convoys proceeded to Libau and Windau to supply the Army Group Courland. For escort, from January, the 13 Type 35 minesweepers of the 1st and 3rd Flotillas, the five Type 40 minesweepers of the 25th Flotilla and, later, the 12th Flotilla with three-to-six Type 43 minesweepers, and 2nd Minesweeper Flotilla with about the same number of Type 43 minesweepers, according to the number of newly-commissioned boats, were employed as submarine-hunters. Soviet submarines were deployed against the German traffic. *Shch–407* was pursued with depth-charges from *TS–8* (ex-*M–375*) on 12 February. On 23 February, *Shch–309* (Captain 3rd Class Vetchinkin) attacked the German freighter *Göttingen*

(6267 tons), torpedoed and sank her. In this action *M–801* (Oberleutnant zur See Damerow) of the 12th Flotilla depth-charged the submarine heavily, but it escaped. The Soviet submarine *Shch–309* missed another ship on the same day. Meanwhile, in Norway, on 11 January 1945, a British force comprising the heavy cruiser HMS *Norfolk*, the light cruiser HMS *Bellona*, the destroyers *Onslow*, *Orwell* and *Onslaught*, attacked a German convoy off Egersund. The freighters *Bahia Camarones* and *Charlotte* were badly damaged, and had to be abandoned. In an engagement with the convoy escort, *M–273* was sunk. On 31 January, in the Ravnafjord, north of Molde, *M–382* was torpedoed and sunk by the Norwegian *MTB–715*.

Back to the Baltic, where, in the meantime, on 17 January, *M–305* foundered in a storm off Brüsterort and, on 30 January, *M–341* and *TS–2* (ex-*M–387*) rescued respectively 37 and 15 survivors from the German passenger ship *Wilhelm Gustloff*, torpedoed and sunk by the Soviet submarine *S–13* (Captain 3rd Class Marinesko). As the Soviets threatened East Prussia and Danzig, from January to March, the 1st, 2nd, 3rd, 12th and 25th Minesweeper Flotillas were extensively employed to protect convoys, and also to take on board refugees in the biggest operation of that kind in history.

Before relating the German surprise attack on Granville, it is necessary to talk about a not very well known fact which took place on 21 December 1944. On that day the German watchers of the advanced post on the Minquiers islands saw a small landing craft, followed in the distance by an escort vessel, about the size of a corvette. The watchers opened fire, and the landing craft started zigzagging and her crew made a lot of friendly gestures. The escort vessel had disappeared. The fire was stopped, and the landing craft went ashore. Aboard the LCVP there were five German fugitive sailors, among them a midshipman, who told that they had been captured in Brest in September 1944, and sent to Granville for unloading colliers. They were very well treated, and got as much food as the American guards had themselves, but nothing to compare with the rations waiting for them in the Islands! They nevertheless decided to escape and rejoin their colleagues, to keep on fighting. On the next day two small patrol boats arrived, and escorted the American LCVP to St. Helier, where the midshipman very quickly told everything he knew about Granville and its coal traffic from England. To give an idea, despite German destructions, the harbour of Granville received 477 ships with 430,382 tons of coal from September 1944 to the end of 1945. Plans were quickly established by Kapitänleutnant Zimmermann, commanding the 46th Auxiliary Minesweeper Flotilla, for sending a raiding party to Granville, to bring back much-needed coal to restart the central power station of St. Peter's Valley, and to get more hours for the stokeholds of the 24th Minesweeper Flotilla's four sweepers. After the fall of St. Malo in August 1944, the four M-boats had set up base in the Channel Islands and, for a short time, continued with occasional patrols between the Islands. But, because of coal shortages, the four were temporarily laid up, and a certain amount of coal was held in reserve so that these ships could be used against an Allied invasion. The majority of the crew were transferred to shore establishments, leaving reliable technical men on board for maintenance purposes, and to ensure that the ships should be kept as near as possible to fighting standards. This method proved very successful, and it was decided to use them for the raid on Granville. It was decided to attack during the night of 6–7 February 1945. The ships sailed, but the weather deteriorated. Mechanical problems took place on different auxiliary vessels; one of them had completely lost contact because of a machinery breakdown. In addition, the only escorting S-boat (*S–112*) had had a skirmish with a US PC-boat and, despite the fact that one group was only 250 metres from Granville's jetties, Admiral Hüffmeier ordered every boat to retreat. The 24th Flotilla was under the command of Korvettenkapitän Mohr after Fregattenkapitän Breithaupt was accidentally killed on 25 December 1944, and he received the whole command of the next expedition, which was to take place during the night of 8–9 March, after plans were fully revised. The attack of the harbour would be accomplished by the four minesweepers, *M–412*, *M–432*, *M–442* and *M–452*, of Group I and a sea-going tug, with a group of a dozen men on board to bring back an eventual prize. Group II was made of three naval gun ferries armed with 88mm. guns, who had to deal with and eliminate any American patrol boats. Group III was composed of three small patrol boats, *FK–01*, *FK–04* and *FK–56*, carrying a commando party to be landed on the Casino beach. Group IV comprised two armed trawlers who had to survey the Chenal de la Deroute, between Jersey and the Continent. The little force comprised a total of 13 boats with about 600 crew members plus about 140 commandos, who had to destroy the harbour installations, to burn depots, and eventually to fight. Allied ships who could not be taken away would be scuttled. Most of the commandos were embarked aboard *M–412*, the Flotilla's leader. At 0015, 15 miles west of Granville, the three naval gun ferries engaged violently the American patrol boat *PC–564* (1942, 370 tons) who, with her 76mm., 40mm. and 20mm. guns out of action after a few minutes, was quickly disabled by 88mm., 37mm. and 20mm. shells. Her Captain, Percy Sandell, USN, decided to beach his ship west of the Pointe du Grouin, north of Cancale. *PC–564* had lost 14 men, killed during the gunfight, 11 wounded in action, plus 14 others who went away on a raft, and were taken as prisoners to Jersey. The engagement had ended at 0045, and the German force was then approaching Granville without any problem, despite the fact that most of its ships were detected by the radar of Coutainville between 2158 and 0023! But the surprise was, nevertheless, astonishingly complete! Shortly after entering the outer harbour, at 0120, *M–412* grounded as she was going to come alongside the western mole, having been misled by a miscalculation of the tide. However, all her commandos landed safely, and the other ones too. In the harbour there were five colliers, and the German commandos controlled it between 0130 and 0300. Three British cargo ships were sabotaged and heavily damaged by German action, and a fourth was slightly damaged. The fifth was captured and brought, with her captain and six of her crew, to Jersey under her own steam. On board the Germans found 112

A camouflaged type 40, the M–411 which was transferred to the Soviet Navy in 1945.

tons of coal and secret documents: maps with the coastal shipping lanes, guidebooks between English coast and French harbours, codes, etc. On her arrival in St. Helier, she was greeted by cheers from German sailors. A second British captain was also captured during the fights. Completely taken by surprise, the local American forces were also quickly overwhelmed, and a dozen American soldiers were taken prisoner, including a colonel and three other officers dressed in pyjamas! A total of 30 Allies were captured in all. The Germans claimed that the Allies had lost about 60 men killed, including six British seamen when resisting the German commandos who boarded the five merchant ships. They also claimed to have destroyed eight cranes, two cars, eight lorries, two locomotives, three trucks, as well as an ammunition depot and a combustible depot. In addition they damaged five cranes and put out of action the tugboat *Servannais* and they scuttled the pilot launch *Pichinette*. The Germans had only six men killed and 30 wounded. They also liberated 67 of their men, and brought them back to Jersey. It was impossible to refloat *M–412*, and she was scuttled with depth charges after her crew was taken off and divided amongst other boats. Her wreck stayed in the outer harbour of Granville until 1951, and then was scrapped. She had been launched on 6 September 1942, in Holland. It seems unbelievable, but Admiral Hüffmeier, by the middle of April 1945, was indeed stubbornly planning another raid on Granville between 5 and 9 May, when moon and tide were

favourable. On 6 May, he even went from Guernsey to Jersey to supervise the last preparations. The Grand Admiral Doenitz ordered him to cancel the operation. Can one imagine another *Eskwood* arriving in St. Helier at about the same time the Capitulation of German Forces was signed in Reims? . . . !

On 22 March, the Soviet submarine *L–21* torpedoed and sank the patrol boat *V–2022*, and the tug *Erni*. After unsuccessful attacks, she was hunted off Kolberg in the next few days by *TS–4* (ex-*M–278*), *M–372* and the fleet sloop *F–8*. In April, in the Bay of Danzig off Hela, embarkations continued under the anti-aircraft cover of warships. Minesweepers were, of course, involved, one of which claimed the destruction of a Soviet MTB. In the last three months of the war German fighters intervened very rarely, because the *Luftwaffe* was completely overstretched, but the German warships put up a very strong defensive fire. Nevertheless, on 11 April, *M–376* was bombed and sunk by Soviet aircraft off Hela. On the night of 15–16 April, the destroyer *Z–34* was torpedoed and damaged by Soviet MTBs *TKA–131* and *TKA–141*. *M–204* and torpedo boat *T–36* brought her to Swinemünde.

South of Norway, on 15 April, *M–368* was sunk in a collision with a U-boat. The end of the war was in sight and, on 2 May, *TS–2* (ex-*M–387*) was scuttled in Lübeck.

On 5 May, *M–453*, patrol boats *V–303*, *V–2002* and training vessel *Nautik* arrived in Hela. They embarked 2700 refugees and, after beating off Soviet MTB attacks

A type 43, the M–806, which survived the war and was also transferred to the Royal Navy in 1945. The armament consists of two 4.1in (105mm) guns, two single 40mm AA guns and a quadruple 20mm AA gun.

from Kolberg, they arrived safely off Copenhagen on 6 May. *M–22* was scuttled on 7 May in the Kiel Canal, which had been navigated in peace and wartime by so many of the *Kriegsmarine*'s ships. It was the day the surrender of German forces was signed in Reims. The long struggle was over . . .

On 14 May, *M–607* arrived in the Firth of Forth. When crossing the North Sea, the crew did not have, at last, the need to watch the sea and the sky, in fear of an attack. It was peacetime now, and the minesweeper was bringing documents on the German mine barrages in the Skagerrak and Kattegat. M-type minesweepers were strongly built

ships, as proved by the experiences of *M–18*, commanded by Otto Köhler. The Commander and First Officer started to say their last prayers as two torpedoes hit – but they went straight through the hull and failed to explode. On another occasion, *M–18* was rammed, first in the bows and, shortly afterwards, in the stern. Minesweepers were frequently used for a variety of other duties and, on the whole, these small ships saw much more action than the larger units. By lack of space, the losses due to aircraft and mines are not covered in this study, with a few exceptions, nor are specifications for which Conway's *All the World's Fighting Ships 1922–46* is recommended.

PERCY SCOTT AND THE DIRECTOR

The reputation of Admiral Sir Percy Scott as the Royal Navy's foremost gunnery expert in the Edwardian era owes much to Scott's own claims. **John Brooks** investigates Scott's remarkable role in improving fire control and separates fact from fiction.

Not least thanks to his own memoirs, Percy Scott has an established reputation as a gunnery innovator and inventor, battling against the conservatism, obstruction and bad faith of the Admiralty. Scott's detestation of the Admiralty (at least in his later years) is evident throughout his book.

> . . . .. in Government offices they do not like suggestions coming from outside which have not originated in the office itself. It was the same with all my proposals. They were all boycotted because the people – mostly my juniors in age, and with far less experience – dealt with those matters at the Admiralty and felt aggrieved that the suggestion had not emanated from themselves

Respecting his greatest invention, the director, Scott asserted that 'in 1905, I revived director firing . . . I submitted the invention to the Admiralty, who had it secretly patented, consigned it to themselves and then boycotted it until 1911'. After he had hauled down his flag on 15 February 1909, 'the Admiralty suggested to me that I should probably not hoist my flag again and that I should be doing more service to the country by continuing my work on director firing than by going to sea. The irony of this assurance appealed to my sense of humour, for I well know that the Admiralty, as a body, were moving heaven and earth to prevent director firing being adopted'.[1] In July 1912, Scott met the First Lord to remonstrate about fitting the *Lion* class battlecruisers with light masts unsuitable for carrying a director. 'Mr. Churchill . . . explained to me that the whole Board of the Admiralty were very much opposed to my system of director firing and that, as they were quite certain that it would never be adopted, he had been obliged to agree to their proposals [for] a light mast . . . thereupon I pointed out to the First Lord that his Board were ignorant and did not know what they were talking about . . .'

Historians have tended to accept Scott's account of how the Admiralty treated his inventions, though they acknowledge his cantankerous, cocksure and outspoken manner; the German naval attaché called him 'an incredible "windbag" and publicity hound.' Scott's biographer, Peter Padfield, after describing the trial of the first fully functional director aboard HMS *Neptune*, noted, 'The date was 11 March 1911. On the outbreak of war, over three years later, just eight battleships had been so fitted in their main armament only – a piece of folly which was only equalled by the Admiralty's no-policy on airships during these critical years.' However, in his later book *Guns at Sea*, Padfield acknowledged that the 'finished Scott/Vickers director system [first fitted in HMS *Ajax* in 1913] was one of infinite refinement which would have been impossible some years earlier.' Marder also deplores the fact that 'When war broke out, only eight battleships had been fitted, and it was not until the time of Jutland that all the capital ships (except *Erin* and *Agincourt*) had the system for their main armament. The work of fitting the secondary armament [directors] . . . had not been finished when the war ended.'

Admiral Sir Percy Scott, Bt., KCB, KCVO, Hon.LL.D. The frontispiece to Fifty Years in the Royal Navy, *1919. (IWM, Q.110329)*

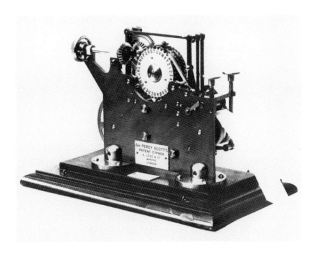

Scott's Pattern I Cipher Machine. The cipher circle could be positioned to produce any of 36 ciphers; any number of circles could be carried. The instrument typed the original and ciphered messages, one above the other, on the paper tape. (PRO, ADM1/8435/302)

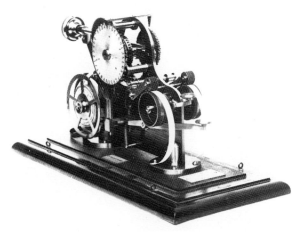

Scott's Pattern II Cipher Machine. In this version, the cipher circle was moved one space relative to the en clair *circle with each letter sent or received. Thus, if an unknown number of letters of a message were to be lost in transmission, the remainder could not be deciphered. (PRO, ADM1/8435/302)*

Sumida recognises Jellicoe's support for Scott's director proposals (also acknowledged by Scott) and refers to the tests of an early prototype director in *Africa* in 1907, continuing: 'The replacement [as Director of Naval Ordnance (DNO)] of Jellicoe by Bacon later that year then appears to have ended Ordnance Department support for director firing . . . In 1908, the Admiralty refused to provide Scott with funds to build a director system for trials in . . . *Good Hope*'. Sumida also suggests that the trials of the *Neptune* director in March 1911 'were successful enough to convince Jellicoe to advise its adoption, but his recommendations were not followed, which may have been the result of the opposition of Moore'[2] (the latter having succeeded Bacon as DNO).

There can be no doubt about Scott's inventive genius or the many important contributions which he made to the improvement of gunnery in the Royal Navy. As early as December 1904, the then DNO (Captain H D Barry) wrote:

I am of opinion that Captain Percy Scott is responsible for the introduction into the Naval Service of
1. The Dotter
2. The Deflection Teacher
3. The general adoption of telescopic sights
4. The signalling shutter now in use with searchlights . . .
5. The Loading Teachers.

Four of these devices were essential components in Scott's system for rapidly firing guns of 6in calibre and less in salvoes by continuous aim. However, Barry's acknowledgement of Scott's many contributions is taken from papers which show quite another aspect of his relationships with the Admiralty. On 13 November 1901, Scott had written complaining of the pecuniary loss he had

suffered by not patenting his ideas; in a further letter of 9 May 1902, he noted that, in March 1899, their Lordships had indicated to him 'that holding patents would contribute a grave objection to . . . selection . . . for any scientific or administrative post in HM Service.' Scott claimed that this meant that he was debarred from patenting in any Foreign Country and at the same time enabled any one 'who heard of my invention to make a slight alteration in it and patent it'. Despite these protestations (less than reasonable, particularly from a serving officer), Scott also admitted to a working arrangement since 1892 with Sir William Armstrong & Co. who had perfected his design for a Truck Flashing Lamp and from whom he had received royalties from time to time (though he claimed to have no record of the sums involved). When Scott submitted his pamphlet on the dotter in December 1899, his covering letter stated that he was already having one made at Elswick for HMS *Terrible*; Armstrongs also received the production orders (of 14 and 119 respectively) placed in October 1900 and June 1901. In November 1900, Elswick had advised the Admiralty that they had worked out an improvement to the design which gave it lateral as well as vertical movement, and Scott was particularly incensed that they had patented 'this improvement which took the invention out of my hands and enabled Sir William Armstrong & Co. to dispose of it to all the Foreigners'.

Scott's letter was accompanied by a printed table listing no fewer than 26 of his inventions, starting in May 1881 with 'an electrical arrangement for conveying the distance of an enemy to the guns'. By July 1904, a new version of the table had grown to 35 items but the DNO commented: 'I would beg to point out that Captain Scott's list contains many items that have been "not approved" or "condemned" by their Lordships. Several items are only practically repetitions of others included in the lists while some . . . are in fact of so trivial a nature that if once included in a consideration for pecuniary reward the term "Invention" would be an absurdity'. Even so, as already quoted, he acknowledged that some of Scott's inventions were indeed important; a generous settlement followed in an award to Scott by the Ordnance Department of £8,000 on 6 December 1904. However, by that date, Scott had made arrangements with the Vickers company which were designed to ensure that, even as a serving officer, he would be very well rewarded in future for his inventive efforts. The original arrangement, concluded on 16 February 1903, was that he would receive royalties of 20% on the selling price of any equipment based on his ideas. Nothing of this close association appears in the autobiography and may well not have emerged, had not Vickers unilaterally attempted, when the director programme was in prospect, to change the terms of payment to a percentage on profits. Since Scott had been receiving substantial if irregular payments for many years, and seems to have had a remarkably casual attitude to the details of his financial affairs, he did not realise the extent of his losses until after the War, when he sued Vickers for sums which were variously estimated during the case but could have been as high as £400,000. 'The inventions concerned were the *Hero* sight, an extension of that device known as the director firing gear; electric range clocks, range transmitters and receivers and a "blow-out" for guns' and, while the payments due for the director dominated the case, it also emerged that, as long ago as 15 January 1905, Scott received £12,000 'in settlement of all royalties on the sighting device'; he was also paid £60,000 between 1915 and 1919. Mr. Justice Coleridge found against Vickers, ruling that Scott should receive either 10 or 20% of the selling prices of sales made (depending on whether there had been competition or not from other suppliers) between 15 January 1905 to 18 January 1913: and 10% on all subsequent sales. Since the latter period covered the whole of the director production programme, which by the end of the War had cost over £1,762,000, it can be assumed that Scott must have received, at the very least, another £100,000 after this settlement in June 1920.[3]

While information requested by Scott for the court case was being prepared by the Admiralty, a memorandum noted that 'the *Hero* Sight Apparatus . . . was the subject of a secret patent in the joint name of [Scott] and Messrs. Vickers. Further that as regards Director Firing Gear patented in the same joint manner in 1907 . . . the Admiralty took the course (unusual in recent years) of allowing an Officer to obtain payment from a firm out of Admiralty contract prices instead of applying for a direct award.' Yet, despite his favourable treatment, Scott continued his complaints of pecuniary losses arising from his inventions and patents. In 1907 and 1908, he submitted to the Admiralty a pair of ciphering machines based on a revolving drum with electrical cross-connections such that it transposed the letters of the alphabet. Following the normal practice with inventions by serving officers, the Admiralty patented the devices but, after trials, did not adopt them; the first was rejected because a single

transposed alphabet was too easy to break: while, with the second, as Scott himself acknowledged at the time, the message became unintelligible if one or more characters were lost in transmission. In late 1913, Scott submitted a new design (based on two drums connected in series between a pair of electric typewriters) to the Committee on the Adoption of Mechanical Cryptography in the Navy. However, the actual device was not completed until six months after the date promised by Scott and the Committee found it 'very complex, very slow and very noisy' and unsuitable for use on board ship with contemporary wireless gear.

Scott's machines are interesting in that they appear to anticipate features of later electric cipher machines. However, as with many of his earlier inventions, Scott underestimated the technical difficulties of realisation and exaggerated the benefits. Also his protestations about financial losses (arising from the Admiralty patents) ring hollow in the light of the large payments received for other inventions made while in the Service.

If Scott's autobiography was economical with the truth about his finances and overstated the importance of many of his inventions, even his own correspondence can give a most misleading impression of the Admiralty's response to some of his other proposals. On 28 February 1903, he wrote to Arthur Craig 'I have proposed to Admiralty a new method of turret sighting and for a wonder it has caught on, it is to be tried in *Hero* and all the sighting of new ships is hung up until after the trial. I use one telescope and one firing trigger for two guns.' Yet on 23 October, as quoted by Padfield, he again wrote to Craig that 'the turret sight in *Hero* has been tried by a Committee and has gone in the waste paper basket along with the Dotter and my other ideas'. These statements are seriously at variance with other sources. By September 1902, the number of dotters ordered had increased further to 178. As for the *Hero* sight, the report of the outgoing DNO (Captain MacLeod) for December, 1903 confirms that improved sighting arrangements 'have been in office for some time but were held over pending the [*Hero*] trials', which had proved 'generally speaking not very promising'. Even so, further trials were recommended. When Captain Barry in turn handed over to Jellicoe in February 1905, he noted that improved sights for older ships were still held up awaiting 'seagoing experience of Captain Scott's design . . . on the chance of its being reported on favourably'. It was not until July 1907 that Jellicoe reported that, after extensive trials in the *Dominion*, the matter had finally been closed.[4] In his memoirs, Scott was highly critical of the older patterns of gunsight and, while claiming most of the credit for their improvement, blamed their Lordships for 'proceeding in their usual dilatory and unbusinesslike way'. In reality, the DNOs' reports indicate that, at a time when Scott was at his most influential,[5] trials of the non-automatic *Hero* sight continued against their advice and, therefore, that Scott himself bore much of the responsibility for the delays in introducing improved automatic sights for ships already in service.

All in all, there are several reasons to doubt the completeness and accuracy of Scott's memoirs. If this is so for

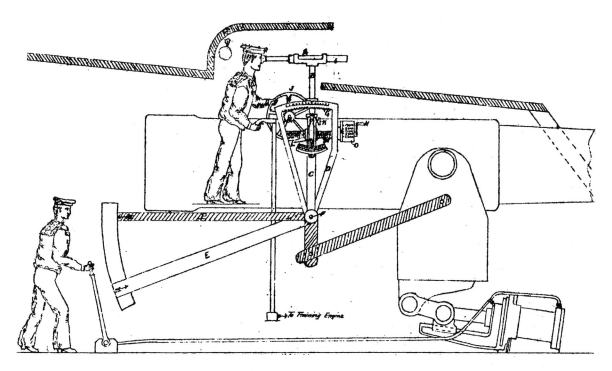

Sketch of the non-automatic sight as tried in HMS Hero. *The gun-layer in the sighting hood trained the turret, set the elevation of the sight and fired whichever gun was ready. The elevation number below was responsible for keeping the two long pointers (P moved by the gun, E by the sight) in alignment. (From* Turret or Barbette Gun Sighting *in the Craig Waller papers, courtesy Commander Michael Craig Waller.)*

more minor developments, how correct is his account of the development of the director, undoubtedly Scott's most important achievement? Confidence is not increased by the realisation that Scott makes no reference whatsoever to the first experimental director, which was installed in HMS *Africa* at the beginning of 1907: nor to a second director which was authorised at the end of 1907 (though it took over two years to complete and test). Scott's account leaps from initial proposals in 1905 to his own improvised director in *Good Hope* to the *Neptune* director. Fortunately, these early directors are reasonably well documented (at least from a bureaucratic, though not from a technical, viewpoint), while the later history of the director is given in post-War reports; the *Handbook of Director Firing 1917* also survives. We can therefore compare these sources with Scott's account of Admiralty boycott and needless delay. However, before doing so, it is necessary first to define certain technical concepts and terms which are required in understanding how the director developed.

Principles of the Director

Before the director, guns were individually aimed using precision sights at each gun. Beginning with *Dreadnought*, new designs of direct-action automatic sights were introduced for turret guns, so that, like the lighter hand-worked guns, the sights were attached to the guns and moved with them in elevation and training. Each sight had two aiming telescopes, one for the layer, who controlled the elevation and also fired the gun: the other for the turret trainer.

The direct action naval sight was designed so that, when the required range was set on its graduated drum or dial, the angle between the axis of the layer's telescope and the barrel (measured in the vertical plane) was precisely equal to the required elevation. Thus, if the gun was fired when the target lay exactly under the telescope's cross wires, the gun was at the correct elevation angle (relative to the surface of the sea) to hit. It must be emphasised that this statement makes no assumption about the angle of elevation relative to the deck of the ship, which would usually be rolling to a greater or lesser extent. Because gun and telescope moved together, the gun layer could choose to position both at whatever angle relative to the deck he found most convenient for firing.

The gun range set on the sight was not the same as the true (or geometric) range from ship to target; the former was obtained by correcting the true range for such factors as the movement of the target during the time of flight of the shell, wind along the range and other ballistic variables. Similarly, the gun was not trained directly at the target; the telescopes of the sight would be given a horizontal deflection to correct for target movement, wind and the drift induced by the spin of the shell. Thus, at the moment of firing, the trainer's telescope, (as well as the layer's) had to be exactly 'on' the target.

There were two methods of aiming. For lighter, hand-worked guns (up to 6in calibre), Percy Scott had introduced continuous aim. Both layer and trainer manipulated their handwheels (for elevation and training respectively) to keep their telescopes continuously on the target; the gun could therefore be fired immediately (or almost) when the signal to fire was given by buzzer, gong, etc. As will be shown, during the early development of the director, continuous aim was not possible for heavy, hydraulically-worked turret guns. The only alternative was, then, to lay and train the guns at fixed angles chosen to ensure that, as often as possible, the movement of the ship brought the sights on simultaneously for elevation and training. This was an infrequent and irregular occurrence, particularly when a combination of roll and yaw gave the ship a twisting, elliptical motion; in these conditions, an attempt at continuous training was necessary in order that the guns were correctly trained when the roll brought the sights on at the fixed elevation. Even then, there were conflicting opinions as to whether the layers should set the fixed elevation so that the sights rolled on near the middle or the extremes of the roll. In the middle, the angular velocity was greater, thus maximising the errors due to the reaction time of the layer and the angular movement of the barrel in the time between pulling the trigger and the round leaving the muzzle. Near the extremes of the roll, the roll velocity was less but more variable; indeed, if the roll was irregular, it was not even certain that the roll would always be sufficient to bring the sights on.

There were three methods of firing guns of the same calibre. The first two could be used with either continuous aim or fixed elevation. In independent fire, each gun was loaded, aimed and fired as quickly as possible; in principle it could give the highest rate of fire but it also maximised the interference between guns due to gun smoke, blast and shock. Second, a ripple was fired in a fixed order, starting with the leeward gun; interference was reduced at the expense of rate of fire. Third, in salvo firing, all guns were fired, as nearly as possible simultaneously, on an audible signal. Salvo firing implied continuous aim; it was the second pillar of Percy Scott's revolution in the firing of hand worked guns: but it was therefore not at first feasible for the great guns.

The requirements for accuracy in laying and training were rather different. The spread of a 13.5in salvo at a range of 12,000 yards was 300 yards, while the range transmitters and receivers worked in steps of 25 yards. Thus an accuracy in elevation equivalent to one or even two such steps was quite sufficient. However, the total increase in elevation required to increase the range of these guns from 10,000 to 15,000 yards was only 4° 32′. Thus, at these ranges, a change in range of 25 yards corresponded on average to a change in elevation of less than 1.4 minutes of arc. Just how small this is can be expressed in terms of a pointer attached to the end of the gun loading arm, about 18 feet (6 metres) from the trunnions; a change in range of 25 yards would cause this pointer to move barely 0.09 inches (about 2 mm). Similarly, a lateral displacement of a salvo by 25 yards at

12,000 yards would have been produced by an angular error in training of 7 minutes of arc: which corresponds to a movement at the turret roller path of 0.7 inches (17 mm).

It might be assumed that training accuracy was therefore rather less of a problem than gun elevation: but when the weights to be moved are considered, it is apparent that this is not the case. Using the figures for *Dreadnought*, a 12in gun, elevated by a single hydraulic cylinder, weighed 58 tons. This was less than one tenth of a complete turret and turntable, which weighed about 600 tons in total and was rotated by a hydraulic training engine working a pinion engaging with a circular training rack. Roll and yaw frequencies were much the same, yet in counteracting them, the training gear had to slew a mass weighing ten times that attached to the elevating cylinder. It should be clear why continuous, precise aim of the turret guns presented a considerable technical problem.

In director firing, the guns were no longer aimed by the turret personnel. Instead, the director, which was essentially a master gunsight, was aimed at the target by its own layer and trainer. The angles of elevation and training of this sight (relative to the ship's deck and keel respectively) were then transmitted electrically to the turrets where they were displayed by receiver pointers. These receivers also had pointers which indicated the elevation of the guns and the angle of training of the turret. The turret layers and trainers had only to manipulate their controls to keep the gun pointers exactly in line with the director pointers. The director layer also fired the guns electrically in a simultaneous salvo from all those turrets with guns ready to fire.

In capital ships, a director sight was always mounted aloft, as far as possible from interference by gun smoke, blast, sea-spray and the splashes from enemy shots falling short. Thus the sight was 90 feet or more above the turret guns; there was also a considerable distance (over 200 feet measured along the keel) between the horizontal positions of the director and, in particular, the aftermost turret. It was therefore not sufficient just to lay the guns parallel to the director sight. Geometric corrections were required, which had to be applied automatically by the director gear. The first, the dip correction, slightly increased the elevation of the guns relative to the director to correct for the guns' lower positions. A second correction to elevation was also needed if the firing was off the beam. In these cases, the after turrets were appreciably nearer or further from the target than the fore turret and director; this correction was therefore needed only in the after turrets.

The training angles also needed correcting for the horizontal distance between the turrets. Had all the guns in a salvo been fired on the same bearing as the director, the inevitable spread for direction would have been increased by the distance between the guns. To prevent this, a convergence correction was applied to ensure that all the sight lines (turrets and director) converged at the range of the target and that the convergence was correct for all target bearings.

Photographs of shipbuilding in the early twentieth century do not exactly suggest precision engineering. There were significant differences in the planes of rotation of the turrets and even between them and the plane of rotation of the director sight itself. It was therefore necessary to correct individually for the misalignment (called the tilt) between each plane of rotation and the notional reference plane, that of the deck.

The terminology introduced here was that in use when the director was fully developed and in quantity production. As will now be shown, it took many years of design and experimentation before all the sources of error in director firing had been recognised and the means for correction developed. However, the essential concepts of gun aiming and director firing having now been introduced, it is possible to follow these developments in some detail, beginning with Percy Scott's revival of director firing in 1905.

The Africa *Director*

Padfield notes that the basic idea of the director dated back to the days of the sailing navy. 'The first recorded system . . . is probably Philip Broke's 1807–13 method of laying all broadside guns to an ordered elevation . . . and . . . angle of training so that their fire could be directed on to a target which the individual gun captains could not see'. A similar system was taught and refined throughout the nineteenth century but fell out of use at the end of the century when ships became larger and more compartmented but electrical means of communication were still undeveloped. Percy Scott seems to have revived the idea in February 1905 in discussions with the DNO and Controller; this was an important moment for the Navy's gunnery organisation, since, in that month, Scott, Jackson and Jellicoe all took up their new appointments as Inspector of Target Practice, Controller and DNO respectively. By August, Scott had developed his ideas into a proposal entitled 'Proposed Method of Fighting the Guns of the Most Powerful Ship in the World, namely HMS *Dreadnought*', which was circulated with a supporting memorandum from Jellicoe dated 17 August. Both documents emphasise the problems caused in independent firing by interference from smoke and shock. Jellicoe stated that the alternative 'Salvo firing by Bell signal where the guns are to be laid independently by their own layers appears to be almost impracticable *unless continuous aim is possible*'. He noted that 'Experiments are now being carried out to ascertain if the elevating and training controls are sufficiently good to make this method applicable' and continued 'As it is not certain that "continuous aim" and bell salvoes will be possible . . . I submit that a trial be made of that part of Admiral Scott's proposal relating to the laying for elevation'. This turned out to be a prudent recommendation; the report of *Dreadnought*'s gun trials, made in October 1906, states that 'it is extremely difficult to readily obtain a slow movement of the guns in elevation which is required to follow the small roll or to keep the sights on at the bottom or top of a larger roll' while the training gear was 'not good enough to keep the sights continuously on for line at a moving object when the ship is under way'.

In February, Scott had suggested that the guns should be 'laid for elevation by scale and the turrets trained by scale'

and his August proposal includes a sketchy description of a converger. However, he agreed with Jellicoe that initially the director should lay 'for elevation by scale passed from aloft as this is . . . more important and also easier carried out than the proposals regarding training'; in any case, Scott's proposal was originally accompanied by explanatory sketches (not finished drawings) only for elevation gear. However, Scott did point out that individual trainers would then remain liable to interference from smoke and blast.

Jellicoe proposed these actions:

(a) To send the original *Hero* sight (without pointers) to Messrs. Vickers, London and to direct firm to tender for converting it into a "director", as suggested by the ITP and including electrical transmitters. Work to be done in consultation with that officer.
(b) To invite Messrs. Vickers to tender for fitting the two right guns in 12-inch turrets in the *Vengeance* with elevation scales.

The *Hero* sight was a suitable basis for development because it was, in effect, a local director sight for the two guns in a turret. It was worked by a single layer who trained the turret, controlled the elevation of the sight and fired the gun. The sight elevation was registered by a long pointer. A second adjacent pointer was attached to the gun and showed the actual gun elevation; a separate number worked the gun's elevation control gear and was responsible for keeping the gun pointer as closely aligned as possible with the sight pointer.

The request to tender was sent to Vickers on 9 September, the *Hero* sight being despatched in October. After a conference at the Admiralty on 22 November, Vickers submitted their tender (for £499), supported by 13 design drawings, on 18 December. However, much work was still required on detailed design; on 17 February, the Director of Naval Construction (DNC) complained that 'The drawings of the electrical arrangements are so meagre as to be practically useless'. Vickers continued to provide additional information and to make changes requested by the Admiralty: requesting an increase in price by £25.10.0 on 2 May. Except for a minor design detail, on 16 May 1906 the DNO recommended acceptance of the firm's designs and tender for the director sight and the formal acceptance of their main tender was sent to Vickers on 25 June.

While the designs and prices were being worked out, the DNO also requested HMS *Excellent* to carry out some experiments to test the concept of the elevation-only director.

> . . . it is desired to carry out a trial to ascertain whether the motion of the ship will preclude keeping the training of:
> (a) The Director
> (b) The various guns
> on the target with the present telescope and sights.

Further instructions relayed through the C.-in-C. Portsmouth added 'Fixing the elevation means that the training of the director and the guns must be kept continuously on in order not to reduce the rate of fire too much'.

HMS Africa *in 1907. This battleship was one of the final three ships of the* King Edward VII *class. Completed around the end of 1906, they were distinguished by a taller foremast with the topmast stepped abaft the fire control tops. The experimental director sight was installed in the upper top. The director controlled the elevation of the 12in guns in her mixed armament of four 12in, four 9.2in and ten 6in guns. (IWM, Q. 38038.)*

In reply, Commander Craig (Commander XP in *Excellent*) warned of possible problems due to vibration aloft and the inadequacy of ordinary service hydraulic gear (though not of training gear under development). He also was first to recognise that 'laying all the guns in the ship to the same nominal angle of elevation [would be] affected by accuracy of roller paths etc. and may vary with the training of the guns, trim of the ship, strain due to rolling and pitching, etc.' Despite Craig's doubts about the usefulness of tests conducted with 'makeshift' gear, they were carried out by HMS *Jupiter* in January 1906, in conditions which produced a total roll of 4–5.5° but this 'was not regular, the actual motion being corkscrew, bringing in a fair yaw'. With the improvised director telescope and the guns at fixed elevation, it was found that, with the gear available, neither could be trained continuously. However, when the director was fitted with 'a 7 power glass, it was found that in three minutes the cross wires rolled past the target with the training sufficiently accurate to fire 30 times', i.e. 10 times a minute. With the guns, the

horizontal and vertical wires were actually on together at most 4 times in a 3 minute run using a 7 power glass but this could be improved to 9 times with a 5 power glass. No specific comments remain on these apparently unpromising results but they were evidently not judged bad enough to cause any alterations in the design.

As to the technical details of this first director, hardly any drawings survive and only an outline of the design can be inferred from the remaining letters and memoranda and a short description in the post-War *Technical History*. In the turret, a wire rope was attached near the end of the gun-loading arm; the rope then led downwards to a sheave (pulley) on the floor of the turret and thence through two more sheaves to the top of a column within which it was attached to a pointer, on a sliding weight. The weight and pointer were guided to move vertically; thus, as the gun elevation changed, the pointer moved up or down. Initially, the design relied on the weight alone to keep the wire taut; as completed, the wire was wound around a drum containing a clock spring.

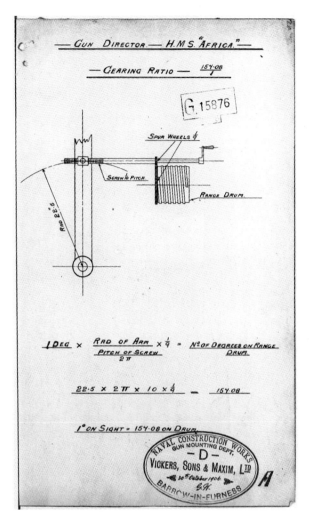

Gun Director, HMS Africa. *The arrangement for altering the sight elevation according to range. (PRO, ADM1/7955.)*

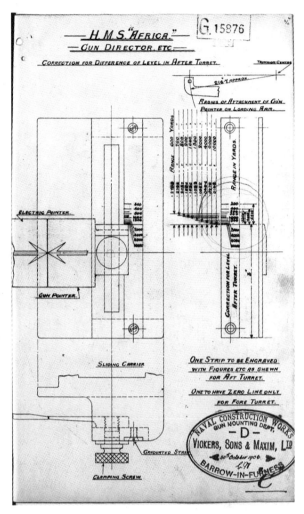

Gun Director, HMS Africa. *Shows the electric pointer (driven by the four receiver motors connected to the Director sight transmitter) and the gun pointer moved by the wire rope attached to the gun loading arm. The gun pointer for the after turret was adjustable for range to correct for the difference in level from the fore turret. (PRO, ADM1/7955.)*

A second pointer, showing the director elevation, was arranged to move parallel with the first. This second pointer was attached to a nut on a long screw, the screw being driven by no less than four receiver motors which were wired to a transmitter switch at the director sight.[6] The operation of laying the gun was therefore to bring the pointer attached to the wire rope exactly opposite to the pointer on the screw. 'The wire rope presented some difficulties owing to the tendency to stretch although after some use it settled down and did not cause any material error.'

The director sight was similar to the *Hero* layout, the telescope being fixed on top of a vertical arm. The elevation of the arm was controlled by a wheel which turned a horizontal threaded rod running through a nut fixed to the arm. The gearing was very high; one turn of the director

elevating wheel corresponded to a change in sight elevation of 7.24 minutes of arc. Clearly there was no question of continuous laying, the whole intent being to devise a very precise method for aligning the guns to the fixed sight elevation; firing depended entirely on the motion of the ship rolling the sight onto the target.

As already noted the original intention had been to fit the director in *Vengeance* (a *Canopus* class battleship completed in April 1902). However, on 23 January 1906, the DNO proposed that 'In view of the fact that there may be some difficulty in arranging this trial in *Vengeance* before that ship completes her refit, it is submitted for approval that it should be fitted instead to two turrets (right guns) in the *Dreadnought*'. Vickers were asked on 5 May if fitting in some other ship than *Vengeance* would increase their price but were told 'the experiment would not be made in

HMS *Dreadnought'*. Jellicoe did not give up, however, suggesting on 16 May that: 'It is for consideration whether the *Dreadnought* should not be wired so far as two of the turrets are concerned . . . as the system is particularly adapted to that ship.' By this time, he must have been concerned about the ability of the revolutionary new ship to develop a rapid and accurate fire in any but the calmest sea conditions. When he handed over as DNO in July 1907, Jellicoe regretfully reported that 'DNO proposed several times that *Dreadnought* should be fitted for director firing, but this was not approved' though it is not clear if he was opposed by his superior, the Controller, or by the whole Board.

Eventually, the Controller gave approval on 8 August to fit the director in *Africa*, a *King EdwardVII* class battleship still being completed at Chatham. Vickers were informed on 23 August; they had previously advised the Admiralty that they would deliver the director gear three months after being informed of the ship to be fitted. Despite strenuous efforts by the Admiralty to bring the date forward (accompanied by a sharp exchange of correspondence), the gear was not ready for inspection by the ITP (Scott) at Vickers' Erith Works until 14 December. One of Jellicoe's officers followed the next day and reported that 'the gear was generally satisfactory [except that] the director trains too stiffly'. However, it was decided to take delivery immediately, Vickers meanwhile to prepare to fit the director with a ball race, a shoulder piece for rapid training and a stronger spring for the rope tension drum. The director gear was finally despatched on 21 December 1906 to Chatham, where the elevating gear and wiring had already been installed in *Africa*.

It is most frustrating to find that these records of delivery are almost the last papers in the PRO cartridge relating to the *Africa* director; the report of the trials has not come to light. The only certain information is in Jellicoe's report of July, 1907 to his successor, Captain Reginald Bacon, which confirms that: 'A system of firing by *director* proposed by Rear-Admiral Sir Percy Scott, has been fitted up to the right gun in each of *Africa's* 12-inch turrets for trial . . . A proposal has been submitted to fit this gear to the other 12-inch guns . . . in order to give it a better trial and it has also been submitted to supply Admiral Scott with materials for fitting extempore director firing gear in the *Good Hope'*. This suggests that the initial trials had been at best a qualified success. Even so, when Bacon in turn handed over as DNO to Captain Archibald Moore, in November 1909, he confirmed that *Africa's* 12-inch guns are . . . fitted up with director gear' and that 'The gear that was in *Good Hope* is being fitted up in *Prince George'*. However, he gave no further information. To obtain some idea on the likely performance of these fixed-elevation-only directors, it is necessary to look at another design which, after much delay, was eventually given a trial in *Bellerophon* in April 1910.

The Dreadnought/Bellerophon *Director*

There are few clues as to why this director design was authorised for *Dreadnought* in the closing months of 1907.

HMS Bellerophon *as she would have appeared in 1910 at the time of the trials of the experimental director; the sight was installed in the forward fire control top.When the production version of the director was fitted in 1916, the sight was located on the platform beneath the fore top. (CPL.)*

It appears to have been an attempt to devise a simpler arrangement in the turret, since one of the few available technical details shows that it dispensed with the sliding pointers and wire rope. Instead, a pointer with an electrical contact was mounted directly on the gun loading arm; this contact made with a movable contact on a graduated arc fixed next to the loading arm. A wheel, remotely controlling the elevation control valve, was mounted at the top of the arc. The gun layer then used this wheel to keep the two contacts closed. Also, it emerges from a later report that the trainer was provided with a pedal-operated switch which he closed only when he was on for training. Thus unless both contacts were made, the gun would not fire. However, unlike the *Africa* design, this director had no electrical transmission of elevation. Instead, a counter (from a spare Vickers range receiver) was coupled to the director elevating wheel. Once the layer had set the elevation, he 'reads off the counter and repeats the indication by voice pipe to the transmitting station' from whence it must have been relayed to the turrets using the normal range transmitters.

The initial design was prepared at Portsmouth, the cost estimate being £216: which, being half that quoted by Vickers, may have influenced the decision to proceed. The whole project was beset with delays: and also an increase of £143 in May 1908 which largely removed any initial cost advantage. The first cost estimate was approved by the Controller on 8 January 1908 and, on 13 January, the DNO (now Captain Bacon) urged that 'It is desirable that the gear should be completed before the ship [*Dreadnought*] goes to sea again as it is proposed to carry out trials of director firing as soon as possible.' However, on 14 January, the Admiral Superintendent, Portsmouth advised that 'The Director and fittings will be completed in theYard by about the first week in March and forwarded to the ship'. Yet an order for mechanical parts was not even placed until 30 April, while it required two formal reminders from the Controller before he was supplied even with a sketch of the general arrangement for *Dreadnought*. By 29 October, Bacon was able to report that 'a 12-inch Director has been prepared at Portsmouth Yard for fitting in *Dreadnought*' but his earlier sense of urgency was quite gone.

> As this method of firing was originally proposed by Rear Admiral Sir P. Scott and as it is understood that he has been carrying out experiments in the *Good Hope* with similar apparatus it does not seem advisable to actually fit up *Dreadnought* for Director firing until the result of Sir P. Scott's investigation is known. . . .

> Also to request Sir P. Scott to forward any proposals he might wish to make for improving the Director gear for *Dreadnought* . . . after he has had an opportunity of inspecting this gear on his return to England.

However, by this date, Jellicoe had returned to the Admiralty as Controller and on 14 November, he insisted that 'If the Director is not fitted during present refit it would delay the work for 12 months and under the circumstances it will be best to carry it out now. Enquiries should be made of Sir P. Scott as proposed by DNO'. Scott responded on 17 January 1909 that the proposed gear could be made 'fairly efficient' though he suggested some minor improvements. Bacon commented to Jellicoe on 2 February 1909:

> It is very satisfactory to note how optimistic Sir P. Scott is of the success of this device from his experience up to date – but at present it is not understood how the time interval between "sights on" and shot leaving the muzzle is allowed for. The firings shortly to be undertaken will be very interesting.

The last sentence confirms other indications that, by the time of writing, the director had at last been fitted up in *Dreadnought* while she was in dock between 20 January and 8 February 1909. However, there had not been time to check the arc calibrations and, in any case, once installed, further modifications were found to be essential. Worse, during *Dreadnought*'s next visit to Portsmouth, *Excellent* advised on 13 August that 'in order to complete director and gun arcs satisfactorily necessary to have director and gun arcs in dockyard for one month from today'. On 18 August, the Admiral Superintendent estimated that the work would take one month to complete. True to form and despite telegraphic prodding by the DNO's department, the gear was not returned to *Dreadnought* at Portland until 9 December.

At this point, an even more potent cause of delay intervened. Herbert Richmond, the Captain of *Dreadnought*, submitted on the same day that 'trials if carried out in the flagship will inconvenience the Commander in Chief, the ship being taken to sea on many days of the week and thus interfering with the administrative work which is centred in the flagship'. He proposed that the gear should be transferred to another ship, the C.-in-C. (Admiral May) concurring and proposing *Bellerophon* as the trial ship. Jellicoe did his best to prevent this further delay and a letter to the C-in-C from the Secretary of the Admiralty dated 13 January 1910 regretted the inconvenience but confirmed that the gear would be tried in

Dreadnought. What happened next is not recorded but, by 17 January, the Controller was urgently telegraphing Portsmouth to 'Report if there are any difficulties in fitting *Dreadnought*'s Director in *Bellerophon*'. After a second telegram brooking no further delay, the Admiral Superintendent replied that 'there would be no difficulty' and on 28 January was ordered to proceed during *Bellerophon*'s current refit. On 18 February, her captain, Hugh Evan Thomas, reported that 'every endeavour will be made to have the gear fitted and tested by 5 March 1910'.

The director sight was installed in the fore top, where a Vickers clock operator was also placed; the latter continually called the range and the sight was adjusted accordingly. 'The Director Officer lays the director by the elevation wheel so as to roll the cross wire across the target in the upper part of the roll and the elevation is passed by voice pipe to the Transmitting Station and thence to the guns.' In the turrets, the gun about to fire was laid to the elevation which had been received and set on the graduated arc. The turret was trained, as continuously as possible, using the sight of the other gun (which was moved in elevation as necessary to keep the target in view); the trainer pressed his foot switch only when on the target. Spotting corrections (as yards up or down) were put only on the director sight, which could be done quickly in from 4 to 6 seconds; since the guns remained at a fixed elevation, this meant that they then fired at a slightly different point in the roll.[7] However, if it was necessary to alter the gun elevation (for example, because the ship was heeling under helm), the change took 26 seconds which 'always means missing two opportunities of firing'. Only a low rate of fire could be attained, averaging 1.53 salvoes or 2.78 rounds per minute. Salvoes consisted 'of one, two or three, very rarely four shots' due to 'the fact that continuous aim by the trainers in any swell is impossible' even though 'the training gear in HMS *Bellerophon* . . . is thought to be as good as any in HM Service. The work of the trainer in Director Firing, with his elevating wheel and pedal switch to think of, is very different from when carrying out independent firing. Then the gun is laid for him by the Gunlayer and he gets warning a few seconds before it is required to fire the round, and can bring the gun accurately on for training for a second or two, long enough for the gunlayer to get his elevation on and fire'.

Evan Thomas' report and covering letter were unequivocal.

> The system . . . is altogether too slow [it] also . . . gives inaccuracy in direction and this . . . gives loss of accuracy in elevation . . . whereas with the Director System there is only one opportunity of firing every 14 seconds [the period of roll] and this opportunity may be lost due to smoke, the independent gunlayer can seize every opportunity of firing a round . . . In view therefore of the slowness of the system and the doubtfulness of the advantages to be gained by it, the system of Director Firing is not recommended for adoption in HM Service.

When asked to comment on this report (which, naturally, he rejected out of hand), Percy Scott was able to point out that, unlike even his improvised director in *Good Hope*, the *Bellerophon* director had no electrical means for transmitting elevation. However, none of the early directors was capable of rapid changes of elevation, so this deficiency was not fundamental. The main difficulties arose from problems not of elevation but of training, and in this respect, there is no reason to think that *Bellerophon* was any worse than *Africa* or *Good Hope*: rather the reverse, since they had less responsive training gear. However, the *Bellerophon* director had taken so long to make and install that, by the time it was tried in March 1910, the assumptions on which fixed-elevation directors had been based had been largely negated by developments in elevation and training gear. Consequently, the decision had already been taken to develop a different and much more elaborate type of director, which, in less than a year, was to be

tried aboard HMS *Neptune*. However, before turning to the second phase of director evolution, some account must be given of Scott's second director which he fitted up in HMS *Good Hope*.

The Good Hope *Director*

Percy Scott was appointed to command the 2nd Cruiser Squadron in the Autumn of 1907. Jellicoe also left the Ordnance Department at this time but the quotation already given from the report to his successor shows that, before leaving, he had recommended that Scott should continue his work on the director while at sea; 'details of extempore fitting' were available as early as 1 August 1907, Captain Bacon's first full month in office.

HMS Good Hope, *1907. The fire control tops on the masts had been added by 1906; the* ex tempore *director sight was probably placed in the fore top. This photograph is unusual in showing guns mounted in the two lower amidship casemates. In the heavy seas at the Battle of Coronel, none of the lower tier of 6in casemate guns could be fought effectively with individual laying. Scott claimed that* Good Hope *(two 9.2in, sixteen 6in) would not have been lost if she had been fitted with director firing, but she was overwhelmed by the heavier fire of* Scharnhorst *(eight 8.2in, six 6in) while silhouetted against a clear sky after sunset. (IWM, Q. 21296.)*

Scott wrote later:

> My attention [when not distracted by the feud with Beresford] was devoted to fitting my flagship . . . with director firing: . . . This operation was difficult as I could get no assistance from the Admiralty and was forced to beg, borrow or steal all the necessary material. Fortunately I had a very competent and clever torpedo officer Lieutenant Charles Rice [who] made out all the drawings and supervised the work.

Perhaps Bacon had rescinded Jellicoe's recommendations to supply materials for extempore gear. As already noted, Bacon was sceptical of fixed elevation directors; in his outgoing report, he repeated his concerns about errors arising from firing as the sight rolled past the target; he also remarked that 'Placing the director aloft [away] from the smoke of the guns . . . is no advantage unless some form of training indicator can be devised'. Despite these reasonable concerns, there are several indications in the records of the *Dreadnought/Bellerophon* director that Scott remained on good terms with the DNO's department; he would have attended the *Dreadnought* trials had they taken place as originally planned. Thus there is no evidence to support Scott's later accusations. It is, however, quite possible that he borrowed transmitters and receivers from Vickers: in view of his established association with the firm this would have caused him no difficulty. Indeed, Vickers were no doubt delighted to learn all about the new developments; it is significant that, in his report, Bacon also states 'Messrs. Vickers have designed gear for laying guns for direction by director and have tendered a working model. Approval has been given to fit *Neptune* with complete set of director firing gear for both elevation and training.'

Little is known of the details of the *Good Hope* director. It was eventually used in battle practice on 10 February 1909, Scott claiming 'It was a great success and clearly demonstrated that all our ships should be fitted with this description of firing. The Admiralty, however, took two years before they ordered it to be fitted to HMS *Neptune*.'[8] However, a rather less satisfactory outcome can be glimpsed in other sources. In the battle practice, *Good Hope* was beaten by *Devonshire*, Hughes-Onslow stating, in his 1909 essay 'Fire Control', that the director firing by *Good Hope* did 'not appear to have given such good results as the individual controlled elevation firing, but the more recent trials in May 1909 appear to have given better results'. In any case, despite the decision to transfer the *Good Hope* gear to *Prince George*[9] and the continuing saga of the *Dreadnought* director, Hughes-Onslow's essay (which is known to have influenced Bacon) coincides with the end for fixed-elevation-only directors. In a 'final note' dated 27 May 1909, he wrote 'It is a curious coincidence that Director Firing with fixed elevation is being brought to the front, just when apparently some serious effort is being successfully made to render, at least the heavy power worked guns, much more mobile . . . As regards elevation, it appears that the latest power worked guns are four or five times as mobile as the latest handworked 6-inch guns, as the former can be elevated at a speed of 2.5° per second

and it is hoped to reach 3° shortly whereas . . . the 6in Mk VII mounted in *Good Hope* . . . could not deal with . . . a velocity of 3/4° per sec.' As regards training (and notwithstanding the problems experienced during the 1910 director trials) the *Bellerophons* were the first battleships fitted with greatly improved training gear comprising a 6-cylinder training engine, worm drive and rotary control valves.

For the first time, it was possible to aim the turret guns continuously: though, to quote Arthur Craig when Captain of *Orion*: 'The term "continuous laying" is used in the sense that the sights are kept approximately laid and can be brought exactly on by a small movement when about to fire.' By 1912, the techniques and training had developed to the point where 'in continuous laying in a seaway by the gunlayers in *Orion* all gunlayers [are] able to follow a roll of 12° out to out without difficulty and some a roll of 18° out to out'. Thus one of the original justifications for developing the director had been removed. Even so, there is no evidence that even the agnostic Bacon proposed that development should cease. As already seen, when he handed over as DNO to Captain Moore, the decision had already been taken to develop an altogether more sophisticated type, capable of directing both the elevation and training of guns that could be aimed continuously. The precise date of this decision is not known though it was probably after Jellicoe (who initiated the first director development and always remained a strong supporter) became Controller in October 1908: but before March 1909 when Scott was encouraged by the Admiralty to work closely with Vickers on the development.

The Neptune *Director*

During the later court case, Sir Trevor Dawson of Vickers said that, from this time, Scott 'was regarded by them as a colleague . . . Sir Percy Scott was almost like a member of the department', although Scott was also a member of the committee supervising the technical aspects of development. In his usual egocentric style, Scott wrote that: 'In conjunction with Messrs. Vickers I prepared drawings which I took to the Admiralty in June 1910. They were approved, the work on them was started and in December 1910 the installation on board HMS *Neptune* was completed . . . In January 1911, I joined HMS *Neptune* to superintend the trials. A month was spent at Aranchi Bay, Sardinia in testing the instruments and in educating the officers and men in their use. On 11 March 1911, at Gibraltar, the final trial took place, and proved most successful . . . Sir John Jellicoe, who by that time had taken up his appointment as Commander-in-Chief of the Atlantic Squadron, was present at the trial, and on the strength of it he advised the Admiralty to fit the director to all ships at once. This the Admiralty were reluctant to do, and they were supported in this opposition by Admiral Sir Francis Bridgeman, then Commander-in-Chief Home Fleet, and flying his flag in HMS *Neptune*.' Jellicoe did indeed write an enthusiastic letter about the trial to Mr McKenna, the First Lord (though it contains no recommendation about fitting all ships at once). The results were considered

HMS Neptune *in 1911 as she would have appeared during the director firing trials in the Mediterranean. The director sight was in the cylindrical tower on the platform beneath the fore top.* Neptune *was the last British dreadnought battleship to have two tripod masts each with a fire control top. (IWM, Q. 21560.)*

sufficiently promising for the DNO to submit 'that ships building should be wired for director gear on the same lines as *Neptune* commencing with *Orion* and *Lion* and that director firing should be provided for in the specification of the 1911–12 armoured ships . . . The orders for Director gear itself should be deferred pending further trials.' This cautious approach, not to mention any opposition from Admiral Bridgeman based on first-hand experience, seems to have been justified by subsequent trials. The initial design had no means to correct for the errors due to tilt which had been anticipated by Arthur Craig in 1905; in a report dated 12 December, 1911 Scott recommended that a turret of *Neptune* should be fitted once Vickers had prepared a drawing embodying his ideas for a tilt corrector. The *Neptune* director was also too unreliable to be used in battle practice, while in May 1912, Captain Moore reported that 'Recent trials [of director firing] in *Neptune* were rather disappointing', but that 'HMS *Thunderer* has been fitted for director firing and it is in proposal to carry out trials as soon as possible after her completion'.

Despite its problems, the *Neptune* director was a major advance on its predecessors in two respects. First, both elevation and direction of the director sight were transmitted to the guns: and, second, it adopted the follow-the-pointer principle so that the gun layers and trainers could follow the movements of the director sight. The director sight itself was similar in layout to all subsequent models, the sight-setter, trainer, elevation-layer and telephone number sitting with their feet towards the centre of a revolving ring-frame; at this stage, the trainer's and layer's telescopes were locked together (in later versions, the trainer's telescope could move in elevation relative to the layer's). It was realised that the fine control required for continuous training would turn the director too slowly when slewing from one target to another; the director was therefore provided 'with separate hand wheels and transmitters for fine training or rapid . . . slewing'.

In the turrets, the wire rope method of measuring gun elevation, first devised by Vickers for the *Africa* director, was used again, only now the rope was arranged to revolve a dial, over which moved a pointer driven by the receiver motor connected to the elevation transmitter at the director. The receiver corrected for muzzle velocity differences and height of gun, provided that a pointer graduated for range was kept set by hand. As already mentioned, the *Neptune* director did not at first correct for tilt and, although two attempts were made, the problem does not seem to have been solved properly until later models.

The training receiver had two concentric dials (for training and slewing angles) which were driven from a large pinion engaging the turret training rack; this method was retained in all later models. Each dial had a pointer driven by a receiver motor connected to the director. The convergence correction was obtained from a simple logarithmic calculator arranged around the body of the training receiver which was adjusted by hand. In director firing, the turret trainer and gun layer both worked their control wheels to keep the dials 'in coincidence with the electric pointers on the "follow-the-pointer" principle'.

The Thunderer *and* Ajax *Directors*

The *Neptune* director was a first prototype and many changes were incorporated in the next model, for *Thunderer*, to improve accuracy, reliability and ease of use and maintenance. At the director, the sights were given follow-the-pointer receivers so that the sight setter no longer had to read ranges and deflections off a counter-type receiver and set the values on the dials. The final form of double motor training and slewing system was introduced; this incorporated an ingenious slewing clutch so that only one control could operate at a time; when the clutch was set back for training, the electrical and mechanical gear ensured that both the training and slewing receivers in the turrets correctly indicated the bearing of the director.

In *Thunderer*, 'considerable alterations were made in the elevation receivers'. The unsatisfactory wire rope system was replaced by a large-radius toothed rack on the gun-slide; this engaged with a special 'spring split gear-wheel' designed to eliminate backlash, which then drove the gun elevation pointer of the receiver; ball-bearings were used to avoid friction and 'a spring shock absorber was also introduced . . . to prevent tooth breakage when the gun was fired'.

Thunderer introduced the standard pattern of Vickers detachable step-by-step receiver motor which was used throughout the system for elevation and training; hence 'one motor could serve as a spare for any instrument'.

Despite its success in competitive trials (see further below), the director required yet one more design iteration before what was in effect the production prototype was installed in HMS *Ajax* in 1913. The director sight was given its own tilt corrector, while an additional training wheel was introduced so that the director layer could also train the sight. In the turrets, the training receivers were at last given automatic correctors which adjusted for convergence at all angles of bearing (provided that the target range was set first by hand). In the elevation receiver, the inertia of the elevation-pointer and drive shaft was reduced so that the shock absorber was no longer required.

The *Technical History and Index* describes the progressive refinement of the tilt correctors, though it is not clear in which of the three ships each improvement was first introduced. The first correctors were operated by a

HMS Thunderer *lying out in the River Thames at Dagenham ready to start on her trip to Sheerness to have her compasses adjusted. The director sight had not then been installed on the platform directly beneath the fire control top. (CPL.)*

mechanical wire and drum arrangement but these were succeeded by a design driven by a step-by-step motor connected to the director slewing circuit. The tilt correctors were also used to correct for the difference in height of the turrets and, finally, to correct 'for the distance between the director and gun when firing at positions other than the beam'.

Padfield hardly exaggerated when he wrote that the final design was one of 'infinite refinement'. It is therefore not surprising that the first elevation-and-training director for *Neptune* was far from satisfactory nor that two further phases of development were necessary before the system was fully developed for deployment throughout the Fleet. However, even the second-generation design appeared, in the famous shoot between *Thunderer* and *Orion*, to demonstrate at last that director firing was superior to individual gunlaying.

The competition with *Orion* on 13 November 1913 was designed to compare the two systems of gunlaying in rough weather. It was stipulated that the sea had to be rough enough to make the ships roll 5° each way, that the firing ships should steam at 12 knots, that the targets should be towed at the same speed and that both competing ships should open fire at the same instant upon their separate targets 9,000 yards distant, and would cease fire after three minutes.

The maximum roll recorded was in fact 13.5° out to out: and the results, as given by Padfield, were certainly in favour of the director.

	Rounds fired		Hits	Ricochets
Thunderer	39	On 30ft target	13	2
		On theoretical ship	23	–
Orion	27	On 30ft target	2	1
		On theoretical ship	4	–

However, a report written by *Orion*'s Captain, Arthur Craig, on 15 November, shows that her lower rate of fire and few hits were due almost entirely to one factor: though the test certainly showed that, in the conditions obtaining, the director aloft had a decisive advantage.

> . . . the interference by smoke was the dominating factor
> in the test run and there can be no doubt that it is of

HMS Thunderer *in 1912 after the installation of the director tower beneath the fire control top. This position on the mast was the same as in* Neptune, *even though the mast itself was stepped abaft the fore funnel. Unlike other capital ships of the 1909 programme, the mast fire control positions of the* Orion *class battleships do not seem to have suffered unduly from interference caused by funnel smoke. (IWM, Q. 21854.)*

HMS Ajax *with the director tower on the roof of the circular fire control top. As completed,* Ajax *had an unstayed pole mast with a very small spotting top built around the base of the topmast, which was stepped ahead of the mast. When the director was fitted, the top was enlarged, the mast was converted to a tripod by the addition of two stays and the topmast was moved abaft the top. (IWM, Q. 38068.)*

more serious moment than the motion of the ship in an ordinary seaway as it militates against both spotting and laying. During this run, one gun was so seriously blanked by smoke that it fired only one round . . . the degree of interference during the test run was exceptional, the wind being in the worse quarter and it is desirable to carry out a test with a lesser amount of interference by smoke while retaining a fair amount of motion.

This test seems to have taken place off Portland on 4 December and Scott acknowledged the appearance of reports of the 'surprising defeat of Sir Percy Scott's "Director" System'.

In the following year, newspapers were reporting *Orion's* success in Battle Practice, in which, aided by her Argo Clock, she attained new levels of accuracy by individual laying and firing i.e. finding the range by salvoes and then breaking into rapid independent to give the highest possible rate of fire. On 4 November 1913, *Orion* and *Thunderer* were once more in company and, in the experimental firings against the old battleship *Empress of India*, there was another opportunity to compare the two systems of gunlaying, though only in calm weather with good visibility. In the individual firings, both ships fired 40 rounds in four minutes, *Orion* scoring nine hits and one ricochet, *Thunderer* seven hits and one ricochet; *Thunderer's* director also proved effective in squadron firing when she made seven hits in the final minute. Afterwards, both the C.-in-C., Home Fleet and the DNO (now Captain Tudor) were in agreement that 'under easy conditions our present system of fire control gives better results than the Director' but that 'both systems have their uses', which were summarised as follows by the DNO:

(a) If conditions are favourable for laying and independent fire, the Director becomes a very necessary Target indicator.

(b) Directly a Turret finds laying interfered with they can lay by the Director entirely.

(c) In rough weather or other unfavourable conditions, or for concentrating, Director firing will necessarily be used.

Jellicoe himself later wrote that . . . 'a very large number of officers were sceptical as to [the Director's] value compared with the alternative system; there was considerable opposition to it and . . . in some cases the system was not favoured even in the ships provided with it'. However, the reports on the *Empress of India* firings show that there were good reasons for not placing total reliance on the new system, since it had not yet demonstrated its superiority under all conditions. It must also be recognised that, not only was the first production model only just entering service, but also the techniques for using the director were still evolving. In 1913, although training was continuous, the guns were still laid to a fixed elevation which was liable to reduce both accuracy and rate of fire; the rate was particularly affected when there was little natural roll, precisely the conditions which suited the alternative system of independent laying. It also appears that, at the beginning of the War, the usual practice was for the director layer also to train the sight. It was not until well after Jutland that new orders laid down standardised principles, at least for the training of new personnel.

(a) The director layer to do all the laying and firing. The trainer to do all the training.

(b) The layer to be taught to keep his elevating wheel still before firing for about two seconds.

(c) The director trainer to be taught to keep continuously on for training but not to reverse the direction of training just before opening fire.

The director layer endeavours to get 'on' towards the top of the roll where the angular velocity is small and where, if he misses the upward roll, he has another chance a moment later as the downward roll commences. A certain amount of hunting the roll will be necessary.

Thus, as finally developed, the technique for director aiming followed as closely as possible that for independent aiming. It could then achieve the same accuracy and rates of fire in easy conditions: while in the actual conditions of wartime engagements (firing at the maximum ranges permitted by the visibility), the director aloft could always give a better view of the target. In any case, war-time developments, notably in ladder firing, methods of concentration and gyroscopically controlled firing, were only possible in conjunction with the director.

Director Production

Immediately the *Thunderer/Orion* trials had demonstrated the utility of the director, the Admiralty, in November 1912, approached Vickers 'concerning the equipment of a large number of ships with director firing gear. The firm replied that they could equip 60 ships with the gear within 14 months.' In 1913, two large orders were placed with Messrs. Vickers to be spread out over several financial years. These were the Twelve Ship Order which provided for the eight battleships of the *King George V* and *Iron Duke* classes (including *Ajax*), *Queen Mary*, *Tiger*, *Monarch* and *Thunderer*: and the Seventeen Ship Order for all earlier ships (except, for some reason, *Conqueror* and *Australia*). By the outbreak of war, five ships had been fitted in addition to *Neptune*, *Thunderer* and *Ajax*: *Iron Duke*, *Marlborough*, *King George V*, *Centurion* and *Monarch*. Scott stated that 'when war came, work was stopped on the other 21 ships and was not resumed until three months afterwards when I returned to the Admiralty'. He also quoted Jellicoe:

Early in 1915, arrangements were made with the assistance of Sir Percy Scott . . . by which the battleships and battlecruisers were supplied . . . without being put out of action or sent to a dockyard.

The *Technical History* does not specifically mention this hiatus (due, it may be inferred, to a desire to get all available ships to sea without delay) but, after listing the situation in August 1914, jumps to 2 January 1915 when decisions were taken:

(1) To take immediate steps to increase the sources of supply of instruments.

(2) To concentrate first on fitting the main armaments of

HMS *Dreadnought* and later types of Battleship and Battle Cruiser.

(3) As regards secondary armaments to complete the ships mentioned in (2) which are armed with 6-inch guns.

. . .

(6) All new Battleships and Battle Cruisers to be fitted during construction.

By May 1915, all the ships of the Twelve Ship Order (except *Queen Mary*) plus *Superb*, *Queen Elizabeth* and *Warspite* had been supplied. By the following month, '16 firms were manufacturing parts of director equipments under sub-contract from Messrs. Vickers [though 22] other firms were unable to undertake manufacture . . . chiefly on account of their other commitments'. Supply was, however, unequal to demand, which now also included monitors. It was therefore decided in June 1915 to concentrate on main armament directors. However, 'the loss of skilled labour, resulting from transfers to the Army . . . was seriously interfering with the output, particularly at Vickers' works, Erith, and Wolseley Motors, Birmingham . . . in July 1915 the Army Council made arrangements for the special release of 100 Turners and 100 Fitters for return to Wolseley Motors'. By December 1915, in addition to the seven capital ships shown in the table, 14 monitors had also been fitted: while, by May 1916, all completed capital ships (except *Erin* and *Agincourt*) had been fitted, i.e. 54 ships in all.

After Jutland had shown, in Jellicoe's words 'not merely the utility, but the essential need for director firing', he 'urged that the fitting of director-gear to all Light Cruisers of the Grand Fleet armed with 6-inch and 5.5-inch guns should be hastened to the utmost possible extent'. Although the case for light cruisers had been raised in November 1914, work on experimental installations had been delayed due to the preference given to capital ships and monitors and only two cruisers, *Centaur* and *Concord*, had been completed with directors before joining the fleet prior to the end of 1916. Eighteen more cruisers were fitted during 1917 and a further 26 by the end of October 1918. However, owing to the decision to hasten the supply to light cruisers, the directors for the 6in secondary armaments of capital ships, ordered in December 1914, were often delayed. Temporary installations were put into *Emperor of India*, *Benbow* and *Queen Elizabeth* in November and December 1916: while *Renown*, *Repulse*, *Glorious* and *Courageous* were also completed in the last quarter of 1916. During 1917, all the remaining ships were supplied: except for *Canada*, *Ramillies* and *Agincourt*, which had to wait until 1918, and *Tiger*, which was apparently never fitted. Of the ships with 4in secondary armament, only *Orion* was given a trial installation but not until mid-1918.

The final phase of the war-time director programme saw the installation, between February and October 1918 of 149 Destroyer directors. In the five years 1914–18, the approximate [sic] cost of the whole programme had been £1,762,004[10] and, at its peak had employed 360 men at Vickers Erith, 800 at Wolseley, 107 at Vickers Barrow and a further 140 working on erection on board ship; these

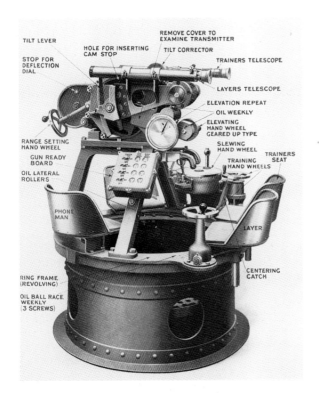

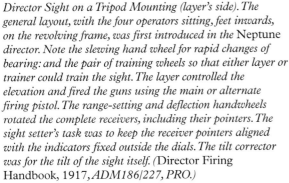

Director Sight on a Tripod Mounting (layer's side). The general layout, with the four operators sitting, feet inwards, on the revolving frame, was first introduced in the Neptune director. Note the slewing hand wheel for rapid changes of bearing: and the pair of training wheels so that either layer or trainer could train the sight. The layer controlled the elevation and fired the guns using the main or alternate firing pistol. The range-setting and deflection handwheels rotated the complete receivers, including their pointers. The sight setter's task was to keep the receiver pointers aligned with the indicators fixed outside the dials. The tilt corrector was for the tilt of the sight itself. (Director Firing Handbook, 1917, ADM186/227, PRO.)

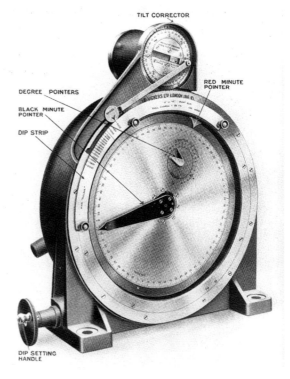

Turret Elevation Receiver. The large dial was calibrated in minutes of arc and the pointers made a complete revolution for every 6° change in elevation. The small dial showed total elevation in degrees. The inner black minute pointer showed the gun elevation, while the outer, triangular minute pointer (which was red) indicated the elevation of the director sight. The tilt corrector was set for the tilt of the turret; it altered the position of the range pointer as the turret trained. This pointer indicated on the detachable dip strip. These strips were individually engraved with ranges and their purpose was to correct for the gun's height and for any difference in its muzzle velocity from that assumed in calibrating the director. The dip setting handle rotated both the ring to which the dip strip was attached: and also the outer rim of the receiver's dial. As the rim rotated, it carried with it both the red director pointer and its receiver motor. Thus, if the handle was turned so that the correct range always lay under the range pointer, the appropriate correction for dip, tilt and muzzle velocity was superimposed on the position of the red pointer. (Director Firing Handbook, 1917, ADM186/227, PRO.)

figures do not include the workforces at the principal sub-contractors, Messrs. Ross, Lagonda, Beyer Peacock, Elliott Bros. and Imperia Co.

Conclusions

The sources for this account of the history of the director suggest that Percy Scott's memoirs on this subject are, to say the least, misleading. He made no distinction between the early designs with only fixed elevation: and does not even mention the *Africa* director, let alone the later design which

ended up in *Bellerophon*. It could be argued that these omissions were because these first directors did not control training: but this was also true of the director in *Good Hope* and, in any case, Scott agreed at the time with the proposal that the *Africa* director should be elevation only.

There was no lack of Admiralty support for the *Africa* director. Jellicoe in particular saw it as an alternative method of salvo firing for the all-big-gun ships, which was needed in case the experiments in the continuous aim of turret guns should prove unsuccessful. Nor did the Admiralty ask for significant design changes during development. Scott and his associates at Vickers were

Table 1: *Director Installation Dates (Latest) for Capital Ships and Monitors, 1910 to 1916*

	1910 to 1913	1914 August	1915 May	1915 December	1916 May	1916 December
					Dreadnought	
			Invincible		Indomitable	
					Inflexible	
			Superb		Bellerophon	
					Temeraire	
				St.Vincent	Vanguard	
					Collingwood	
	Neptune					
				New Zealand	Indefatigable	
					Australia	
				Colossus		
				Hercules		
	Thunderer	Monarch	Conqueror	Orion		
			Lion	Queen Mary	Princess Royal	
	Ajax	King George V				
		Centurion				
		Iron Duke	Benbow			
		Marlborough	Emperor of India			
			Tiger			
			Queen Elizabeth		Malaya	
			Warspite		Barham	
					Valiant	
					Revenge	Resolution
					Royal Sovereign	(Ramillies
					Royal Oak	June 1917)
				Canada		Erin
						Agincourt
						Repulse
						Renown
				14 monitors		2 monitors
Installations per period	3	5	9	21	16	7
Total Installations	3	8	17	38	54	61

responsible for the time taken to convert Scott's outline proposals of August 1905 into the equipment finally installed at the beginning of 1907.

Had he mentioned it, Scott might have had more justification for lambasting the Admiralty over the delays in completing the *Bellerophon* director. The main causes were the inability of the DNO's department to hasten work in Portsmouth Dockyard: and the difficulties of synchronising the construction and fitting of prototype gear with the refits of ships in service. The initial delays occurred when Jellicoe was still DNO and, while Bacon initially pressed on with the development, his memorandum of October 1908 could be seen as a typical bureaucratic ploy to stifle the project. If it was, Jellicoe, lately returned as Controller, insisted that installation should proceed, but even he could

not prevent another round of delays, some technical and some arising from the unfortunate choice of the Home Fleet flagship as the trial ship.

There is no evidence to suggest that Bacon actually denied Scott the materials required to construct the *Good Hope* director, though Scott could well have borrowed step-by-step gear from Vickers. It should also be remembered that Bacon was responsible for moving the *Good Hope* gear to *Prince George*, where the fixed elevation director would have been worth trying with an older type of elevation gear. In any case, by the autumn of 1908, Bacon would have been justified in his sceptical attitude concerning the accuracy of fixed elevation directors. During his time as DNO, the early experiments in improved elevation and training gear had born fruit so that the main

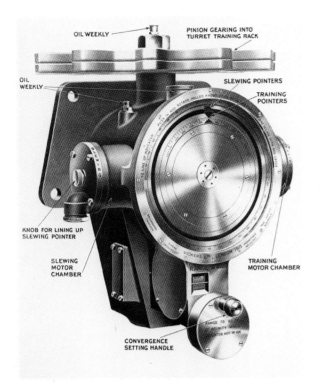

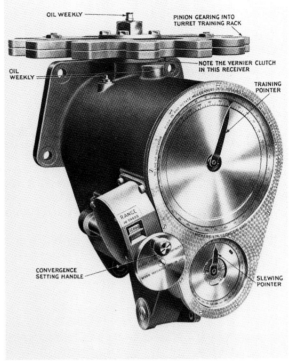

Training Receiver – turret single dial type (fitted in Queen Elizabeth *and all 12in and 13.5in ships except* Erin*). The training receivers were mounted under the turret training rack, to which the split pinion engaged directly. In the single dial type, the slewing dial (with black zero pointer) rotated outside the inner training dial. The slewing dial rotated 1° for every 1° rotation of the turret, while the training dial made one complete revolution for every 6° of turret training. The turret trainer kept the black dial pointers in line with the red pointers, which indicated the angle of training of the director sight. The training dial was calibrated not in minutes of arc but in the equivalent lateral displacement in feet at a range of 10,000 yards. The receiver corrected automatically for convergence if the range was properly set using the convergence setting handle. (*Director Firing Handbook, 1917, ADM186/227, PRO.*)*

Training Receiver – turret double dial type (fitted in all 15in ships except Queen Elizabeth, *in* Canada *and in* Erin*). While operating on identical principles to the single dial type, this receiver had separate dials for slewing and for training. (*Director Firing Handbook, 1917, ADM186/227, PRO.*)*

justification for this first type of director had been removed. Furthermore, there are no indications that either the *Africa* or the *Good Hope* directors were significantly better than the *Bellerophon* gear eventually proved to be. Lastly, it was during Bacon's time as DNO that the much more radical director for *Neptune* was approved: and that Percy Scott was assigned to working full time with Vickers on its development. If the Ordnance Department under Bacon did withdraw support, it was only from the obsolete form of director firing: and Scott was never a gunnery outcast in the way that Pollen was, eventually, to be.

Scott's later claim that the Admiralty boycotted the director until 1911 was absurd. Indeed, it obscured his and Vickers' considerable achievement in getting the new design completed in about 15 months and in installing the prototype by the end of 1910. Even so, it would have

been miraculous if they had got everything right first time and, despite the success of the initial trials, it is not surprising that major design changes proved necessary to improve reliability, to correct for tilt and to develop a more accurate method of measuring gun elevation. The cautious approach of the then DNO, Captain Moore, after the *Neptune* trials was not unreasonable and certainly did not indicate outright opposition; since the greatly improved *Thunderer* director had been installed by mid-1912, the design and development work must have continued at full pace throughout his period in office.

Once the *Thunderer* had demonstrated that the problems and deficiencies of the *Neptune* director had been overcome, the Admiralty were not slow in placing production orders, even before the final round of design changes had been made and tested in *Ajax*. The rate of installation of the initial programme was not, however, very fast, being still dictated by peacetime priorities and financial constraints. The three-month hiatus at the start of the War is harder to explain but was probably due to the pell-mell attempt to get all available ships to sea, at a time when many thought all would be over by Christmas. Once the wartime production programme got into its stride in 1915, any delays were caused not by Admiralty lassitude but by production difficulties arising from shortages of skilled labour, and the problems of installing complex gear in ships which could not be taken out of service. Capital ships also had to compete for the limited supply with other ships. Despite the demand for monitors, almost all battleships and battlecruisers had received their main armament directors before Jutland. Afterwards, the delays in fitting their secondary armament were due to the greater priority given to light cruisers.

There was no Admiralty boycott of Scott's directors, nor was the Board ever 'very much opposed' to his system. His original design (about which he was later so reticent) was overtaken by developments in gun aiming gear and, while the full elevation-and-training director might have been put into production somewhat earlier, it is now impossible to attest that a complete phase of development could have been safety omitted. It is ironic that Scott's splenetic account of his greatest invention has not only obscured the considerable scale of the wartime production programme: but has detracted from the great technical achievement of himself and his collaborators at Vickers in perfecting the full director well before the outbreak of the War.

Notes

[1] Scott's sea-going career ended after his extremely public disputes with the C-in-C, Channel Fleet, Lord Charles Beresford, following the 'paintwork affair' (4 November 1907) and a second incident when, on 1 July 1908, Scott refused to obey a signal from Beresford which would have resulted in a collision between *Good Hope* and *Argyll*.

[2] Jon Tetsuro Sumida, *In Defence of Naval Supremacy*, London, 1989, pp. 154 and 207. On p. 154, it is suggested that, by mid-1909, 'Scott and Pollen thus found themselves sharing the status of gunnery outcasts'.

[3] The case was fully reported in *The Times* from 29 June to 6 July and is summarised in *Aim Straight*. Scott's rewards contrast starkly with those of, for example, Admirals Dumaresq and Dreyer, who received £1,500 and £5,000 respectively for their inventions: 'Recommendations of The Royal Commission on Awards to Inventors, 30 October 1925' in Anthony Pollen, *The Great Gunnery Scandal*, London, 1980. p. 253.

[4] *Papers prepared by the Directors of Naval Ordnance and Torpedoes for the information of their successors.* Copies courtesy Professor Jon Sumida.

[5] Scott was appointed Inspector of Target Practice, reporting directly to Fisher, on 24 February 1905. In his autobiography (p. 190), Scott claimed that, during the ensuing parliamentary debate of 7 March, Mr Gibson Bowles referred to him as 'a rather peculiar wild animal to let loose on a tame Board of Admiralty'. Unfortunately, this story (pretty unlikely anyway, in view of the outsize personality of the new First Sea Lord) is not borne out either by *Hansard* or *The Times*. The

latter for 8 March (although cited by Scott) reported Gibson Bowles as saying only that 'the personality of ... Sir Percy Scott was enough to justify almost any appointment (hear, hear)'.

[6] Vickers explained that four motors were provided to give an adequate reserve of power, even if one broke down.

[7] With this sight, it was therefore possible to change the elevation of the telescope without altering the transmitted elevation; this new feature may have been an additional reason for constructing this director.

[8] It was actually two years before the completed *Neptune* director ran its trials.

[9] This contradicts Scott's claim (*Fifty Years . . .* p. 213) that 'the director firing I had installed [was] put on the scrap heap' as soon as he left his squadron. However, *Prince George* (*Majestic* class) was much damaged in a collision on 5 December 1909 (Oscar Parkes, *British Battleships*, London, 1966, p. 388) which presumably put an end to any further testing.

[10] For comparison, the cost of a single *Queen Elizabeth* class battleship was £2,685,799.

Sources

Published Works

Adm. Sir Percy Scott, *Fifty Years in the Royal Navy*, 1919

John Brooks, 'The Mast and Funnel Question' in *Warship 1995* and 'All-Big-Guns' in *War Studies Journal*, Kings College, London, Spring, 1996

Adm. Sir William James, *The Sky was always Blue*, 1951

Arthur Marder, *From Dreadnought to Scapa Flow, Vols. I and II*, 1961–5

Peter Padfield, *Aim Straight*, 1966 and *Guns at Sea*, 1974

John Roberts, *The Battleship Dreadnought*, 1992

S W Roskill, *Admiral of the Fleet Earl Beatty*, 1981

Jon T Sumida, *In Defence of Naval Supremacy*, 1989

Unpublished Sources

Public Record Office (Crown copyright acknowledged)

ADM1/7761, *Inventions of Captain Percy Scott*

ADM1/7955, *Director for Turret Firing (Africa)*

ADM1/8145, *Director Firing Gear (Bellerophon)*

ADM1/8330, *Notes on Director Firing*

ADM1/8346, *Sinking of HMS Emperor of India*

ADM1/8435/302, *Mechanical Cryptography*

ADM116/611, *Scott's Aiming Apparatus*

ADM137/293, 'Notes on Director Firing' in *GFG&TOs*

ADM138/231 and 348, *Ships' Covers, Dreadnought* and *Lions*

ADM186/227, *Director Firing Handbook 1917*

ADM186/236, *Range Tables 1918*

Craig Waller Papers (courtesy Commander Michael Craig Waller)

P Scott, *Gunnery*, 1905

Letters from Scott to Arthur Craig

Turret or Barbette Gun Sighting (n.d.)

A W Craig, *Hydraulic Training Gear*, 1907 and *Rough Weather Test Firing*, 1912

Naval Library, Ministry of Defence

Spotting Rules, 1916

'Fire Control in HM Ships' in *Technical History and Index*, 1919

Churchill College, Cambridge

Capt. C Hughes-Onslow, *Fire Control*, 1909, PLLN 1/5

Jellicoe to McKenna, 14 Mar. 1911 in MCKN 3/10

WARSHIP NOTES

This section comprises a number of short articles and notes, generally highlighting little-known aspects of warship history.

GUN DRAWINGS

Antony Preston adds a short supplementary comment to David Hughes' notes on the naval gun collection held at the Cumbria Record Office in Barrow-in-Furness. (Warship 1995, p183)

An important source of data on gun-mountings is the collection of drawings, manuals and microfilm held by the National Maritime Museum in its Brass Foundry archive. These were all that was left of the old Elswick Ordnance Company's archives, which had been very brutally 'weeded' by the management of Vickers-Armstrongs – roughly four tons of assorted drawings were being pulped or burnt each week before the NMM Ship Department got to hear about it, and asked the company for permission to retrieve what it could. However, the vandalism has started much earlier, as I found a book dating from the 1930s which summarised drawings which had been destroyed.

Despite this, some very interesting items survived:

- numerous manuals relating to Japanese mountings, the proto-type triple 6in turret mounting for the Argentine Navy's cruiser *La Argentina*, etc
- a number of projects 'between the wars' for coast defence and ship mountings
- the drawings for the Chilean Navy's 102mm automatic mountings
- numerous light guns such as 12pdr and 4.7in QF guns for the RN and other navies
- rail gun outfits of various calibres

Among the more esoteric items was a drawing of the 9.4in tubes for the Norwegian coast defence ships *Bjoergvin* and *Nidaros*, with a marginal comment showing that Nos 1–3 were relined to 9.2in and No 4 was completed to the new calibre. Another curiosity was a Russian 130mm (5.1in) tube ordered post-June 1941 to make good Soviet Navy shortages – the gun had originally been designed at Elswick in 1913 for Imperial Russian Navy light cruisers!

COAST DEFENCE GUNS IN WORLD WAR II

Antony Preston raises a point arising out of John Campbell's article on British Second World War coast defence guns. (Warship 1995, p79)

Although John Campbell rightly wasted no powder and shot on the myth of the 18in guns at Singapore, it is quite remarkable how durable this story has proved. Undoubtedly they exercise a hold over naval enthusiasts' minds, partly because of their sheer size, and partly because they are linked with the canard of the 'guns pointing the wrong way'. Only recently I was engaged in correspondence with the quarterly magazine *Warship World*, in which I energetically 'shot down' the story. To my amazement I found that one correspondent quoted with confidence a 1947 account by Ronald Bassett, in which he claimed to have seen the guns lying in the jungle on Blakang Mati island.

Knowing that the gun registers at Priddy's Hard showed quite unequivocally that two 18in Mk I guns were sold for scrap in 1933, and the third was sold for scrap after a long period at Shoeburyness, I turned to Ian Hogg for help. Former Master Gunner Hogg RA is an authority on British coast artillery, and he reached the conclusion that the guns which Bassett saw must have been old 9.2in guns dumped when Connaught Battery was modernised in the mid-1920s.

Ian Hogg's studies show that the original guns on Blakang Mati were two 9.2in Mk VIII guns . These were replaced by three Mk X guns in the 1920s (the Mk VIII was declared obsolete in 1927). It was very common for guns to be dumped locally because the cost of shipping them home for scrapping at Woolwich was too great. It is possible that in 1942 the Japanese scrapped two of the damaged Mk X guns without even noticing the old guns lying in the jungle. The old guns have since been mounted on plinths in two former 6in emplacements at Fort Siloso at the western end of Blakang Mati, and Hogg's photographs confirm they are 9.2in Mk VIII.

In 1921–26 one 18in Mk I and its mounting were installed at the Proof & Experimental Establishment at Silloth, Cumbria for proving cordite. The other two, ex-*General Wolfe* and ex-*Lord Clive*, went to Shoeburyness, Essex and Yantlet on the Isle of Grain, Kent also for proof-firing. Register Nos. 2 and 3 were sold in 1933, and Register No.1 was sold in 1947.

Information on the fates of the 15in guns at Singapore is vague. The RA regimental history says that the Johore Battery guns were destroyed but does not mention the Buena Vista battery. A PoW reported that the guns were cut up for scrap and shipped back to Japan. A Japanese report said that it would be possible to 'cannibalise' spares to make one gun in each battery serviceable, but nothing was ever done.

Today even the sites of the batteries cannot be verified as they have been built over.

WARSHIP ODDITIES IN CHILE

During a recent visit to the Chilean Naval Museum in Valparaiso Antony Preston came across two oddities.

One is a rare example of the Harvey towed torpedo, developed by the mid-Victorian British Navy and presumably sold to Chile.

In the gardens of the Museum are two examples of a rare model of the Gatling machine-gun, one of many rapid-fire weapons produced after the American Civil War.

GERMAN AUXILIARIES

Pierre Hervieux has provided the following, additional information to his article 'German Auxiliaries at War' in Warship 1995, *p. 108*

In the Kriegsmarine's diary (KTB), there is no trace of the attack of 26-27 June by British MTBs off St Helier. No M-boat was sunk, so *M-4620* was not lost that night. The mistake of the identification comes from the fact that the 2nd *M-4620* was the ex-*M-4611* and she was sunk on 28 June by the destroyers HMS *Eskimo* and HMCS *Huron*. There were two *M-4620s*.

1. *M-4620* (ex-German trawler *Harvestehude*, 523 tons, commissioned first as *M-1201* in 1939 and transferred on 1 November 1942 to the 46th MS Flotilla as *M-4620*. She was sunk on 11 March 1943, in 48°56 N/ 03°38W, by French MTBs.

2. The ex-French trawler *Etienne Rimbert*, 193 tons, was repaired and commissioned in the German Navy on 26 June 1942 as *M-4611* and was sunk on 27 April 1943 in St Helier by an air attack. Salvaged and repaired she was recommissioned on 23 January 1944 as *M-4260* and sunk again on 28 June 1944, in 48°51N/02°02W by the above mentioned destroyers.

AERONAVAL ODDITIES OF THE FIRST WORLD WAR

The First World War saw some unusual juxtapositions of aircraft and surface vessels, some for obvious reasons but others difficult to explain. RD Layman discusses six examples.

1. Friedrichshafen FF.29 (navy number 204) perched on the foredeck of *U-12* in Zeebrugge harbour on 6 January 1915 at the start of an experiment testing the feasibility of taking an aircraft to sea aboard a submarine and thus extending its operational radius. The scheme was concocted jointly by *Kapitänleutnant* Walter Forstmann, captain of *U-12*, and *Oberleutnant zur See* Friedrich von Arnauld de la Perrière, commander of the Zeebrugge seaplane detachment. The photograph shows von Arnauld, the pilot (in the rear cockpit), and his observer, *Oberleutnant zur See* Herman Moll, just before *U-12* sailed into the English Channel.

The seaplane was placed in takeoff position by trimming the submarine down by the bow until the aircraft floated free. A successful flight was made over the Kentish coast, unobserved from the ground. Rough seas prevented a scheduled rendezvous of aircraft and submarine, and both returned independently to Zeebrugge. The experiment was criticized by higher authorities, who forbade its repetition (although the use of aircraft by submarines was proposed later in the war and special seaplanes designed for the role).

Von Arnauld continued in aerial command at Zeebrugge until becoming a PoW when his plane was shot down by a French warship. He was the brother of Lothar de la Perière (who chose a different spelling of the family name), the famous submarine commander. Forstmann also gained fame as a U-boat skipper. Under the Third Reich, von Arnauld and Moll rose to the rank of general in the *Luftwaffe* and Forstmann to that of admiral in the *Kriegsmarine*. (Photo: courtesy of the late *Konteradmiral* A D Walter Forstmann)

---

2. Single-seat Sopwith Schneiders, Admiralty serial Nos. 3730 and 3743, aboard a two-track wooden ramp on *E-22* in a photograph undoubtedly taken at the Felixstowe Royal Naval Air Service station and probably on 24 April 1916. That was the date they were taken to sea, launched by trimming the boat down, and flown back to Felixstowe.

The experiment was undertaken to determine if submarines could carry aircraft into the North Sea to intercept German airships; although the test was successful, the scheme was dropped because the ramp hindered *E-22*'s submerged performance. It was still aboard, however, when *E-22* was sunk by *UB-18* the next day, and one of the British vessel's only two survivors clung to two pieces of it until he was picked up by the German submarine.

E-22's logbook, which might have shed more light on the experiment, was, of course, lost with her. (Photo: RDL)

3. During 4–6 February 1916 the German battlecruiser *Goeben* (nominally the Turkish *Yavuz Sultan Selim*) took two aircraft of the Ottoman 7th Air Squadron, an all-Turkish unit, from Constantinople to the Black Sea port of Trabzon, from whence they were transported overland to the Caucasian battle front. Here we see one of them on her deck during the voyage. It is an Albatros two-seater; the shape of the radiator and what is obviously a ring mount for a machine gun in the rear cockpit indicates it is a C.II or C.III type. To facilitate shipboard carriage its wings have been detached; they can be seen stacked forward of the aircraft. The other aeroplane was an unarmed Rumpler B.II.

Goeben also transported the aircraft personnel (four officers, 30 enlisted men) and equipment, including fuel and bombs. Also aboard were a battery of mountain artillery, eight machine gun sections and their personnel and a medical unit with its supplies. (Photo: Peter M Grosz)

---

4. Wight Twin (officially Admiralty Type 187, Admiralty serial No. 1451) being transported on 15 July 1916 aboard *Golden Eagle* from East Cowes, Isle of Wight, where it was constructed by J. Samuel White & Co., to the Felixstowe RNAS station for testing.

The Twin, of which only three were built, was, as its unofficial name implies, a twin-engine, twin-fuselage floatplane. It was designed as a torpedo plane but No. 1451 was unable to take off under the weight of the 18-inch missile, and that put paid to the type.

At the time this photograph was taken the 793-ton paddle-wheel *Golden Eagle* was still a civilian vessel, serving as an RNAS transport rated as a mercantile fleet auxiliary. She did not become an officially commissioned Royal Navy vessel, entitling her to receive the HMS prefix, until 1918. Returned to her civilian owner after the war, she was again taken into RN service in 1939 and became an anti-aircraft ship. (Photo: IWM)

5. What is going on here is a mystery. The aircraft appears to be a twin-engine Gotha WD.7, one of eight built to train pilots in torpedo-dropping techniques. The ship, readily identifiable as a torpedo boat or destroyer, could be one of any number of classes that bore strong resemblances to each other.

Perhaps the seaplane has had a mechanical failure of some sort and the ship has come to its aid, but the circumstances remain unknown. (Photo: Peter M. Grosz)

6. Certainly, the Swiss Navy never had an aircraft carrier, but there was something of an approximation. It was a barge on which was secured an old-fashioned spherical balloon named *Theodor Schaeck* and towed by a steam launch named *La Broye* on the Bielersee (Lac du Bienne) sometime in 1915.

The Swiss had become touchy about violations of their air space after British aircraft, flying from France, allegedly crossed over Swiss territory during a raid on the Zeppelin works at Friedrichshafen in 1914, and used observation balloons to watch for any future such incursions (one was shot down, apparently inadvertently, by a German aeroplane in 1918). But why a balloon should have been placed on a body of water so remote from the French border is puzzling.

The photograph shows smoke from the launch's funnel billowing around the *Theodor Schaeck* – a terribly dangerous situation, for a single funnel spark could have touched off the balloon's highly flammable hydrogen. (Photo: Bundesarchiv Bern)

Aero historian Harry Woodman has established that the photograph on page 36 of *Warship 1994*, accompanying R D Layman's article 'Naval Kite Trials,' shows Russian naval kite pioneer *Leitenant* Nicholai N Schreiber being lofted from the Black Sea Fleet torpedo gunboat *Kapitan Saken* on 21 September 1901 (old style) off Sevastopol. Mr Woodman has also forwarded to the author another photograph of the same experiment, as seen here.

In addition, he has supplied a photograph supplementary to the article 'The Shipboard Balloon' by R D Layman and Stephan McLaughlin in *Warship 1992*. This shows a spherical balloon named *Chaika* (Seagull), one of those constructed by Fyodor A Postnikov at Vladivostok during the Russo-Japanese war, over the armoured cruiser *Rossia*. It may be tethered to the vessel, but is more likely to be in free flight. *Rossia's* mainmast flies in addition to the national ensign the flag of Admiral Karl P Yessen, commander of the Vladivostok cruiser squadron.

NEWS FROM VARIOUS WARSHIP MUSEUMS

David McLean has compiled the following listings and invites further news items from Warship museums around the world for future issues.

HMS *BELFAST*

HMS *Belfast* is Europe's last Big Gun Armoured warship of World War II and is permanently moored in the Pool of London.

Belfast served throughout the Second World War, playing a leading part in the sinking of the German battle cruiser *Scharnhorst* at the Battle of North Cape and in the Normandy Landings. After the war she supported UN forces in Korea and remained in service with the Royal Navy until 1965. On Trafalgar Day, 21 October 1971, she became the first British warship to be preserved for posterity since Nelson's flagship HMS *Victory*.

A new permanent exhibition telling the story of HMS *Belfast* from her inception in the mid-1930s to the decision to save her for the nation in 1971 was opened in July 1996.

Using original artefacts, documents, plans, and drawings as well as contemporary paintings and photographs, ship models and audio-visual displays, 'HMS *Belfast* in War & Peace' provides a comprehensive account of the life and times of this great historic warship and of the men who served in her.

Over the next five years or so, HMS *Belfast* will benefit from the 'Tower Environs Scheme', a major project designed to enhance the setting of the Tower of London and its surrounding area including the adjacent Thames.   DM

IMPERIAL WAR MUSEM

The Baltic Diaries of Commander Francis Goodhart DSO RN.

One of the most outstanding recent acquisitions by the Imperial War Museum are the diaries and photographs of Commander Francis Goodhart DSO RN. Francis Herbert Heaveningham Goodhart joined the Royal Navy in 1900, entered the Submarine Service in May 1905 and was appointed to his first command, HM Submarine *C.6*, on 1 September 1908. After two years mandatory general service in the battleship HMS *Magnificent*, he took command of HM Submarine *D.3* in October 1912 before being appointed in command of the new submarine *E.8* in 1914. In August 1914 he was one of the first British submariners to put to sea and thereafter he and his crew endured the boredom and monotony of patrols in the Heligoland Bight, where, to quote another distinguished submariner, all that they usually saw was 'water and a damn sight too much of that'.

In August 1915 Goodhart was ordered into the Baltic and it is this period of his naval service which is featured in the diaries which come in two small volumes closely filled with Goodhart's small and erratic handwriting. The style of the diaries is very fluid, written without much in the way of punctuation and evidently as Goodhart would have spoken. Some of the entries are extremely long and one cannot but wonder how Goodhart managed to write as much as he did, particularly when the submarine was at sea. Goodhart remained in the Baltic until December 1916 when he was appointed to the submarine *K.14*, then under construction. During this period the diaries record his experiences of operating with the Russians, the tensions among his fellow British submariners and his experiences at sea. The most significant episode was his sinking of the German light cruiser *Prinz Adalbert* on 23 October 1915. His attack technique may be of interest to modern submariners:

> . . . it was a really simple attack. I never altered course at all until well- after firing! Fired bow tube . . . one destroyer crossed our bow about two hundred yards off and I left our periscope up rather a long time just as she was coming on to fire. But torpedo HIT after 75 seconds just under 1600 yards. I followed the track of the torpedo when I fired and saw it was running well. I was

Commander Francis Goodhart (right) with his First Lieutenant, Alexander Greig (left). Goodhart is wearing the ribbon of the St George's Cross awarded to him for sinking the German cruiser Prinz Adalbert. *(IWM. Goodhart Collection HU 57575.)*

looking right ahead when I saw a red line of flame along the waterline under the forebridge. I thought they had fired fore turret at me! I looked at the ship again and all there was an immense cloud of thick smoke. she must have gone off in one act! A MkVIII is some stuff!

Mechanical problems kept *E.8* in dock throughout the summer of 1916 and not even a tour of the Crimea and Galician front could assuage Goodhart's frustration. In December 1916 he was delighted to learn that he was being relieved and sent back to England. He was then appointed to command *K.14* one of the new steam driven fleet submarines, 'they seem great boats', he wrote. On 29 January 1917 Goodhart went out in *K.13* to observe her performance on the final part of her acceptance trials. That afternoon during her third dive the submarine flooded through an engine room ventilator which had remained open. All efforts to bring the boat to the surface failed and she settled on the bottom of the Gareloch. Goodhart volunteered to make a daring escape with Lt Cdr Godfrey Herbert, *K.13's* commanding officer, from the conning tower to alert the authorities. Herbert reached the surface safely but Goodhart struck his head on the roof of the wheelhouse, was rendered unconscious and subsequently drowned. Two days later the bows of *K.13* were brought to the surface and the forty nine survivors of the eighty who had been onboard the submarine were dragged out through a hole cut in the bows. The submarine was repaired and returned to service as *K.22*.

The diaries show Goodhart to have been a competent and determined officer who never tired of seeking out the enemy and who was frustrated when opportunities failed to materialise. The diaries also reveal him as a commanding officer who, by the standards of the time, was concerned for the welfare of his ship's company and who enjoyed the camaraderie of a lively wardroom. They also show him to have been a man devoted to his wife and their children. His youngest daughter, Barbara, had been born while he was in Russia, and he had barely seen her by the time of his death. Goodhart's peers in the submarine service included officers of the calibre of Horton, Laurence, Nasmith and Talbot, all of whom subsequently achieved flag rank. Had he lived there is no reason suppose that Goodhart would have fared any the less well in his career.

The Goodhart diaries constitute a detailed record of one of the little known aspects of the war at sea during the Great War. They offer an excellent picture the early days of submarine warfare and show the enthusiasm of the early submariners with no hint of the unbelievably squalid conditions in which they lived at sea. The diaries are also an evocation of the late Edwardian period and with their talk of 'bucking up', 'good shows' and 'strafing', they recall the naively with which the generation of 1914 approached the age of total war.

The last entry in the diaries is written by Goodhart's wife Isabel.

[Monday 29 January 1917] Frank left at 6 a.m to go with Mr Herbert in *K.13*. He never came back. The boat sank at 3 p.m off Shandon and on Tuesday the 30 at 1 p.m Frank was drowned trying to get out of the boat to get help. His body was found on Feb 1st and on the 6th he was buried at Faslane Cemetery – Garelochhead.

Paul Kemp

HISTORIC WARSHIPS AT BIRKENHEAD

There are three important warships open to the public at Birkenhead and of interest to *Warship* readers. They are berthed at East Float Dock, Dock Road, Birkenhead, on the Wirral Peninsula.

The frigate, HMS *Plymouth*, is a veteran of the Falklands Campaign of 1982. The surrender of South Georgia was signed in her wardroom and she led the invasion fleet into San Carlos Water. Later, while carrying out a bombardment of Argentine positions in West Falkland, she was caught in open water under Fanning Head by five Argentine Daggers, who attacked at mast level. She was hit by four bombs, none of which exploded (probably because the planes had to fly so low), though one hit a depth charge which *did* explode. She ran for the shelter of Carlos Water in order to put out an internal fire. There were no serious casualties.

Another Falklands veteran is HMS *Onyx*, which was the only non-nuclear submarine to take part in the conflict. Her main role was to insert and extract SBS patrols on the enemy-held islands usually at night - using canoes and rubber boats.

The third exhibit is a German U-Boat (U534), the only U-Boat to be raised from the seabed after having been sunk by the Allies. Her sinking on 5 May 1945 marked the end of the Battle of the Atlantic, the long struggle against the U-Boat threat to Britain's survival. U534 opened to the public in August 1996.

(Details on all three warships from Woodside Tourist Information Centre Tel: 0151 647 6780, Fax 0151 666 2448) DM

RUSSIAN WARSHIP OPEN FOR FISHES

One redundant Russian warship is destined to go on public display in Cayman Brac, one of the Cayman Islands in the Caribbean...but not in the conventional sense. She will be sunk off the island and will become colonised by a multitude of colourful fish and be an exciting environment for scuba divers. Fish will swim in and out of the gun barrels, along corridors, round the bridge and pop out of ports to frighten divers. Several other warships have been sunk in this way in environmentally acceptable locations and more will undoubtedly follow. Indeed a warm coral reef might be a more agreeable fate for a hard-worked warship than the scrapyard crushers.

DM

USS *MISSOURI*

In August 1996, it was announced by the US Department of Defense that the veteran US battleship USS *Missouri* will be preserved as a ship museum at Pearl Harbor in Hawaii. The 'Mighty Mo' was launched in 1944 and the Japanese surrender was signed on board in August 1945. She was decommissioned after the Gulf War, her career having spanned half a century. (*see also p.220*) DM

The 25ft model of HMS Victory *being unloaded at Chatham Historic Dockyard in July 1996.*

CHATHAM HISTORIC DOCKYARD

This extensive naval museum-in-the-making continues to expand slowly. The restoration and preparation of exhibits relies heavily on the voluntary efforts of a small band of enthusiasts and on bids for Millennium Fund money.

Several exhibits will be of interest to *Warship* readers. HMS *Gannet* , the *Doterel* class sloop built at Sheerness in 1878 – the quintessential Victorian 'gunboat' - continues its steady restoration. HMS *Ocelot (S17)*, the last submarine built at Chatham in 1962, has been open to the public since August 1995. A diesel-electric *Oberon* class patrol submarine, she is now berthed in No 2 Basin, Chatham Maritime.

Recently arrived is a 25ft long 4-ton model of HMS *Victory* which was originally made for shooting the ship scenes in *'Lady Hamilton'*, a 1941 Hollywood film starring Laurence Olivier and Vivien Leigh. After use the model was looked after at the United States Naval Training Center in San Diego where it remained for 50 years. After the Center closed it was brought to Chatham thanks to financial help from The Hudson Trust and other benefactors and is now on view in the Mast House and Mould Loft where the *Victory*'s lines were originally laid off. This model is believed to be the largest ship model in Great Britain and reinforces Chatham Dockyard's links with the famous *Victory*, which is such an important part of Britain's maritime heritage.

There is a ten-year capital projects programme, designed to increase income and to secure the long-term future of the site. Major projects for Heritage Funding include restoration of No 1 Smithery and Gallery featuring shipbuilding in the age of iron and steam, a new gallery featuring HMS *Ocelot* and the story of the dockyard in the twentieth century. DM

WARSHIP WRECKS DISCOVERED

In the summer of 1996 two wrecks of Royal Navy warships from the First World War were discovered.

The first was in July, when a fisherman off the coast of Donegal recovered torpedo warheads from the destroyer *Racoon*. She was a destroyer of the *Beagle* or 'G' class, wrecked in a snowstorm on 9 January 1918 while serving in the 2nd TBD Flotilla. Apart from her age (launched in 1910), the most interesting point is that the *Beagles* were the first ships in the Royal Navy with the 21in torpedo, a weapon which had a major effect on fleet gunnery because of its increased range.

The *Racoon* was fitted with two single tubes, with four torpedoes embarked. The 21in (533mm) RGF (Royal Gun Factory) Mk VII was fitted with the new Hardcastle heater to improve performance, and carried a 225lb charge of wet guncotton. Range was 1000 yards at 50 knots, an impressive performance by the standards of the day.

The second wreck to be discovered was that of the submarine *C.29*, found 70 miles off Scarborough by divers in August. She was on of 11 'C' class boats known to have been used as decoys in an attempt to trap German U-boats. The U-boats had taken to shelling the North Sea trawler fleet, and someone at the Admiralty came out with a unique solution, to use requisitioned naval trawlers to tow submerged submarines. A telephone link between the submarine and her towing trawler allowed information on the range and bearing of the U-boat to be sent down the line. The submarine would then slip the tow and work into position for a torpedo shot.

The submarines used were:
- *C.23* towed by HMT *Ratapiko*
- *C.24* towed by HMT *Taranaki*
- *C.26* towed by HMT *Wolsey*
- *C.27* towed by HMT *Princess Louise*
- *C.29* towed by HMT *Ariadne*
- *C.33* towed by HMT *Malta*
- *C.14*, *C.16*, *C.21* and *C.34* (no trawler identified).

Despite technical problems the *C.24*/*Taranaki* combination sank *U.40* off Aberdeen on 23 June 1915, and the *C.27*/*Princess Louise* combination sank *U.23* off Fair Isle on 20 July. Sadly *C.29* appears to have been towed into a German minefield on 29 August, and was sunk with all hands (17 officers and ratings). The 'submarine trap' concept might have claimed more U-boats, but by an oversight the survivors of *U.23* and *U.40* were allowed to mix with German civilian detainees who were subsequently repatriated. They told the German Navy on their return to Germany, and the secret was out, but of course it did put paid to surface attacks on the fishing fleet for the time being. AP

NAVAL BOOKS OF THE YEAR

This section is divided into full-length reviews, short descriptive notices, a list of books announced, and naval videos.

Jane's Warship Recognition Guide.
HarperCollins, 1996. 190 × 125mm, 241 pages, c500 photographs and drawings.
ISBN 0 00 4709810. £14.99

At last Jane's Information Group has produced a book within the reach of the ordinary warship-enthusiast. It is also a great improvement over the limp-covered pocket books published some years back, with good line drawings and well-reproduced photographs. Bearing in mind that most naval personnel, and naval pilots in particular, are not experts in ship-recognition, this will be useful to the professional as well as the amateur.

The choice of ship-classes is puzzling – the introduction says the 300 classes are largely chosen for importance, unusual features and the fact that they are likely to be encountered away from their home waters. This does not explain why space is devoted to an obscure class of North Korean frigates, for example, and a large series of Japanese escorts, yet the numerous *Leander* class is covered by only two examples in the Royal New Zealand Navy. The Chilean *Almirante Riveros* class destroyers are no longer in service, and so will not be sighted at sea. Was the choice dictated by what was available rather than what is useful?

The editor does not seem to be familiar with some fairly standard features of warship design. Spray-deflecting bulwarks in the Aegis cruisers are described as 'unusual raised sides surrounding forecastle", and as 'raised solid sides to forward end of forecastle' in the *Perry* class frigates. The mast closest to the forecastle has always been the foremast, and the mainmast is the second mast – irrational, perhaps, but standard nomenclature nonetheless and well known. 'Transom' is a type of stern, not an alternative term.

Although some would claim that pennant numbers will always be deleted in time of war, the current likelihood of crisis and local flare-ups means that most warships are easily identified by their pennant numbers. Perhaps it might have been better to drop one or two of the more obscure warship classes to make room for a pennant list like the one published in *Jane's Fighting Ships*. The composite warship drawings are a very useful guide to the beginner, and the national flags and ensigns are particularly useful in colour.

Antony Preston

Ed. by Elisabeth Rowell, In Peace and War – Tyneside, Naples and the Royal Flying Corps.
E. R Rowell, 1996. 170 × 240mm, 212 pages, photographs and drawings.
ISBN 0 9527716 0 8. £17.50

This privately published memoir covers the careers of a father and son, Sir Herbert Rowell KBE and Sir Robin Rowell CBE, AFC, DL. Rowell Snr was apprenticed to J Wigham Richardson, before working for Sir W G Armstrong, Mitchell & Co. He went to the company's Pozzuoli ordnance factory outside Naples, an early example of technology-transfer, and much later joined R & W Hawthorn Leslie & Co. Rowell Jnr fought in the First World War, first with the Royal Engineers, then with the Royal Flying Corps and Royal Air Force, becoming an experimental pilot with the Aircraft Directorate and serving with the Design Department of the Air Board.

The book has interesting insights into the warship-building activities of the Armstrong company, including the Elswick cruisers, and a very rare view of the early days of military aviation. Although hardly a mainstream work of naval history, it has much to interest the reader, and is extremely well produced. The photographs and drawings are all unusual, if not unique.

Antony Preston

Tarrant, V E, Jutland, The German Perspective.
Arms & Armour Press, London, 1995, 318 pages, many line diagrams and charts.
ISBN 1 85409 244 8. £20

The author has tried to provide a new outlook on the Battle of Jutland by describing it from the German point of view. The main source is the official history, *Der Krieg in der Nordsee* by Groos, written in 1925 with additional material from personal accounts by German officers. These sources have been used by previous writers from the British point of view so that there are no great surprises.

The daylight battle is seen in fairly similar ways by the two navies, though there is still no good explanation of why Scheer and Hipper thought that Beatty was running for home in the so-called 'Run to the North' (The course was east of north). It did not occur to them that Beatty was joining the Grand Fleet. The new approach comes into its own in describing the night action. From the British viewpoint this was a confused series of attacks, largely unsuccessful, but seen from the German side it is much clearer. They were running steadily for the safety of the Horns Reef passage, and were only slightly distracted by the British attacks.

For both day and night actions there are very clear charts, and the student of Jutland will obtain a new insight. The text concludes with a collection of signals made by the German side during the battle. A point of great interest is to discover how long it took for a signal to pass from the bridge of one ship to the bridge of another, passing coding rooms and transmitter/receiver on the way. It is not possible to do this in all cases since differences between clocks suggest that some signals were received before they were sent. A reasonable interpretation suggests a time of about seven minutes for transmission, perhaps a little faster than in the RN.

There are a few minor quibbles. Early on the author refers to the much heavier deck protection of the German ships but there was little difference, with 1–2 inches in modern ships (a little thicker on the slopes). It should be appreciated that the protective deck was intended to keep out splinters from shells bursting above and not to stop shells impacting directly. One, perhaps two, splinters pierced the deck of surviving British ships. It is also said that the Germans improved flash protection after the fire in *Seydlitz* turrets at the Dogger Bank. This seems to be incorrect, the only additional precautions were to reduce the number of charges in the turret.

It is also said that German shells penetrated British armour without difficulty. The thickest armour hit in surviving ships was 9 inches (ships lost did not have anything thicker than 9 inch) and several shells failed to penetrate and burst behind. The failure of British shells is beyond dispute.

This is a well-written and interesting contribution to the story of Jutland and at £20 should find its way on to many bookshelves.

David K Brown, RCNC

Sumrall, RF, Sumner-Gearing Class Destroyers, Their Design, Weapons and Equipment.
Conway Maritime Press, London, 1995, 320 pages, 225 photos, 25 plans, 23 colour illustrations.
ISBN 0 85177 657 4. £35

The book opens with a short section on the development of US Navy destroyers between the wars, a topic which is not as well known in the UK as it should be. This development led to superb ships with welded, longitudinally-framed hulls, the best guns and fire control system in the world and machinery which was light, ompact, well subdivided, easily maintained and, above all, reliable. (I will return to US machinery later).

By 1940 development had led to the *Fletcher* class which on a design displacement of 2110 tons (standard) carried five single 5inch guns and 10 torpedo tubes and had a design speed of nearly 38 knots. The arrangement of five single mounts and a quadruple 1.1inch on the centre-line made the upper deck arrangement very cramped, and, even before they entered service, an improved design

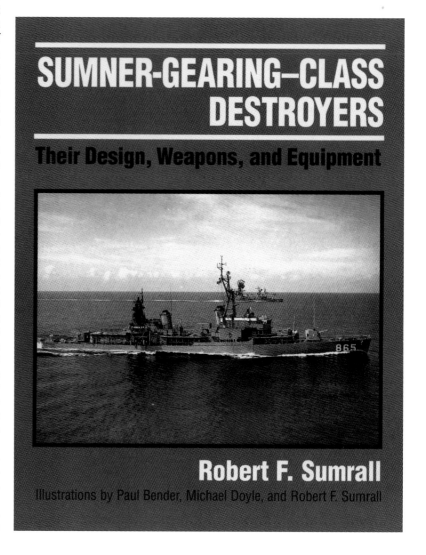

SUMNER-GEARING–CLASS DESTROYERS

Their Design, Weapons, and Equipment

Robert F. Sumrall

Illustrations by Paul Bender, Michael Doyle, and Robert F. Sumrall was sought. There were numerous studies, most of which are illustrated, and opinion soon hardened on a design using the same machinery as the *Fletcher*s and an almost identical hull (beam increased by a foot) but with the upperworks entirely changed around three twin 5 inch mounts. This became the *Allen M. Sumner* class; later an extra 14ft was inserted amidships to increase the fuel stowage, leading to the *Gearing* class.

There is then a detailed 'walkthrough' description of the ships. The first 19 are described as having a 'British style' bridge which was greatly disliked. I am not surprised; though loosely based on Mountbatten's ideas, used in most British Second World War destroyers, the USN derivative was obstructed and had poor visibility.

About the only complaint made of these classes were that they were wet. Again, I am not surprised as their freeboard was inadequate, even by the standards used by British constructors in 1939–45. Freeboard/sq rt length is a useful guide and British destroyers were expected to have a value of over 1.1 and on completion, most achieved at least 1.2 (and there were complaints from sea that *they* were wet!). The *Sumner*s seem to have achieved about 1.0 and the *Gearing*s 0.9. I would have given them a little more flare but that is a matter of hot debate. At the time, their wetness was blamed on the weight of two twin 5in turrets, well forward, but it is unlikely that this had much effect. Their bridge was rather far forward at 0.29 of the length which would have exacerbated the perceived motion.

The book continues with a description of the many conversions during and after the war. Their large hulls made this relatively simple and they became radar pickets, minelayers, specialist A/S vessels and carried prototype missile launchers, Dr Friedman, in his introduction, suggests that the British *Daring*s, whose concept owed much to the *Gearing*s, could not be modernised because their turrets were too high. I think this is wrong; the reason was, at their half-life guns were seen as outdated and there was no way of getting Seaslug into a *Daring*. The elaborate gun-bay of the 4.5inch Mk 6 made alteration difficult.

There are detailed sections on armament, radar and other equipment. These are clear and well illustrated but it is likely that most readers already have this information in other books. Only four of these ships were lost and there are some fascinating photos of ships which survived incredible damage. These classes must rank as the best destroyers of the Second World War and the author has done them justice, helped by excellent drawings by Paul Bender and Michael Doyle. The numerous photographs are well chosen and clear. Some foreign designs inspired by the *Sumner*s are mentioned but, strangely, the *Daring*s are not included, and their machinery, at least, was based on the *Sumner*s.

Machinery

It is worth looking in a little more detail at USN machinery and the author's views on its development. The first USN designs between the wars had machinery built by the shipbuilder to a (British) Parsons design. The Bureau of Engineering became unhappy with the design ability of Parsons and in May 1935 the US Espionage Act was invoked to prevent further involvement of foreign companies. This was partly due to intense lobbying by the design agency Gibbs & Cox (and Gibbs was related to the Roosevelts by marriage) who preferred machinery based on power-station experience, particularly by Westinghouse. Admiral Bowen, who became head of the Bureau in May 1935, gives[1] two specific, technical reason for his choice. The Westinghouse company had carried out a great deal of research into blade vibration and, though this work had been published, it had not been adopted by Parsons. The RN had put an experimental high-temperature, high-pressure plant into *Acheron* which never performed well. Its failings have been dismissed as teething troubles but the few accounts available suggest that

the fundamental problem was blade vibration. Bowen also points out that the number of moving parts was greatly reduced – eg *Benham* had 1,750 blades compared with 17,500 in a similar Parsons design – reducing first cost and improving reliability.

The *Mahan* class were given a Westinghouse-derived plant but the lack of experience of Gibbs & Cox led to a very congested layout which was very unpopular and got the new machinery a bad reputation. It was overweight and the promised savings did not materialise. However, the trials of the *Somers* in November 1937 showed a reduction of 20% in fuel consumption, with a considerable saving in weight. By this time the shipbuilders were fighting back and the *Gridley*s had Bethlehem machinery, which Sumrall says fully matched the performance of the Gibbs plant preferred by the Bureau. Bowen gives very different figures and your reviewer lacks the knowledge to decide.

In a decade, steam temperature had risen from 648 to 850°F and pressure from 400 to 580 lbs/in^2. Double reduction gearing had been introduced and, though there were teething troubles, these were soon overcome. It is not possible to detect any great change in cost of the ships, either way, due to the introduction of advanced machinery but, using conventional exchange rates, US destroyers were very expensive. Costs are very difficult to compare and the fact that US shipbuilders could compete in export markets suggests that the real costs may not have been very different from European builders.

Many books have been published about the destroyers of the Second World War but none have looked seriously at the technology of naval architecture and marine engineering and how these differed between navies (I have a draft!). Mr Sumrall gets closer than most and reminds us that the *Sumner* and *Gearing* classes were not only the best destroyers of the war but that other navies took a long while to catch up after the war. It is a book to be read with attention by enthusiasts and engineers alike.

[1] Vice Admiral Harold G Bowen, USN. *Ships' machinery and Mossbacks*, (Princeton, 1954).

David K Brown RCNC

Kingsley, FA (Ed, 10 authors), Radar, The Development of Equipments for the Royal Navy 1935–45.
Macmillan, Basingstoke, 1995, 310 pages, 95 illustrations.
ISBN 0 333 61210 8. £42.50

This book follows from *Radar at Sea* (Howse), going into considerably more technical detail. It is a tribute to the clarity of the authors' writing that your reviewer, whose electronics is barely A-level, could always follow what they were getting at.

The first section begins at the end of the First World War, with developments in radio and valve design which were to affect early radar development. Indeed, LSB Adler took out a provisional patent setting out the essential features of radar in 1928 while at the Signal School but it was not pursued. The Admiralty was quickly informed of Watson-Watt's classic trials of 1935 and speedily directed the Signal School to start work on naval radar. There was considerable debate, then and later, as to whether the navy should take part in a tri-service development or go it alone, based on the very great expertise of the Signal School in valve technology. The arguments seem closely balanced and naval work was concentrated at the School, though co-operation with developments elsewhere seems to have been good. This section leads on through gunnery sets to the cavity magnetron and the detection of U-boats.

The second section deals with basic theory with such interesting asides as height-estimation from the range at which various lobes were entered. It is followed by a section on valve technology and, as the writer points out, silica technology, which was so important, is dead and almost forgotten. This detail alone makes the book a valuable historical record. There is then a section on the metric air warning sets starting with type 79, the first production British naval radar – still in successful use in my first ship – followed by type 281 and the post war 960. The combined fit of 79/281 in Pacific Fleet carriers enabled them to estimate height at a greater range than the more sophisticated USN height-finders. There is then a shorter section dealing with Identification Friend or Foe (IFF).

The last three sections cover ship fitting, maintenance, and miscellaneous problems on a more personal level, usually involving 'unsocial hours', difficult travel and much hard work.

The story of radar in the Royal Navy was a great success, reflecting credit on all concerned. One might have welcomed a little more discussion of how this came about. First was the brilliance of the young scientists concerned; the number of those who achieved at least FRS is remarkable, with quite a few knighthoods, and some who even won popular renown. (What was the basis on which they were selected?) The attitude of the Board seems to have been understanding and helpful, whilst there were few problems at ship-level when the team came to fit their gadgets into an already overcrowded ship.

Appendices list the various types designed and fitted, the date at which sets were first fitted in individual ships (If accurate, this will be invaluable for dating photos of ships) and a list of manufacturers involved.

The book will be of most interest to the serious reader but there is a great deal for every one.

David K Brown, RCNC

Kingsley, FA (Editor), The Applications of Radar and other Electronic Systems in the Royal Navy in World War 2.
Macmillan, Basingstoke, 1995, 294 pages, 52 illustrations.
ISBN 0 333 62748 2. £42.50

This is the third book published for the Naval Radar Trust, devoted to recording the history of the introduction of radar in the navy. The first, *Radar at Sea*, was a general survey whereas the book now under review is a more technical study of the applications of radar. The subject is covered under the headings of Weapon direction and control, AIO, Fighter Direction, Electronic Counter Measures, HF/DF and German developments.

The first section is strong on the effectiveness of the whole system in that improvements in the radar soon showed the need for better directors, computers and, eventually, VT fuses. Little could be done about the proverbial 'way of a ship in the sea'. There are many useful tables of detection ranges and estimated kill probabilities.

Prior to the war the only input to the Action Information Organisation (AIO) was from visual observation and a single ARL table was adequate to keep the command in touch. As more and more information came in from air and surface radars more and better plots were required and fitted. There were many problems in ship-fitting and in its use, deriving from the secrecy attached to radar; those not in the know could not appreciate its importance. In the 1930s, with short-range fighters and no radar there was little which could be done to develop fighter-direction. The first modern carrier, *Ark Royal*, never had radar and information was supplied by visual signalling from *Sheffield*. Operation 'Pedestal' in 1942 was seen as a landmark as *Victorious* had the best AIO in the fleet. It was reasonably successful but near saturation. By the time the Pacific Fleet was formed, a good plotting team could handle 12 tracks per minute.

ECM was somewhat less glamorous, but vital when the Germans started to use radio-controlled bombs. The section on HF/DF is particularly welcome as it has not received enough credit for its vital role in the Battle of the Atlantic and it is hoped that historians will re-assess the value of this equipment. If anything, HF/DF was regarded as more secret than radar as much of its value would be lost if the Germans had realised that it was in use. Luckily, they decided that such equipment was impossible to fit in a ship. Credit is give to a Polish team for their important contribution.

The Germans has a small lead in surface and gunnery radars at the outbreak of war but this was soon lost when Hitler ordered work to be stopped on all projects which would not complete in six months. The British ASV sets were a particular shock to them and work was belatedly restarted.

This book is aimed at the informed reader, who will find it fascinating. It is hope that many of the points made will, in time, filter down to general historians.

David K Brown, RCNC

Plummer, R, Paddle Steamers at War 1939–45.
GMS Enterprises, Peterborough, 1995, 64 pages, c 80 photographs (Paperback).
ISBN 1 870384 39 3. c. £6.95

Few readers of *Warship* will be aware that the Royal Navy (RN) operated over 50 requisitioned paddle steamers as minesweepers and as estuary anti-aircraft (AA) ships during the Second World War. Their story is told in this fascinating little book.

The first section lists each ship by its peacetime area of operation, supplying brief notes on its operational history. For two of them the cycle had gone full circle, as the *Queen of Kent* and *Queen of Thanet* had been built as minesweepers in 1916 and converted into paddle steamers after that war. There are then a number of personal accounts by men who served in them dealing with the dreary but always dangerous task of minesweeping, the perils of the Dunkirk evacuation, etc.

The illustrations are mainly of the ships spiced with a few shots of life on board. They are well chosen, many have been drawn from private collections and not been used before, but the reproduction could have been better. If your interest lies in ships of the RN you will enjoy this book.

David K Brown, RCNC

Brown, A & Polglaze, R, HMS *Aristocrat*, A Paddler at War.
Waverley Excursions Ltd, Gwalia Buildings, Barry Docks, CF62 5QR. 72 pages, 55 illustrations.
£4.95 post free.

The LNER paddler *Talisman* was built in 1935 by Messrs A & J Inglis for service on the Clyde. Though she looked to be a typical Clyde paddle steamer she was actually very different, being diesel-electric with the motor on the paddle shaft. The main advantage was that bridge control was

easy and there were also savings in fuel and in wages. However, there were many problems; the entablature castings cracked, as did their replacements and there were problems with the salt water cooling system. When war broke out she was undergoing a major engine refit and was not taken over by the Admiralty until June 1940. Since the name *Talisman* was in use by a submarine she was renamed HMS *Aristocrat*.

Her early war service was in the Thames and Medway as an anti-aircraft (AA) ship; her armament varied but, eventually, she had four single pom-poms, three Oerlikons, two power-operated quadruple .303in turrets and two twin .303 Lewis. She took part in several rehearsals for the Dieppe raid but was lucky to be refitting at the time of the actual attack. Her days of glory came as Headquarters ship for the building of Mulberry B at Arromanches. Later, she provided AA protection round the Dutch coast.

This book tells the story of the ship and her men and gives a vivid picture of wartime life in a small warship. During five years of war service she had covered 46,583 miles without any further machinery problems. After the war she returned to the Clyde until laid up in 1966, and was scrapped the following year.

David K Brown, RCNC

Friedman, Norman, US Submarines since 1945 – An Illustrated Design History.
Naval Institute Press, Annapolis, (UK distributors, Airlife, Shrewsbury), 1994, 284 pages, 120 photos, many plans.
ISBN 1 55750 260 9. £52.95

As one would expect from Dr Friedman's earlier books, this new work is fascinating, revealing much of the thinking which lay behind the numerous designs of US submarines since the Second World War. When the war ended in 1945 the USN had a superb and numerous force of submarines intended to attack surface targets. They had scored against submarines but only on the surface. (HMS *Venturer* attacked a U-boat in

the only submerged sub v sub engagement of the Second World War). Trials with a pair of captured Type XXI U-Boats showed they were much quieter than contemporary US boats, demonstrating both the potential of similar craft in ASW and the threat from the large number of such boats being built in the USSR.

The *Tang* class incorporated most of the early lessons and were reasonably successful once their original, unreliable diesels had been replaced. A number of radical alternatives were also considered involving High Test Peroxide (HTP) or liquid oxygen in various plats. Hydrodynamic studies at DTMB led to the radical fat hull form of *Albacore* with a single propeller. The author points out the similarity with airship studies; in the UK this was even closer as the best of the post World War I airship forms had been proposed by Haslar, based on submarine work. The *Albacore* form and diesel-electric propulsion then came together in the *Barbel*s, largely copied in Holland and Japan.

Rickover was insistent that the innovation of nuclear power should not be endangered by failures in other parts of the ship and the first nuclear attack boats (SSNs) were of conventional twin-screw configuration. There were two reactor designs, water-cooled in *Nautilus* and sodium-cooled in *Seawolf*, both tested in shore prototypes. Though sodium cooling seemed the more promising, the problems proved insuperable. Early exercises with *Nautilus* showed the capability of the SSN; with very high speed for the day and the ability to remain submerged almost indefinitely, she could attack at will with very little chance of a successful counter-attack. It is interesting that *Nautilus* was said to have cost as much as two destroyers.

Skipjack was the first single-screw SSN, much improved in the *Thresher* class, particularly with her big spherical passive sonar. After her loss a redesign of the *Thresher*s became the *Sturgeon*s. The emphasis was turning to quiet submarines rather than very high-speed types, and there were a number of difficult problems to overcome. Dr Friedman says that blade-rate noise was not recognised before 1960 but I seem to remember joint discussions with US experts before that. He also says that computer-controlled milling machines were necessary to overcome the problem but all the early – and fairly successful – RN skewed propellers were made in the old-fashioned way.

As in this country, there were numerous studies into 'cheap' SSNs which resulted in the big, fast and expensive *Los Angeles* class, built in very large numbers. There is much mention of the sonar equipments and of the torpedoes which they fired – the Mk 45 Astor nuclear torpedo was said to have a kill probability of 2.0 as the risk to the firing ship was so high! There is so much of interest in this book that the only criticism is to ask for more – and more 'ship' technology would have been welcome. There is only passing reference to the structural problems of the large-diameter submarine, solved for both navies by Bill Kendrick at Dunfermline – the US classified his work more highly that the UK did (now largely declassified). Control problems and propeller-noise are mentioned, but there were many other aspects, and it was an area in which Anglo-American collaboration was particularly close. It is often argued that air-purification and its measurement was the greatest engineering achievement in the development of the SSN, while many on both sides of the Atlantic will remember difficulties with the materials for seawater systems.

Later chapters deal with the genesis of the *Seawolf* and later attempts at a cheaper submarine, the 'Centurion'. The missile submarine, from the early, clumsy boats to carry the Regulus cruise missile to the Polaris and Trident boats, have another chapter, and there is an interesting appendix on midgets. Like the UK Royal Navy, the USN looked at submarine aircraft carriers, landing ships and store carriers; they are described and illustrated, but, other than a few commando carriers, none were built.

The author makes very good use of photos taken while building, to show how equipment such as sonars were fitted into the outer envelope. Both photographs and plans have extensive captions which add greatly to their value whilst the detailed text is amplified by extensive end notes. The problems faced by the USN were similar to those experienced by the RN

and it is a mistake to assume that the former had a bottomless purse, particularly on the R & D side. This book is essential – and fascinating – reading for anyone wishing to understand the awesome power of the modern nuclear submarine.

David K Brown, RCNC

Stobart-Hook, B, Warships for the World.
Cross Publishing, Newport (IoW), 1994, 216 pages, 154 photographs. ISBN 1 873295 50. 2.

This book tells the story of Vosper-Thornycroft (VT) following the merger of the two famous founding companies in 1966; earlier books tell the separate histories before merger. The new company has been very successful in the export market and the author, who was Sales Director, explains at least some of the secrets of their success. The first step is to understand what the customer wants, point out opportunities which he may not have thought of and then to offer a package which he can afford. The package includes weapon integration, through-life support and, with RN assistance, training.

One can see the success of this policy through early corvettes, the very fast Mk 5 frigates for Iran and the powerful Mk 10 frigates for Brazil as well as in the numerous, successful fast patrol boats for many navies. In addition the company has built many ships for the Royal Navy (RN); it is surprising, however, that the author does not know that his customer and the design authority is MoD(PE), not MoD(N). The company has been well to the fore in new technology such as GRP construction, fast patrol boats, hydrofoils (through their work on HMS *Speedy* is not mentioned) and their own ideas for hovercraft.

It is well worth reading, though anecdotal in style and not always accurate. One would expect that VT with their close involvement in mine countermeasures (MCM) would know that the magnetic mine was not a German innovation of the Second World War but used in large numbers by the RN in 1918–19. The illustra-

tions are well chosen and a number are in colour.

David K Brown, RCNC

Ware, Chris, The Bomb Vessel.
Conway Maritime Press, London, 1994, 128 pages, 80 illustrations. ISBN 0 85177 631 0. £25

This fascinating book reminds the reader that the UK Royal Navy (RN) has always had an important role in coastal attack. One may recognise the Landing Craft Tank (Rocket) as being a close Second World War parallel and wonder if there is a current need. The bomb ketch originated in the late 17th century and the book describes their development until the early 19th century, surprisingly omitting the mortar vessels, mortar floats and mortar frigates of the Crimean War. This series of books from Conway is intended to make more readily available the wonderful plans collection of the National Maritime Museum, and the many plans reproduced in this book are both clear and interesting.

The earlier vessels had mortars fixed to fire forward and at constant elevation, which necessitated a rather strange rig, but in later vessels the mortars could train and elevate, permitting a more conventional rig. Like many other, my interest in these craft was kindled by Hornblower's success in *The Commodore* but it is now clear that C S Forester erred in describing bomb vessels of a century earlier. It seems strange that the armament of many of these vessels was mixed, with one 10in and one 13in mortar. The hulls had to very strong to withstand the recoil of the mortars and hence they proved very suitable for Polar exploration.

As is usual in this series, much use is made of the Navy Board questionnaires on sailing qualities. Your reviewer very much doubts if these heavy, bluff vessels could reach the speeds of 5–6kts so often claimed by their captains.

These interesting warships are little known and the author and publisher have done well to make their history better known.

David K Brown, RCNC

FROM MONITOR
TO MISSILE BOAT

COAST DEFENCE SHIPS AND COASTAL DEFENCE
SINCE 1860

George Paloczi-Horvath

FOREWORD BY ANTONY PRESTON

George Paloczi-Horvath, From Monitor to Missile Boat, Coast Defence Ships and Coastal Defence since 1860.
*Conway Maritime Press, 1996. 160 pages, 125 illustrations, 267 × 267 mm.
ISBN 0 85177 650 7. £30*

This book covers the development of coast defence and coast defence ships from the American Civil War to the present day. The major part concentrates on the development of the classic gun-armed coast defence ship which originated with the British and French floating batteries of the Crimean War, and evolved via Ericsson's *Monitor* and the early turret ships to the small coast defence battleships which formed the core of the major coast defence navies of the late 19th and 20th centuries. Coverage is also given, on a lesser scale, to static coastal defences including fortifications, artillery, minefields, etc. The final part, about 25 per cent of the total text, covers modern coast

defence from 1950, with particular emphasis on the evolution of coastal forces craft into the small to medium sized missile armed vessels of today.

It is not, however, a simple run through the development of ship design and fortifications. The author gives details of political and military background, discusses the meaning of important operations and other occurrences in the evolution of coast defence and the place of coast defence in naval strategy and tactics, its value in the past and present and its potential value in the future. In the process he has produced a very readable and thought-provoking narrative which is wide-ranging in its coverage of a subject which is complicated by difficulty of definition. For a start, coast defence vessels can as easily be used for attack as defence – the CSS *Virginia* and USS *Monitor* for example, are both in the class of coast defence vessels but when they had their famous engagement in Hampton Roads in 1861 one was attacking while the other was defending a harbour. More specifically the British First World War monitors were built for coastal attack

rather than defence (acknowledged in this book with their description as Coast *Offence* Monitors) but they still fit into the class of ships limited to coastal operations by a lack of seaworthiness and/or endurance. In a sense this is what sets the coast defence vessel apart: the sacrifice of oceangoing qualities reduces the requirements of size and weight providing ships of relatively high offensive power at a reasonable cost. This also makes them a first-class option for any country looking for deterrent defence against coastal assault, a strategy most successfully demonstrated by Sweden whose coast defence navy, aided by extensive coastal fortifications, has helped substantially in maintaining her neutrality.

At another level the complications of definition can be seen in the Russian *Sevastopol* class dreadnoughts – not coast defence vessels in the true sense (and not mentioned in this book) but nevertheless designed primarily to defend St Petersburg from a German assault (see *Warship 1994*). The book does mention the German 'Pocket Battleships', or more correctly 'armoured ships', of the 1930s which evolved from a series of design studies for coast defence vessels to become, in effect, long range armoured cruisers for attack on ocean trade, although this would not and did not prevent their use as coastal warships.

Whilst the larger coast defence vessels are described in some detail the smaller coast defence vessels – torpedo boats and coastal forces craft up to 1945 – are not the subject of close examination, which is not intended as a criticism merely as comment – a detailed coverage of these vessels on an international scale would have produced a book of greater size and price without adding greatly to its value as a study of coast defence issues. The post Second World War section does, however, cover these craft in some depth. The advent of the guided missile has enabled the development of coast defence vessels which, although still limited in ocean-going capacity, have substantial offensive capability and therefore deterrent qualities, enabling them to take over the role that was once the province of much larger and, relatively, more expensive ships.

From Monitor to Missile Boat is a well produced book, on good quality paper with well reproduced illustrations and, vitally important in a reference work, a good index. It provides a valuable insight into the true value of coast defence, a function often dismissed as the weapon of a weak nation, and is highly recommended to those with an interest in warship development.

John Roberts

Andrew Gordon, The Rules of the Game.
John Murray, 1996. 720 pages, over 40 photographs and drawings.
ISBN 0 7195 5533 7. £30

After so many books on the Battle of Jutland it is tempting to say, 'Not again', but this one is very different. It is in part a study of the system which led to the failure of the Royal Navy, the Grand Fleet and the Battle Cruiser Force to inflict a decisive defeat on the German High Seas Fleet, and in part a detailed discussion of how that victory was thrown away.

The 'Rules of the Game' of the title are all relevant to the story of how the Royal Navy accomplished the change from oak and canvas to steel and turbines. It is Gordon's submission that during the 50 years of that transition, the Royal Navy's stock of clear, empirical understanding of its 'product' (a battle- and war-winning machine) was 'pilfered' by the vested interests of 'process' (theoretical doctrine). He lists 28 themes:

- In times of peace, empirical experience fades and rationalist theory takes its place
- The advent of new technology assists the discrediting of previous empirical doctrine
- The purveyors of new technology will be the most evangelising rationalists
- Rationalism, unlike empiricism, tends to assume an accretion of vested interests
- The training establishment may try to ignore short bouts of empirical experience to preserve its 'rationalist' authority
- Military cultures impart doctrine by corporate ambience as much as by explicit teaching
- In long periods of peace 'ambient' doctrine may be no more than the habits of the years in which war has been forgotten
- In peacetime doctrine is vulnerable to commandeering by 'systems lobbyists'
- Innovations adopted in accordance with peacetime doctrine may lock the Fleet into both systems and doctrines which will fail the empirical test of war
- Purveyors of technical systems will seek to define performance criteria and trials conditions
- A service which neglects to foster a conceptual grasp of specialised subjects will have too few warriors able to interrogate the specialists
- The volume of [signal] traffic expands to meet capacity
- Signals 'capacity' tends to be defined by how much the senior end can transmit, rather than by how much the junior end can conveniently assimilate
- Signals' prioritising mechanisms become dislocated in times of overload
- Incoming traffic can act as a brake on decision-making
- The more signals, the more the sun shines on signallers
- The 'centre' must subject its own transmissions to the strictest self-denying ordinance
- Signalling promotes the centralisation of authority
- There is an inverse law between robust doctrine and the need for signalling
- Heavy signalling, like copious orders, is symptomatic of doctrinal deficiency
- The promise of signalling fosters a neglect of doctrine
- War-fighting commanders may find themselves bereft of communications facilities on which they have become reliant in training
- Properly disseminated doctrine offers both the cheapest and the most secure command-and-control method yet devised by man
- Every proven military incompetent has previously displayed attributes which his superiors rewarded
- Peacetime highlights basic 'primary' skills to the neglect of more advanced, more lateral 'secondary' abilities, the former being easier to teach, easier to measure and more agreeable to superiors
- The key to efficiency lies in the correct balance between organisation and method
- Doctrine draws on the lessons of history.

To illustrate the relevance of these 'syndromes' Gordon traces the evolution of tactical doctrine from the time of Adm Sir George Tryon in the early 1890s to Jutland in 1916. The death of Tryon in the notorious collision between his flagship HMS *Victoria* and her consort HMS *Camperdown* in 1893 set back the cause of tactical innovation for at least 25 years, and over-centralisation became the dominant doctrine of command.

The second part of the book gives the most informative account of just how the Grand Fleet worked in 1916, and tells in chilling detail the horrors of being under fire from massive guns. He points out that the High Seas Fleet offered the British four golden shots at serious damage, if not partial annihilation. The fact that all four chances were missed is an awful indictment of the system of tactics.

To sum up, the book presents the author's arguments clearly and with sufficient shafts of wit to sustain interest throughout. Where pedantic detail is needed to explain such things as discrepancies in track-charts and signal logs, it is there; where it is superfluous, the narrative says it all. Perhaps not the last word, but certainly the most profound study of Jutland this reviewer has ever read.

Antony Preston

SHORT NOTICES

David Davies, Fighting Ships – Ships of the Line 1793–1815.
Constable, 1996. 150 × 235mm, 8 plates, 24 maps and drawings.
ISBN 0 09 476020 9. £19.95

A concise account of the achievements of the line-of-battle ships which fought the Great War against France. Readable and informative, but a book for the non-specialist.

Bob Nicholls, Statesmen & Sailors – Australian Maritime Defence 1870–1920.
Australia, 1995. 150 × 210mm, 19 photographs, 2 maps.
ISBN 0 646 23609 1. Price not known

Endorsed by the Navy League of Australia, this book covers the politics of creating the fledgling Royal Australian Navy out of the old State navies and the Royal Navy's Australian Squadron. Politics is inseparable from personalities, and this well-researched book sheds light in many forgotten corners of Victorian and Edwardian imperial policy.

Frank Pearce, Heroes of the Fourth Service.
Robert Hale, 1996. 130 × 215mm, 24 photographs, 5 maps. ISBN 0 7090 5879 9. £16.99
A tribute to the courage and endurance of the civilian seamen who kept the Merchant Navy going through the Second World War. Although little new ground is covered it is an eloquent tribute to the people who stood firm against a ferocious onslaught. Had the Allied merchant seamen (who included many from neutral countries) ever refused to sail, the Axis would have won the war before the might of America could be mobilised.

A O 'Cappy' Masters, Memoirs of a Reluctant Batsman – New Zealand Servicemen in the Fleet Air Arm 1940–45.
Janus, London, 1995. 135 × 220mm, 35 photographs. ISBN 1 85756 148 1. £15.95
An affectionate memoir dedicated to the memory of three Royal New Zealand Navy pilots who lost their lives. The photographs are mostly standard, but the text gives many insights into wartime naval aviation.

Jon Guttman, Defiance at Sea.
Arms & Armour, 1995. 155 × 235mm, 32 illustrations. ISBN 1 85409 240 5. £16.99
A total of 14 concise accounts of naval actions, starting with the *Revenge* in 1591 and ending with the Argentine submarine *San Luis* in 1982. The choice of subjects is eccentric, to say the least, and the student of naval warfare will learn little that has not been done in greater depth elsewhere.

James Foster Tent, E-Boat Alert, Defending the Normandy Invasion Fleet.
Naval Institute Press, Annapolis, Maryland, 1996 ISBN 1 55750 805 4
Most books on the Allied invasion of Normandy in June 1944 concentrate on the amphibious operations and subsequent land battles without much more than a passing reference to the naval campaign that secured the invasion shipping lanes and beach heads against German naval intervention. J.F. Tent has made a substantial contribution to redressing the balance with this thoroughly researched analysis of the threat posed to the invasion fleet by the *Kriegsmarine*'s E-Boats.

The E-Boats' potential to cause disruption to the invasion shipping was vividly demonstrated in an attack on an American training exercise just weeks before D-Day. Oral history and original source material is used to good effect in providing a detailed insight, from the perspective of both sides, into how the Allies were able to prevent a repetition of this catastrophe and deal a crushing blow to the E-Boat force in just over a week after the landings. *E-Boat Alert* is recommended as an enlightening account of an otherwise neglected episode in naval history.

NAVAL BOOKS ANNOUNCED

Chris Bennett, Supercarrier: USS George Washington. *Motorbooks, 1996. £9.95*

D K Brown, The Design and Construction of British Warships 1939–1945
Volume I: Major Warships
Volume II: Submarines, Escorts and Coastal Forces
Volume III: Amphibious Warfare Vessels and Auxiliaries
Conway Maritime Press, 1996. £25 each

Yves Buffetaut and Jean Restayn, U-Boat 1939–45. *Histoire & Collections, 1996. £16.95*

An illustrated survey of the submarines of the *Kriegsmarine*.

Conway, Conway's All the World's Fighting Ships 1947-1995. *Conway Maritime Press, 1995. £75*
Comprehensive overview of the world's navies since the Second World War; covers recent shake-ups in the world's navies and assesses developments in the Soviet Navy in the light of the flood of new information.

WJR Gardner, Anti-submarine Warfare. *Brassey's 1996. £25*

Denis Griffiths, Steam at Sea: Two centuries of steampowered ships. *Conway Maritime Press, Feb 1997. £30*

David Hobbs, Aircraft Carriers on the Royal and Commonwealth Navies: The Complete Illustrated Encyclopedia from World War I to the Present. *Greenhill Books, Aug 1996. £35*

Jane's Battleships of the Twentieth Century. *Ed Tony Gibbons and Bernard Ireland, HarperCollins, Oct 1996. £25*

David Jefferson, Coastal Forces at War: Royal Navy Little ships in World War 2. *Patrick Stephens, 1996. £17.99*

R D Layman, Naval Aviation in the First World War: its impact and influence. *Chatham Publishing, Sep 1996. £22.50*

David Lyon, Sea Battles in Close-up: The Age of Nelson. *Ian Allan, 1996. £24.99*

Brendan A Maher, Passage to Sword Beach: Minesweeping in the Royal Navy. *Naval Institute Press, Annapolis, distributed by Airlife Publications, Shrewsbury, 1996. £24.95*

Gerhard Koop/Klaus-Peter Schmolke

Die deutschen Zerſtörer 1935-1945

Bernard & Graefe Verlag

The Imperial Japanese Navy's attempt to take Midway's Atoll.

David Stevens, The Royal Australian Navy in World War II. *Allen & Unwin, Aug 1996. £19.95*

Ian Sturton, All the World's Battleships 1906 to the Present (re-issue). *Conway Maritime Press, Nov 1996. £15*

Cdr Jeff Tall and Paul Kemp, HM Submarines in Camera 1901–1996. *Sutton Publishing, Nov 1996,. £17.99*

Julian Thompson, Imperial War Museum War at Sea. *Sidgwick and Jackson, 1996. £25*
Naval actions of World War II.

Ian Trenowden, Stealthily by Night: The Coppists. *Crecy Books, 1996. £18.99*
The first full-length book about Mountbatten's combined operations men who secretly surveyed enemy beaches prior to invasion. The information they gathered on gradients, currents, sandbars, beach exits, mines, etc was of vital importance to invasion plans. Operating on dark nights, they were dropped a few miles off shore from submarines or launches and paddled or swam in to do their exhausting work.

Nathan Miller, War at Sea: A Naval History of World War II. *Scribner, 1996. £20*

Bob Nicholls, Statesmen & Sailors, Australian Maritime Defence 1870–1920. *published by the author, 1995. £14.95*
This important account of how Australia acquired a navy is available from the author at 25 Duke Street, Balmain, NSW 2041, Australia. Tel/fax: [02] 810 7417 (£19.75 incl. p&p)

Robert S Parkin, Blood on the Sea: American Destroyers lost in WWII. *Spellmount, 1996. £20*
The histories of 71 US destroyers.

Jurgen Rohwer, War at Sea 1939–1945. *Chatham Publishing, Aug 1996. £28*

Gerhard Koop and Klaus-Peter Schmolke, Die deutschen

Zerstorer 1935–1945. *Bernard & Graefe Verlag, Bonn, 1995 250 × 210 mm, 272 pages, numerous photographs, plans and maps, ISBN 3-7637-5940-9*
This comprehensive account (in German) of the destroyers of the Third Reich includes some remarkable photographs of warships in action during the Second World War.

Don Sheppard, Blue Water Sailor: The Story of a Destroyer Officer. *Presidio Press distributed by Greenhill Books, 1996. £17.99*
Operations in a destroyer during the 1950s and 60s.

Peter C Smith, Eagle's War: War Stories of HMS Eagle. *Crecy Books, 1996. £18.99*

Peter S Smith, The Battle of Midway. *Spellmount, 1996. £18.95*

VIDEOS

The Destroyers. *Castle Vision, 1991, 48 mins. £14.95*

Great Sea Battles of World War II. *Castle Vision, 1991, 58 mins. £14.95*

U-Boat War. *Castle Vision, 1990, 55 mins. £14.95*

The Battle of the Atlantic. *Luther Pendragon, 1993, 90 mins. £14.95*

London stockists: National Maritime Museum, Nauticalia Ltd, yacht chandlers, etc

THE NAVAL YEAR IN REVIEW

The events covered in this review stretch from approximately May 1995 to June 1996, with some information about earlier and later events.
Compiled by Antony Preston

After five years of uncertainty the navies of the Western Alliance seem to have achieved a plateau of stability. Budgets remain tight but the worst of the massive 'downsizing' has come to an end, and there is no more talk of using military cutbacks to finance some mythical 'peace dividend'. Although the Russian Navy continues to grapple with its internal problems it shows little sign of returning to the menacing status it adopted before the fall of communism. Outside the traditional framework of the Cold War, non-aligned countries continue to expand their navies, notably in the Asia-Pacific region.

It is fortunate that the potential flashpoints of the Gulf and Bosnia produced no naval crisis during the period under review, but the dispute over territorial waters in the South China Sea will not be solved unless China chooses to compromise with its neighbours.

WESTERN EUROPE AND NATO

Belgium: a rumoured sale of three *Aster* class coastal minehunters to Greece did not materialise, and the ships are still laid up. Approval was won, however, to build four new coastal minesweepers equipped with the French Sterne influence minesweeping system. The first is to start construction in 1996 at the SKB-Polyship glass fibre-reinforced plastic (GRP) facility.

Canada: In the summer of 1995 the Department of National Defence announced the deferment of plans to acquire submarines to replace the ageing *Ojibwa* class. This would seem to put an end to hopes of buying the *Upholder* class from the Royal Navy, but the latest plans are to acquire them in 1997 and to retrofit a Canadian-developed Proton-Exchange Membrane Fuel Cell (PEM-FC) air-independent propulsion (AIP) system. Alternatively the system could be developed for a class of new-built submarines.

Plans to build four air defence variants of the 'City' class patrol frigates have been abandoned. Instead four ships will be retrofitted with the Signaal APAR and SMART-L radars and the US Standard 2 (SM-2) missile system, around the turn of the century.

HMCS *Kingston*, first of 12 maritime coast defence vessels (MCDVs) was delivered in December 1995 and will be formally commissioned later in 1996. Plans to equip them with a full mine countermeasures (MCM) capability were dropped as an economy measure, but an advanced indigenous system is under development.

France: The *Marine Nationale* has been hit by severe budget problems, and there is now no chance of a second nuclear-powered aircraft carrier (CVN). The *Clemenceau* is to pay off in 1997, and it is likely that her sister *Foch* will go into reserve when the CVN *Charles de Gaulle* becomes fully operational in 1998–1999. Eventually a smaller and less capable carrier may be built, possibly a slower helicopter carrier.

With all four *Rubis* class nuclear attack submarines (SSNs) now modernised to the standard of the later *Amethyste* class, resources will be concentrated on building the third and fourth *Triomphant* strategic submarines (SSBNs). The second of class, *Le Temeraire*, will be rolled out in 1996. The diesel-electric submarine (SSK) force will not be replaced.

A new air defence coordination system designated OP3A has completed trials in the destroyer *Jean de Vienne*, and will be retrofitted to another 21 surface combatants. Only five *La Fayette* class frigates will be built, and work on the fourth, the *Jaureguiberry*, started at Lorient in July 1995. The *Courbet* is running trials and will be fully operational by the end of 1996.

Germany: The German armed forces are severely constrained by budget cuts, but little has been done to rationalise the naval industry. There are still two submarine builders, four frigate builders and two minehunter builders, an expensive luxury. The submarine force is to be reduced to 12 SSKs, but only four of the new Type 212 have been funded. By the time they are ready from 2003 onwards the Type 206A boats will be close to the end of their effective lives. Hopes of selling most of the unmodernised Type 206 boats to Singapore came to nothing and they are being offered to other countries, including Poland.

The second of the Type 123 *Brandenburg* class frigates, the *Schleswig-Holstein*, was commissioned late in 1995, and her sisters *Bayern* and *Mecklenburg-Vorpommern* will be in commission before the end of 1996. Final authority was given on 13 June 1996 to build three Type 124 air

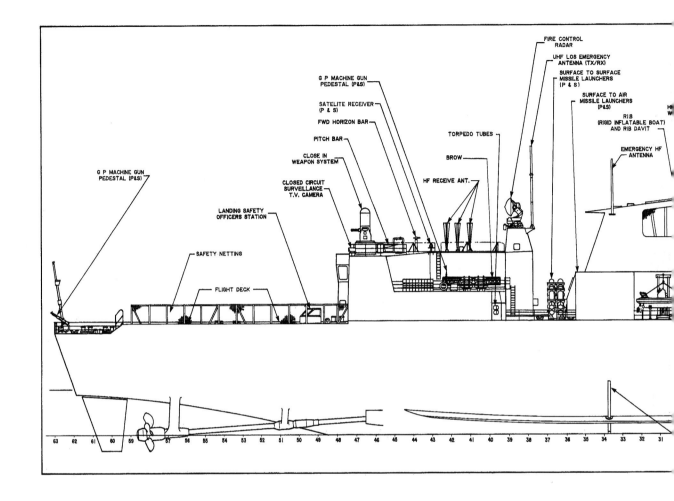

defence frigates at a cost of DM2.9 billion, with an option for a fourth unit. First steel is, however, unlikely to be cut for some months.

A total of 36 fast attack craft (FACs) remain in service, and it likely that some will be modernised. The original order for Type 332 *Frankenthal* class minehunters was completed in April 1996, but a supplementary order has been placed for two, to be delivered in 1998.

The plans to build an 18,000-tonne amphibious transport have been cancelled, but it is hoped to build a cheaper 10,000-ton ship for out-of-area operations.

Greece: The Hellenic Navy has acquired a number of modern ships in recent years, including four ex-US Navy *Charles F Adams* (DDG-2) class air defence destroyers, three ex-*Knox*

(FF-1052) class frigates and a fifth *Kortenaer* class frigate from the Royal Netherlands Navy. The second of four MEKO 200 type frigates, HS *Spetsai*, is scheduled to be completed in a Greek shipyard in 1996.

A major upgrade for the four IKL Type 209/1100 *Glavkos* class submarines will be finished in 1997, but there is no report of funding for bringing the newer Type 209/1200 *Poseidon* class to the same standard. Notwithstanding, the Navy is considering the acquisition of more submarines to counter the strength of the Turkish Navy.

Two more Type 148 FACs have been acquired from the Federal German Navy, bringing the total to four. Two very old minehunters have been acquired from the Italian Navy, but there is an urgent need for a modern MCM capability.

Italy: The Italian Navy's long suspended 'S 90' submarine project has now been officially cancelled, and in its place is a new Memorandum of Understanding (MoU) to build a variant of the German Type 212 design at Fincantieri's Monfalcone shipyard. Details are being worked out between Fincantieri and the German Submarine Consortium, but the present timetable allows for a start to be made in 1998. Two boats would be delivered in 2004, and the Italian Navy will take an option on two more.

Three major surface units, the veteran helicopter-carrying cruiser *Vittorio Veneto* and the two *Audace* class air defence destroyers, will reach the end of their effective lives by the end of the century. As the third partner in the 'Horizon' frigate project, the Italian Navy has officially declared an intention to order six ships, but a

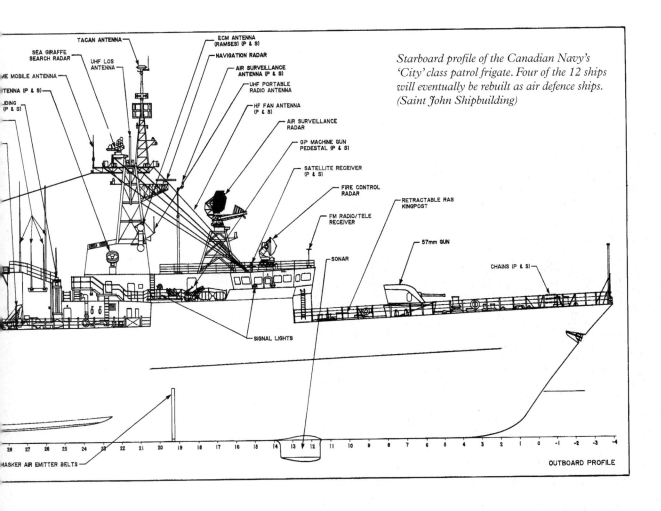

Starboard profile of the Canadian Navy's 'City' class patrol frigate. Four of the 12 ships will eventually be rebuilt as air defence ships. (Saint John Shipbuilding)

total of four seems more realistic.

The *Granatiere*, last of four ex-Iraqi frigates taken over for general patrol duties, completed her overhaul in January 1996. A new class of eight 25-knot 1000-tonne patrol craft is projected but no further details have been released. These ships will supplement a new group of four coastal patrol craft now ordered. Drug smuggling and illegal immigration are now serious problems.

With the minehunter *Rimini* delivered in March 1996 the *Gaeta* class is now complete. Six new coastal minehunters of an enlarged design are planned but chronic financial problems have caused this project to be deferred. However the Italian Navy now has 12 modern MCM ships.

The Netherlands: Budget-cutting in the wake of the Cold War has reduced the submarine force to only four *Walrus* class boats, and two of the surviving four *Kortenaer* class, HNlMS *Abraham Crijnssen* and HNlMS *Piet Hein*, were sold to the United Arab Emirates (UAE) in April 1996. However the last of the *Karel Doorman* class, HNlMS *Van Speijk*, was commissioned last summer. The keel of the first of two air defence/command frigates (*Luchtverdedingings en Commando Fregaat* or LCF) will be laid in August 1997, followed by the second in May 1998, both at the Royal Schelde shipyard in Flushing. Latest reports suggest that one or two more may be funded, as an alternative to modernising the two *Jacob van Heemskerck* class frigates.

Late in 1995 work started on converting three of the *Alkmaar* class Tripartite minehunters to control ships for the German Troika drone mine clearance system. Another four *Alkmaars* will receive a new command system and the Franco-Swedish Propelled Variable Depth Sonar (PVDS).

The new underway replenishment ship (AOR) *Amsterdam* joined the fleet in September 1995 and the amphibious dock transport (LPD) *Rotterdam* will be ready for launching in January 1997.

Norway: The Royal Norwegian Navy (RNorN) plans to build up to six frigates to replace the four surviving *Oslo* class. Design-study contracts were let in September 1995 to Dutch, French, German and Norwegian shipyards. This is a reversal of a previous policy of relying only on FACs as the core of the fleet, but work is proceeding on a new class of advanced FACs (see below).

The Finnish fast attack craft Oulo *firing a Swedish RBS-15 anti-ship missile. (Saab Dynamics)*

The French frigate La Fayette *(F710) shows how 'stealth' characteristics can affect the appearance of warships. (DCN)*

The layout of radars, electronic warfare antennas and satellite communications receivers on the island superstructure of the French nuclear carrier Charles de Gaulle *(DCN).*

The French offshore patrol vessel Flanant *fitting out at CMN's Cherbourg yard in January 1996. (Antony Preston)*

The Royal Netherlands Navy 'M' type frigate HNIMS Van Amstel. *(RNethN Audio Visual Service)*

The new amphibious dock transport (LPD) Rotterdam *is to be launched in 1997. (RNethN Audio Visual Section)*

All four of the *Oksöy* class mine-hunters have been delivered, as well as the first of five *Alta* class minesweeper variants. These ships are the most unconventional mine countermeasures (MCM) vessels in existence, using a surface-effect catamaran hull. With production tailing off early in 1997 the RNorN is looking for a replacement for its ageing fleet of FACs. In November 1995 design-study contracts were awarded and the prototype *Skjold* was ordered from Kvaerner Mandal last September. *Skjold* would be completed in 1998–99, and the rest would follow by 2003 at the latest.

Portugal: Despite severe financial cutbacks the Portuguese Navy has striven hard to maintain effectiveness. No replacement is in sight for the three ageing *Daphne* type submarines, but a choice will probably not be made until the Spanish Navy makes its own decision on a *Daphne* replacement.

A second priority is the modernisation of the MCM force. The Portuguese

Navy is an observer in the Belgian minesweeper programme, but an alternative is collaboration with the Spanish CME programme. Negotiations began in 1995 to buy the redundant US Navy tank landing ship USS *Newport* (LST-1179).

Spain: The age of the submarine force gives cause for worry, but there is no sign of a decision on the future size of the force. The 'Scorpéne' design is under development jointly by Empresa Naçional Bazán and DCN in France, but this is an export project, with no guarantee of Spanish Navy interest.

The projected in-service date for the first of the planned F-100 type frigates is in some doubt. The cancellation of the agreement to buy the Signaal APAR radar and SEWACO XI command system in favour of the US Navy's SPY-1F radar and Aegis weapon control system will necessitate a total redesign of the hull.

The first GRP-hulled *Contra Minas Español* (CME) was laid down in 1995 at Cartagena, for delivery in

1998. Another four minesweeper variants are planned but no funds have been allocated. The new AOR *Patiño* has been delivered and the new LPD, probably to be named *Juan de Austria*, will be launched at Ferrol in July 1996.

Sweden: Despite a round of defence cuts the Royal Swedish Navy has secured key elements of its new construction programme. Following her launch in February 1995 the A 19 type submarine *Gotland* started sea trials in July and was formally commissioned in April 1996, the world's first submarine designed with an AIP plant. Her sister *Uppland* was launched at Kockums' Malmö yard in February, and will be commissioned in 1997 with the last of the class, HSwMS *Halland*.

The 'Submarine 2000' is no more than a conceptual study, but Kockums has launched the 'Viking' project to pave the way towards a common submarine for Denmark, Norway and Sweden, and perhaps Finland. The Royal Swedish Navy would require

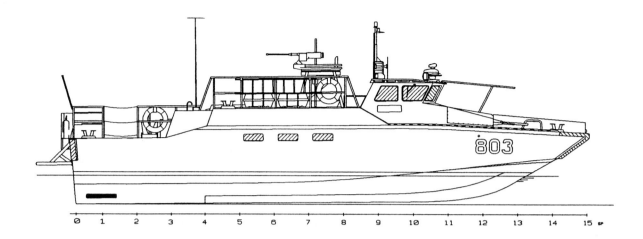

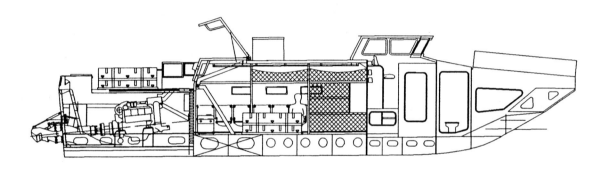

The Royal Norwegian Navy has ordered 16 Stridsbåt-90 *fast assault craft from Dockstavarvet in Sweden. (Dockstavarvet)*

Masthead array of a Portuguese Navy MEKO 200 type frigate of the Vasco da Gama *class. Note the MW-08 surveillance radar and the STIR tracker, as well as various antennas. (Signaal)*

Four Landsort *class minehunters of the Royal Swedish Navy helped to sweep old Soviet minefields off the Estonian port of Paldiski in May 1996. (Celsius Tech)*

five submarines to replace the two modernised *Sjöormen* class and the three *Näcken* class. The A 14 type *Sjöbjörnen* has been sold to Singapore for training, and it seems likely that the submarine force will decline from its present total of 13 to as few as nine or ten by the end of the century.

Karlskronavarvet started construction in 1996 of the first of two YS-2000 type missile-armed FACs,

with an option on two more. Some 'stealth' features from the technology-demonstrator *Smyge* are incorporated into the design and armament includes the new Bofors 57mm L/70 Mk 3 gun mounting, the Saab RBS-15 Mk 3 and anti-submarine sensors and weaponry. If the later units are built they will be configured for surface warfare. A new class of 36-metre GRP minehunters is also under

(Below left) A Goteborg *class corvette of the Royal Swedish Navy, configured for anti-submarine warfare with lightweight torpedo-launchers replacing heavyweight torpedoes and missiles. (CelsiusTech)*

(Below) The Swedish submarine Gotland *is the first in the world built from the keel up with an air-independent propulsion (AIP) system. (Kockurns)*

construction. The first, HSwMS *Styrsö*, is to be delivered in 1996, and the *Spärö*, *Skiftö* and *Sturkö* will follow in 1997.

Turkey: The third and fourth IKL Type 209/1400 submarines are under construction at Gölcük Shipyard, but in spite of having eight modern German-designed submarines in service the Turkish Navy retains nine elderly ex-US Navy boats, mainly for harbour training.

The *Oruc Reis*, second of four lengthened MEKO 200 *Barbaros* class frigates, was commissioned in March. Her sisters *Salih Reis* and *Kemal Reis* are expected to be commissioned in 1998, by which time a decision can be expected on the next generation of frigates. Current plans are to build six new frigates, and already bidders are trying to interest Turkey in various designs. The US Navy has offered three *Oliver Hazard Perry* (FFG-7) class for delivery in 1996, subject to Congressional approval. Names selected are *Gaziantep* (ex-*Antrim*), *Giresun* (ex-*Flatley*) and *Gelibolu* (ex-*Clifton Sprague*), but at the time of writing Congress has delayed delivery because of a diplomatic dispute over aid-flights to Armenia.

The smaller Taskiszak Shipyard has delivered two *Yildiz* class 56-metre FACs and three more are on order. Six coastal minehunters are required to replace 40-year old vessels, but funds have not yet been allocated.

United Kingdom: The second Trident missile-armed nuclear submarine (SSBN) HMS *Victorious* began her first deterrent patrol late in 1995, and the *Vigilant* completed contractor's sea trials at the end of May 1996. The last of class, HMS *Vengeance*, will not become operational until 1999, but the last of the A3 Polaris-armed *Resolution* class, HMS *Repulse*, completed her last patrol in mid-May 1996. In theory, at least, the higher reliability of the *Vanguard* class design and the Trident II missile system allows the deterrent patrols to be maintained temporarily with only two SSBNs.

The projected Batch 2 *Trafalgar* class (B2TC) project has moved a step closer to fruition with the award of the prime contract to GEC-Marconi. The arming of five SSNs with BGM-109 Tomahawk cruise missiles will go ahead, and the contract to upgrade the SMCS command system was awarded to Loral and GEC Marine in October 1995. Although only three SSNs are included in the current long-term costings (LTCs), a total of five will be needed to maintain a total of 12 SSNs.

HMS *Ark Royal*, the ten-year old support carrier, is currently laid up and will start a two-year modernisation in 1997. Her two sisters have been taking turns to maintain patrols off Bosnia, flying the upgraded F/A.2 version of the Sea Harrier, armed with the Blue Vixen radar and AIM-120 AMRAAM missile.

The Type 23 'Duke' class frigate HMS *Somerset* has been commissioned recently. Her sister *Grafton* will be delivered in November 1996, followed by the *Sutherland* in February 1997. Three more, to be named *Kent*, *St Albans* and *Portland*, were ordered at the end of February 1996, and will be delivered in 1999-2001.

The formal go-ahead to the 'Horizon' project's Principal Anti Air-warfare Missile System (PAAMS) last December helped to head off attempts to cancel the whole project. The Aster-15 missile, the core of PAAMS, passed a number of milestones in 1995 and is expected to start sea trials off France in December 1996.

Despite the transfer of four *Broadsword* class frigates to Brazil the Royal Navy's total of escorts will not

Layout of the Type 2076 Integrated Sonar Suite designed for the Royal Navy's new Batch 2 Trafalgar *class (B2TC). (Ferranti-Thomson)*

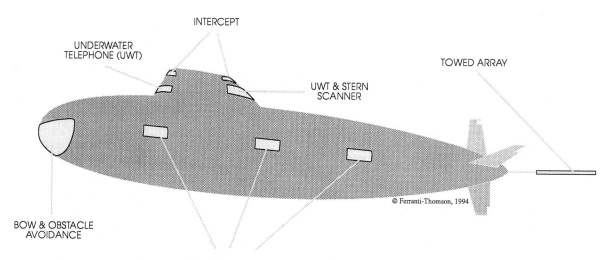

The nuclear attack submarine HMS Trafalgar *on completion of a major refit at Devonport in April 1996. (DML)*

HMS Cornwall, *a Batch 3 Type 22 frigate undergoing a refit at Devonport in 1996. (DML)*

sink below the ordained figure of 35 because of new construction. However, it does imply that the commissioning of the remaining Type 23 frigates will result in some of the older Type 42 destroyers going into reserve.

The new amphibious assault helicopter carrier *Ocean* was launched in July 1995, but sustained some damage during the launch. She is to be repaired on the Clyde before proceeding to Barrow in Furness for final fitting-out. The logistic landing ship *Sir Bedivere* completed a major SLEP at Rosyth and rejoined the Royal Fleet Auxiliary in April 1996. Two of the five remaining ships have not been given the SLEP, but funds are likely to be available for only one more. Two LPDs to replace the *Fearless* and *Intrepid* were ordered this year, to be named *Albion* and *Bulwark*.

THE UNITED STATES

It has been said in jest that the US Navy's problems give poverty a bad name, but the fact is that the 'drawdown' imposed by Congress has cut a mighty swathe through President Reagan's 600-ship Navy. As the euphoria subsides President Clinton has come to realise that he cannot use the Department of Defense budget as an endless source of money to balance the federal budget, and there are welcome signs that the worst of the cuts are over.

The fourth *Theodore Roosevelt* (CVN-71) class nuclear aircraft carrier, the USS *John C Stennis* (CVN-74) was commissioned in December 1995. Work is well advanced on her sister *Harry S Truman* (CVN-75) and the keel of the *Ronald Reagan* (CVN-76) was laid at the end of

1995. The original nuclear carrier, the USS *Enterprise* (CVN-65), returned to service in the summer of 1995, bringing the total of carriers up to 13, but the conventionally-powered USS *America* (CV-66) will decommission in September 1996, followed by the USS *Constellation* (CV-62) late in 1997. The process of securing funding for *CV/CVN-77 is under way,* but the debate on the design continues. Some in the naval aviation community think that there is scope for improvement over the 30-year old *Nimitz* (CVN-68) design which is itself a derivative of the original *Forrestal* (CV-59) design.

After seven years under construction the new nuclear attack submarine *Seawolf* (SSN-21) is complete, and one of her two sisters, the *Connecticut* (SSN-22) will follow in 1998. The unnamed *SSN-23* has been

The destroyer USS John S McCain *(DDG-56) moving down the Kennebec River in Maine after delivery by Bath Iron Works. (BIW)*

The newly converted mine countermeasures support ship USS Inchon *(MCS-12) was an amphibious assault carrier (LPH) until last year. (Ingalls Shipbuilding)*

authorised despite strenuous opposition, but she will not be ready until the next century. Completion of the last of the 59 *Los Angeles* (SSN-688) class in the summer of 1996 brings to an end a colossal programme spanning nearly a quarter of a century. The class has been in production for so long that the time has come to consider the future of the oldest units. The *Baton Rouge* (SSN-689) was stricken at the beginning of 1995 after damage sustained in an underwater collision with a Russian submarine. The cost of re-coring nuclear reactors has forced the US Navy to retire many older SSNs, and only 24 of the *Sturgeon* (SSN-637) class were still active in 1995.

The SSBN force is also being run down in numbers, with all the older boats stricken or converted to non-strategic roles. The *Ohio* (SSBN-720) class have a mix of Trident I and Trident II missiles, and although all 18 of the class have been commissioned, a decision to reduce the SSBN force to only 14 units suggests that four of the earlier Trident I submarines will be laid up. The others will be rearmed with the longer-range Trident II to simplify logistics.

According to a recent fleet summary published in the US Naval Institute *Proceedings*, the status of the four *Iowa* (BB-61) class battleships is unclear. The Navy maintains that it cannot afford to run them, a view supported by the House National Security Committee, which initiates budget appropriations. In contrast, the Senate Armed Services Committee has responded by opposing the move, on the grounds that the battleships' firepower is essential to littoral warfare. As a result the Defense Department Appropriations Bill of December 1995 forbids the spending of any money on the ships to reinstate them or maintain them, whereas the Defense Department Authorization Bill of January 1996 requires the Navy to reinstate the two battleships which are in best condition. The Navy is asking Congress to clarify its intentions, and, pending that decision, is keeping the *Iowa* (BB-61) and *Wisconsin* (BB-64) as Category B Mobilization Assets rather than reserve warships. But that is not the end of the story; like the *New Jersey* (BB-62), the *Missouri* (BB-63) is earmarked for preservation as a memorial, on account of her historical importance. However, the 'Mighty Mo' is one of the two best ships (the *Wisconsin* (BB-64) is the other).

The nuclear cruiser fleet has been thinned out, and only two of the *Virginia* (CGN-38) class remain in service, along with the two *California* (CGN-36) class and the 34-year-old *Bainbridge* (CGN-25). With 27 conventional Aegis cruisers in service, production has switched to the *Arleigh Burke* (DDG-51) class Aegis destroyers. By the end of 1996 18 will have been delivered and 13 more are under construction or authorised. The first improved Flight IIA ship, to be named *Oscar Austin* (DDG-79), and later ships will have the latest Baseline 6 variant of the Aegis weapon direction system.

All the *Knox* (FF-1052) class frigates have been reduced to training duties or are available for transfer to friendly navies. Influential officers in the surface warfare community wanted to do the same to the *Oliver Hazard Perry* (FFG-7) class missile-armed frigates, but the acute shortage of escorts forced a reappraisal of these under-valued ships. So far only 11 have gone, leaving 50, either active or serving with the Reserves.

The US Navy's new emphasis on 'littoral' warfare has proved a blessing to the amphibious warfare community. Although the older *Newport* (LST-1179) class tank landing ships have nearly all been stricken or transferred to other navies, a new class of amphibious dock transport, the *San Antonio* (LPD-17) class, is nearly ready to be ordered. These large and capable ships will replace older LPDs and dock landing ships (LSDs) early in the next century. The launch of the *Pearl Harbor* (LSD-52) by Avondale Industries early in 1996 marks the final phase of production of the 12 *Whidbey Island* (LSD-41) and similar *Harper's Ferry* (LSD-49) class LSDs. Only two of the *Iwo Jima* (LPH-2) class amphibious assault helicopter carriers remain in service.

With eight *Osprey* (MHC-51) class coastal minehunters in service by the end of 1996 and another four to be completed over the next three years, the modernisation of the US Navy's MCM fleet is well advanced. To improve mobility for the minehunters the former assault carrier *Inchon*

(LPH-12) has recently been converted to an MCM support ship and redesignated MCS-12. She has elaborate workshop facilities and will also operate an airborne MCM squadron of eight MH-53E helicopters.

EASTERN EUROPE

Croatia: This infant force retains many of the former Yugoslav Navy's ships, and before the ruinous civil war provided most of its personnel. A second Type 400 53-metre missile-armed FAC is under construction at Kraljevica Shipyard. Information is sparse, but she is reported to have been launched two years ago. Armament is largely Swedish: RBS-15 anti-ship missiles and a 57mm Mk 1 gun, but some Russian/Yugoslav light weapons are also mounted.

Estonia: The withdrawal of the Russian Navy from its base at Baltiisk (now Paldiski) highlighted a severe problem with mines. Not only had the Soviet Navy mined the approaches but the German mines from the Second World War had not been swept. This has prevented Estonian fishing vessels from getting out to their fishing grounds off the coast of Finland, a serious economic loss for the fledgling state. As a form of economic aid the Royal Swedish Navy sent a task force of four minehunters, a support ship and a hydrographic survey vessel to Paldiski to clear a channel, in May 1996. In three weeks the Swedish force succeeded in clearing a channel, but some 3600 mines remain, and a German MCM force is expected to resume the task later in 1996.

Russia: Still beset by appalling financial problems and a shrunken industrial base, the Russian Navy is still trying to maintain itself as a front-line force. The Baltic Fleet (largely a training force) has been reduced by a third, the Black Sea Fleet has seen much of its shipbuilding and repair capability fall into Ukrainian hands, and the Pacific Fleet seems to be beyond salvation for the time being. The Northern Fleet, however, remains the main force, but operates at a reduced tempo.

Late in December 1995 the aircraft carrier *Admiral Kuznetsov* was sent to the Mediterranean as a prestige gesture to celebrate the 300th anniversary of the founding of the Navy. At about the same time the Ukraine was reported to be trying to sell the incomplete sister *Varyag* to China once more, but it is not clear if the ship will be scrapped or completed by the Chinese with Russian technical assistance. An official source confirmed that the damaged hybrid cruiser-carrier *Admiral Gorshkov* will be repaired, and not sold to India. Thus only a decade after the Soviet Navy's attempt to establish a major carrier capability, including the aborted CVN *Ul'yanovsk*, only one carrier is serviceable.

The only effective nuclear-powered cruise missile-armed submarines still in service are 11 Project 949/949A 'Oscar I' and 'Oscar II' types. Two more cancelled 949A hulls are being offered for commercial conversion.

Efforts are being made to maintain continuity of SSN building, with the first of the new *Severodvinsk* class submarines scheduled to be launched in 1998, and at least two more planned. Two Project 971 *Bars* class (known to the West as the 'Akula'), the *Vepr* and *Drakon*, were delivered in 1995, and one launch is planned for 1996. The backbone of the SSN force remains the Project 671RTM *Schuka* class ('Victor III'), and only five of the Project 671T/671RT *Kefal* class ('Victor I/II') remain.

Only three or four Project 636 improved 'Kilo' type diesel-electric submarines are in service in the Russian Navy, but two more are destined for China, the first to be launched in 1996.

Two large surface warships were delivered to the Northern Fleet in 1995, the Project 1155 improved *Udaloy* class destroyer *Admiral Chabanenko* and the fourth Project 1144 *Kirov* class large nuclear-powered cruiser *Petr Veliky*. The Project 956A improved *Sovremennyy* class destroyer *Vazhnyy* is fitting out, and the last of the class, *Aleksandr Nevskiy* (ex-*Vedumchivyy*) is still under construction. Three partly-built sisters have been scrapped, according to official statements.

The second Project 1154

Neustrashimyy class large frigate, the former *Nepristupnyy*, has been renamed *Yaroslav Mudryy*. She is reported to be some years away from completion, while the third unit, possibly to be named *300 Let Rossykomy* in honour of the tercentenary, is to be the last. The Project 1166.1 *Gepard* type light prototype, intended for export, failed to appear at any naval review in 1995 or in 1996, despite reports of having run trials in 1994.

The once numerous light forces have also been run down significantly, and very few of the obsolescent Project 206M 'Turya' type hydrofoils and Project 205 'Osa' type missile boats remain. Production of the successful Project 1241.1MP 'Tarantul III' 56-metre missile-armed corvettes continues.

Ukraine: The newly independent Republic of the Ukraine has been forced to scale down its grandiose claim to half the Russian Black Sea Fleet. What is emerging is a coast defence force more in keeping with the nation's needs and resources.

Completion of the Project 1164 *Slava* class missile cruiser *Chervona Ukraina* was stopped, and the ship has been returned to the Russian Navy, which renamed her *Varyag* in February 1996. Little progress appears to have been made with work on two Project 1124EM 'Grisha V' type 1200-tonne frigates at Kiev, and a rumoured Project 1232.2 'Pomornik' type hovercraft has not appeared. Some 170 ex-Russian ships and minor craft were scheduled to be handed over by April 1996, but absorbing such a large number of vessels into the inventory has proved very difficult.

Yugoslavia: The rump of the former Yugoslavia (including Montenegro) should not be forgotten, as most of its ships are operational. In particular the naval forces operating off Bosnia keep a wary eye on the five submarines, at least one of which puts to sea regularly.

MIDDLE EAST

Egypt: In the wake of the successful modernisation of four Chinese-built 'Romeo' type submarines, negotiations have been completed with the US State Department to acquire two new-built submarines. As no US shipyard can bid competitively after a 30-year 'holiday' from diesel-electric submarine construction, the German Submarine Consortium has been asked to transfer technology to Ingalls Shipbuilding. Approval for the deal is now assured, and an order is expected before the end of the current fiscal year, with Foreign Military Sales funding.

The US Navy has also offered two *Oliver Hazard Perry* (FFG-7) class frigates, the USS *Copeland* (FFG-25) and USS *Duncan* (FFG-10), subject to Congressional approval. Three small US-built coastal minehunters (ordered in 1990) arrived in Alexandria late in 1995, and another US contractor completed delivery of a series of 45-ft patrol boats to the Coast Guard.

Iran: The third Project 877EKM 'Kilo' type submarine was expected to be delivered this spring, but reports of more purchases seem premature. The second batch of five 'Hudong' type missile-armed FACs has not yet been delivered.

Israel: The first IKL Type 800 'Dolphin' class submarine is now afloat and should be ready for sea trials by the end of 1996. The second will be launched in the autumn, and all three are intended to be in service by 1999.

It is reported that the three *Sa'ar 5* type *Eilat* class corvettes are not fully operational because of difficulties in integrating the Barak 1 missile system with the Elbit combat system. The operational evaluation did not take place until the end of March 1996, during firings from an older *Sa'ar 4.5* type FAC, and the *Eilat* herself will probably not have a functioning air defence missile system until 1997 or the year after. The ships were delivered in 1994-95 by Ingalls Shipbuilding in the USA, but with no electronics installed. It had been widely assumed that Barak 1 is operational as it has been sold to Chile and Singapore.

Kuwait: Work on the eight PB-37BRL 42-metre patrol craft at CMN's Cherbourg yard is well advanced, and the first is scheduled for delivery in 1997. If the latest reports are correct these ships will be the first in the world to be armed with the ship-launched variant of the British Aerospace Sea Skua light anti-ship missile. There is no sign of an order for the projected Offshore Missile Vessels (OMVs).

Oman: The new corvette *Qahir al Amwaj* started her sea trials late in 1995 and was commissioned in March at Vosper Thornycroft's Woolston yard. Her sister *Al Mua'zzar* is currently fitting out and will be commissioned in November.

The first of two *Al Bushra* class offshore patrol vessels (OPVs) were commissioned at CMN's Cherbourg yard in the summer of 1995 and the *Al Najah* followed in April 1996. The planned anti-submarine armament has not been purchased (an active towed sonar array and lightweight torpedoes) so the Royal Navy of Oman still has no means of dealing with submarines such as the Iranian 'Kilos'.

Qatar: Two of the four *Barzan* class 56-metre FACs have been delivered to the Qatari Emiri Navy, leaving the *Al Udeid* fitting out and the fourth, as yet unnamed, under construction.

Saudi Arabia: At the time of writing the contract for two air defence frigates based on the French *La Fayette* design has not been signed. As the Aster-15 missile system is unlikely to be operational before 2000 current plans are to arm them with the latest version of the Crotale short-range missile.

The first of four *Madina* class frigates and the oiler *Boraida* arrived at Toulon in December 1995 to be overhauled, and the rest of the ships, including the oiler *Yunbou*, are to follow at nine-month intervals. Under the so-called 'Mouette' programme the work on the frigates will be limited to refurbishing hulls and equipment, upgrading the Otomat missiles, Tavitac combat system and sonars, and replacing the helicopter handling system. The frigates have had major problems with their diesel engines.

The first three *Al Jawf* class (modified *Sandown*) minehunters have

The superstructure and foremast of the Royal Navy of Oman's new corvette SNV Qahir al Amwaj. *(Vosper Thornycroft)*

Launch of the Omani offshore patrol boat SNV Al Najah *at CMN's Cherbourg in April 1996. (Antony Preston)*

finally been accepted and two sailed from the United Kingdom at the end of 1995. Funding for the second batch of three under the 'Al Yammamah' agreement has not yet been released.

United Arab Emirates: The competition to build up to four air defence frigates for the UAE Navy is still unresolved, but the Dutch government secured an important advantage in April by selling two *Kortenaer* class for only US$362 million. The UAE has expressed an interest in buying the advanced LCF frigate.

ASIA-PACIFIC REGION

Australia: HMAS *Collins*, first of the new class of six submarines, was commissioned in July 1995, and her sister *Farncomb* is fitting out. The third boat, to be named *Waller*, will be in service towards the end of 1997 and the last will be ready in October 1999. An option to build two more lapsed three years ago, but there is growing political pressure to reinstate them to maintain employment at the Australian Submarine Corporation's yard. The Defence Department is opposed to the idea as funds have been earmarked for more urgent programmes, and the RAN has made it clear that additional money would have to be voted by Parliament.

The frigate programme is also running to time, with HMAS *Anzac* commissioned in mid-May 1996, her sister *Arunta* launched on 28 June and first steel cut for the *Warramunga*. The remaining six will be delivered at yearly intervals thereafter, through to 2005. Late in 1995 two project-definition study contracts were awarded for the proposed modernisation of the six *Adelaide* class (*Oliver Hazard Perry* type) frigates. They will be rearmed with the Standard SM-2 missile and a new surveillance radar if funds permit.

The GRP hull of the first of six *Huon* class coastal minehunters was delivered in September 1995 by Intermarine SpA in Italy, and fitting out has begun at Australian Defence Industries' yard in Newcastle, NSW. The ship will start sea trials in April 1998, and her sisters are under construction by ADI under a technology-transfer agreement. The last of class is expected to be in service by 2002.

The Australian Government has worked hard to coordinate Navy plans for 12 Offshore Patrol Combatants (OPCs) with the Royal Malaysian Navy's plans to build OPVs (see below). If the joint venture goes ahead the OPC programme will be brought forward, but if not the original timetable will be adhered to, and the *Fremantle* class 42-metre patrol craft will be given a service-life extension.

A contract has been awarded to Forgacs Dockyard to carry out a major conversion of the two ex-US Navy *Newport* class LSTs, HMAS *Kanimbla* and HMAS *Manoora*. The ships were bought in 1994 for conversion to training and helicopter support ships (THSSs), to operate and maintain Army Blackhawk helicopters. The costings were reviewed by the incoming government after public criticism about extra costs incurred by 'emergent' work to deal with corrosion, but the review failed to find evidence of any incompetence or dishonesty in the procurement procedure.

Brunei: The Royal Brunei Armed Forces announced in mid-December 1995 that it had awarded a contract to Yarrow Shipbuilders to build three 95-metre offshore patrol vessels (in reality 1500-tonne corvettes) armed with Harpoon and Seawolf missiles. The first ship will be ready by the beginning of 2000.

China: The SSN and SSBN forces are unchanged, although the US Director of Naval Intelligence has stated that work is in hand on new designs, designated Types 093 (SSN) and 094 (SSBN), to come into service early in the next century. The conventional submarine force is being modernised, with the second Project 877 'Kilo' delivered from Russia in September 1995 and the first two Project 636 boats to be launched in 1996. No further news is available on the indigenous design (codenamed 'Song'), but production of the 'Ming' continues locally.

The last Type 051 'Luda II' destroyer, the *Zhuhai*, appeared at a fleet review in Indonesia in September 1995, accompanied by an oiler and the 'Jiangwei' type frigate *Huainan*.

Sketch design for the conversion of the tank landing ships HMAS Kanimbla *and HMAS* Manoora *into LHAs.*

(Overleaf) *HMAS* Collins *on trials in late 1995. Note the light boom over the rudders for deploying the Kariwara towed array. (RAN)*

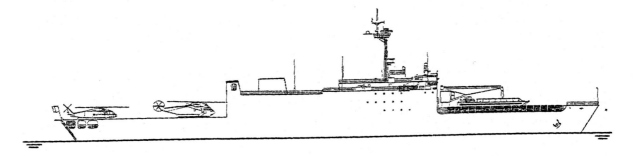

Model of the Yarrow corvettes ordered by the Royal Brunei Armed Forces in December 1995. Armament is only speculative as details are not yet decided. (R Coltart)

There is some dispute about the armament of the 'Jiangwei'; US intelligence sources credit it with having a sextuple air defence missile-launcher, whereas other sources say it is a dual-purpose launcher capable of firing anti-submarine missiles as well. Two more of the class are expected to become operational in 1996.

Production of the modern Type 052 'Luhu' destroyer has slowed down because of a shortage of gas turbines, and the second unit appeared in 1995. Although the importance of light strike forces is diminishing as the People's Liberation Army-Navy becomes more involved in blue-water operations, production of the 'Houjian' and 'Houxin' type FACs continues.

India: In theory the projected aircraft carrier is still on the agenda, although original in-service date of 1997 has long been irrelevant. The Naval Staff insist that large carriers are required, as replacements for the British-built *Vikrant* and (eventually) *Viraat*, but even a smaller design such as the Italian *Giuseppe Garibaldi* seems to be beyond the Indian Navy's means. The acquisition of the Russian *Admiral Gorshkov* is no longer an option.

The submarine force is being modernised by discarding the Russian-built Project 641 'Foxtrots' and replacing them with Project 877EKM 'Kilos'. There is no sign yet of work starting on an improved 'Kilo' design in 1997, and rumours of more IKL Type 1500s built locally have come to nothing. Plans to build an SSN seem to be very long-term.

The new Project 15 air defence destroyer *Delhi* is to be delivered in 1997 by Mazagon Dock in Bombay, followed by the *Mysore* in 1999 and the *Bangalore* the following year. The Project 16A frigate *Brahmaputra*, first of three improved *Godavari* class also being built by Mazagon Dock, is expected to be commissioned at the end of 1996, but some major items of equipment may not be ready in time. The Project 25A *Khukri* class corvette *Kora* was delivered by Garden Reach Shipyard in Calcutta in 1995 and three more may be completed by the end of the century.

No decision has been announced on the urgently needed replacements for the MCM force. At least ten minehunters are needed, but rumours of an order for GRP-hulled vessels placed with Goa Shipyard have not been verified.

Indonesia: Negotiations with the German Submarine Consortium over the acquisition of two more Type 209 submarines continue, but to date no order has resulted.

As predicted, the purchase of 'Parchim' type corvettes, 'Kondor II' type minesweepers and 'Frosch' type tank landing ships from the former East German Navy has imposed a heavy burden of maintenance. More 57-metre German-designed patrol craft may be ordered locally.

Japan: The Japanese Maritime Self Defence Force (JMSDF) sticks to its scrap-and-build policy, ensuring a modern fleet and a steady flow of orders to the shipyards.

The submarine force is to remain at 16 boats, so as the improved *Harushio* class come into service from 1998 onwards the older boats will be phased out. Some will be relegated to training duties.

The third Aegis destroyer, the *Myoko* (DD-175), was commissioned in March 1996. Seven more are planned through to the end of the century. Also commissioned in March was the anti-submarine destroyer *Murasame* (DD-101), first of a planned class of eight. With so many powerful escorts in service and under construction the JMSDF has built very few frigates in recent years, and has no plans to build any more for five years. Retirement of older frigates (rated as destroyer escorts) will reduce the number of smaller escorts.

A third missile-armed hydrofoil was delivered in 1995, but construction of three more has been delayed. These are the only examples of this unorthodox but expensive type projected in any navy. Work continues on the new 500-tonne minehunters and two

MCM support ships. The first of three 8900-tonne LPDs should be delivered in 1998.

North Korea: The ageing collection of Russian and indigenous designs is a wasting asset, and the nominally large submarine force of 22 'Romeo' type is the most potent element. Large numbers of a small coast defence midgets (designated 'Sang-O' in the West) are reported to be under construction, with perhaps 12 in service.

South Korea: In contrast to the North, the Republic of Korea Navy has made giant strides, and has just announced an 18-year expansion plan costed at US$15.4 billion. By 2012 it is hoped to acquire an aircraft carrier capable of operating 20 aircraft, a number of large air defence ships, and ocean-going submarines.

Five *Changbo-go* class (Type 209/1200) submarines are in service and four more are in various stages of construction. Longer-term plans have been drawn up for larger submarines similar in capability to the Australian *Collins* class, but nothing is likely to happen for some time.

Work is in hand on three KDX type destroyers, but plans to build up to 18 have been modified. The second batch will be some 1000 tonnes larger and a third batch will have a full air defence capability, with Standard SM-2 missiles. These may be the 7000-tonners recently announced as part of the new expansion plan.

A 3300-tonne minelayer was ordered two years ago, and the MCM force is to be expanded by building a larger minehunter than the existing *Kang Keong* class.

Malaysia: the new frigate KD *Lekiu* will not be delivered to the Royal Malaysian Navy (RMN) until the end of 1996, with her sister *Jebat*. Delivery has been held up by late delivery of software for the Nautis-F command system. In other respects the *Lekiu* is complete, and she has completed gunnery trials.

A decision is awaited on what is undoubtedly the largest naval construction programme ever seen in South East Asia, the selection of a design and builders for the New Generation Patrol Vessel (NGPV)

project. Up to 27 1200-tonne OPVs will be built over the next 15 years, starting with a batch of six. Many shipyards are bidding for this prestigious US$2.2 billion programme, including Australia's Transfield Defence Systems (see under Australia earlier).

In a surprising move the RMN also agreed in 1995 to buy two ex-Iraqi corvettes from Italian builders Fincantieri. They will be delivered in 1997, following a short overhaul and refurbishment. According to the latest reports the RMN may buy another three, a move which would almost certainly cause the NGPV decision to be deferred. The RMN also has long-term plans to buy submarines, but they too fall outside the scope of the next five-year Malaysia Plan.

New Zealand: The first of two *Anzac* class frigates, the *Te Kaha*, was launched in Australia last summer and will be commissioned in March 1998. Her sister *Te Mana* was laid down on 28 June 1996, for completion in November 1999, and the RNZN is asking for permission to take up its option for two more. This option must be exercised by September 1997, and the Navy is looking for ways to find the necessary funds.

Pakistan: Work has started at DCN Cherbourg on the first of three *Agosta-90B* type submarines, and she will be followed by two built at Karachi. After completion all three will have the new MESMA (AIP) system retrofitted by inserting a 'plug' or additional hull-section.

PNS *Muhafiz*, second of three Tripartite type minehunters, was launched at DCN Lorient in July 1995, while the GRP hull of No.3 was shipped out to Karachi for fitting out.

Philippines: After many years of neglect the passage of the Armed Forces of the Philippines Act promised funding for a massive modernisation of the Navy over a period of 15 years. The first stage includes 33-metre patrol boats, 45/50-metre patrol craft, search-and-rescue craft, 85-metre OPVs, 80-metre corvettes and 120-metre frigates. In April 1996 requests for proposals (RFPs) were sent to foreign shipyards to build the

first three OPVs, two corvettes, six patrol craft, two patrol boats, a mine-hunter and helicopters and amphibious vehicles.

Singapore: Following evaluation of an offer to buy up to five Type 206 submarines from the German Navy, as well as a training session aboard an Indian Navy 'Foxtrot', the Republic of Singapore Navy (RSN) bought the Swedish A 14 type *Sjöbjörnen* from the Royal Swedish Navy. The submarine will remain in the Baltic, and experience with her will help the RSN to make its choice for new construction.

The first of six *Fearless* class gun-armed patrol craft was launched in February 1995, and a second batch of six was ordered immediately afterwards. Details of their armament is sparse, but it is believed to include missiles and the new Gudgeon sonar from Thomson Sintra. All four *Bedok* class minehunters were commissioned in October 1995 as the 194th MCM Squadron. Up to four large amphibious ships are planned.

Taiwan: The *Kang Ting*, first of six frigates ordered from France four years ago, has been delivered by DCN Lorient, and armament will be fitted at Kaohsiung. The remainder will be delivered by 1998, but there is no confirmation of the original intention to build ten more in Taiwan.

The 'Kwang Hua Flight II' project to build four air defence frigates was cancelled late in 1995, possibly because the basic *Oliver Hazard Perry* (FFG-7) design was over-stretched by all the additional systems proposed. The acquisition of surplus *Knox* (FF-1052) class frigates from the US Navy will continue, however, and six out of the planned total of 12 are already undergoing upgrading.

Thailand: The Royal Thai Navy's (RTN) new support carrier *Chakkrinaruebet* was launched in Spain in January 1996, and delivery is planned for April 1997. The second *Naresuan* class frigate was delivered from China in September 1995.

The RTN intends to buy submarines but the situation is complicated by periodic denials and confirmations, culminating in a report that the funding must come from

Fitting the bow-section of the Royal Thai Navy's new light carrier Chakkrinaruebet *at Ferrol in NW Spain. (EN Bazán)*

within the existing budget. Sweden has offered two unmodernised A 14 type submarines for interim training as part of a new construction deal including two A 19 *Gotland* class.

Two minehunters are projected, and these are believed to have a higher priority than the submarines. The Italian *Gaeta* design has been selected, with German electronics.

LATIN AMERICA

Argentina: The *Armada Republic Argentina* is close to collapse, with only two out of 49 warships fully operational. Seven of the others are in poor condition and ten are completely unserviceable. The carrier *Veinticinco de Mayo* has been out of service for nearly ten years and the vaunted Super Etendard force of 14 aircraft is down to one aircraft, following a fatal crash earlier in 1996.

Brazil: The Type 209/1400 submarine *Timbira* was launched at Rio de Janeiro in January 1996, and a fifth, to be called *Tamandare*, was approved early in 1995. Since then, however, the submarine programme has slowed to a halt because of financial problems. The SSN project has been the subject of financial scandal, and funding has dried up, making it unlikely that any results will be seen before 2010 at the earliest.

The frigate *Greenhalgh* (ex-HMS *Broadsword*) was handed over by the Royal Navy in June 1995. Her sisters *Bosisio* (ex-HMS *Brazen*) and *Dodsworth* (ex-HMS *Brilliant*) will be handed over in August, and HMS *Battleaxe* will become BNS *Rademaker* in April 1997. Work is in hand on the *Barroso*, first of the modified *Inhaúma* class light frigates, and details are being finalised for the modernisation of the *Niterói* class.

Chile: The last of four ex-Royal Navy

destroyers, the *Latorre*, is completing a major modernisation at Talcahuano, with Barak 1 missiles and a new combat system. The old destroyers *Almirante Williams* and *Almirante Riveros* are both out of service, but the two ex-Royal Navy *Leander* class frigates, *General Baquedano* and *Ministro Zenteno*, are undergoing a major modernisation.

The two British-built submarines *Hyatt* and *O'Brien* have been brought up to the same standard as the German-built *Simpson* and *Thomson*, with the same sonars and electronics. Despite rumours, the acquisition of two or three more IKL Type 209 submarines is virtually certain.

Colombia: The reported acquisition of two ex-Iraqi frigates from Fincantieri has fallen through, but the experimental Spanish FAC *Cormoran* has been bought for the Coast Guard and renamed *Espartana*.

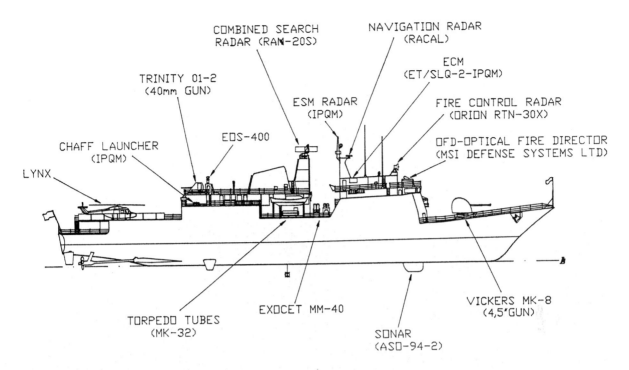

COMBINED SEARCH
RADAR (RAN-20S)

NAVIGATION RADAR
(RACAL)

TRINITY 01-2
(40mm GUN)

ECM
(ET/SLQ-2-IPQM)

ESM RADAR
(IPQM)

FIRE CONTROL RADAR
(ORION RTN-30X)

CHAFF LAUNCHER
(IPQM)

EOS-400

OFD-OPTICAL FIRE DIRECTOR
(MSI DEFENSE SYSTEMS LTD)

LYNX

TORPEDO TUBES
(MK-32)

EXOCET MM-40

SONAR
(ASO-94-2)

VICKERS MK-8
(4,5'GUN)

Profile of the Barroso, *first of a class of modified* Inhaúma *class light frigates for the Brazilian Navy. (EMGEPRON)*

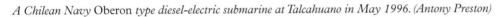

A Chilean Navy Oberon *type diesel-electric submarine at Talcahuano in May 1996. (Antony Preston)*

The offshore patrol boat Vigilant *was delivered to the Mauritius Coast Guard by Chilean builders ASMAR at Talcahuano in May 1996. (Antony Preston)*

AFRICA

Mauritius: The Mauritian Coast Guard took delivery of the offshore patrol vessel *Vigilant* from Chilean builders ASMAR last December. The ship has only a light armament of one 40mm gun, but is equipped with a flight deck and hangar for a Chetak light helicopter.

Morocco: The *Marine Royale Marocaine* took delivery of the 64-metre offshore patrol vessel *Rais Bargach* in December 1995, from the Brittany yard of Leroux & Lotz. Her sister *Rais Britel* followed in June 1996, and the other two will follow in December 1996 and June 1997 respectively. A option for a fifth may be taken up.

The widely reported deal to purchase two ex-Iraqi corvettes from Fincantieri has fallen through.

South Africa: The plan to build four corvettes was deferred in 1995, partly because of funding problems but also because of aggressive lobbying by European contenders for the contract. Spanish shipbuilders Empresa Naçional Bazán would have won the contract, but there may have to be a second round of bidding after the current defence review is completed.

The 'Minister' class FAC *Frederick Cresswell* has completed a major modernisation, with a new locally-developed combat system and all sub-systems overhauled. A variant of the combat system is being retrofitted to the three *Daphne* type submarines as well.

WARSHIP GALLERY

In this new section of *Warship*, we are publishing pictures of warships which are unusual, remarkable as pictures, mysterious or otherwise of special interest to readers. This section is not intended for standard ship portraits, but for out-of-the-ordinary pictures which illuminate aspects of warships not evident in the usual views. Some pictures will be from the wide-ranging and largely unknown Conway Picture Library, some will be published in an effort to glean more information about them. In these cases, help in identification from readers will be much appreciated. Indeed the editors would be happy to hear from readers with unusual pictures of post-1860 warships which might appear in future issues.

The iron screw troopship Serapis *(6,211 tons) was launched at Blackwall on 2 September 1866. After a distinguished career she was sold in 1894 and scrapped. (CPL)*

Figurehead from the iron screw frigate HMS Raleigh. Launched at Pembroke in 1873, she was re-rated as a cruiser in 1889 and finally scrapped in 1905. (CPL)

The six screws of the extraordinary circular Russian estuarine defence vessel, Novgorod, 1874. (CPL)

With a seagull escort, a destroyer officer keeps watch at sunset, December 1941. Most wartime hours were like this. (CPL)

The crew of the battleship USS Missouri observe the fourth anniversary of VJ Day, August 1949. (CPL)

INDEX

Page numbers in *italics* refer to illustrations; those in **bold** refer to diagrams and maps